AN INTRODUCTION TO
SYMBOLIC LOGIC

by SUSANNE K. LANGER

SECOND EDITION

(REVISED)

DOVER PUBLICATIONS, INC.
NEW YORK

FIRST PUBLISHED IN 1937

SECOND EDITION, 1953

COPYRIGHT 1953 BY SUSANNE K. LANGER

Library of Congress Catalog Card Number: 53-12389

Manufactured in the United States of America

Dover Publications, Inc.
180 Varick Street
New York 14, N.Y.

TO MY MOTHER
ELSE U. KNAUTH

CONTENTS

CONTENTS

PREFACE TO THE FIRST EDITION

SYMBOLIC LOGIC is a relatively new subject, and the easiest methods of approach have not yet been determined. In point of arrangement, therefore, this *Introduction* has no predecessor. That is just why it was written: the need of some systematic guide, from the state of perfect innocence to a possible understanding of the classical literature, has become acute and commánding.

But, although my text has no predecessor, it has had at least one inspirer: my debt to Professor Sheffer of Harvard is too great to be expressed in any detailed acknowledgments. The underlying ideas of the book—its emphasis upon system, its progress from the specific to the general, from the general to the abstract, its whole treatment of logic as a science of forms—all this is due to his influence. How many lesser ideas also derive from him I am unable to say; it is the mark of a great teacher that one cannot render to him the things that are his. They become part of one's own mentality, and ultimately of the intellectual commonwealth.

To my friend Professor Paul Henle I wish to express my heartiest thanks for his kindness and patience in reading the entire manuscript, uncovering various errors, and checking all the algebraic formulae. He has suggested many improvements, and sometimes found simpler or briefer explanations or formal demonstrations. I would also thank Dr. Henry S. Leonard for some excellent suggestions, and for reading a part of the proof.

S. K. L.

WHEN THIS book was written, there was no systematic textbook of symbolic logic in English except the *Symbolic Logic* of Lewis and Langford. Perhaps Couturat's little Summary, The Algebra of Logic, could also be regarded as a text, in that it set forth a system developed by various persons, notably De Morgan, Boole, and Schroeder, making no claim for itself to originality; but that was, after all, an outline rather than an introduction. For the rest, every exposition was still in connection with a contribution: Lewis's *Survey of Symbolic Logic* had been written mainly to propose the system of "strict implication," Russell raised many questions he did not claim to settle, Quine was almost completely original; and even the most "digested" work (Lewis and Langford) entered into no elementary discussion of the basic logical notions—generalization, abstraction, relation, form, system. Such fundamental concepts were taken for granted.

They have always been taken for granted in that paragon of pure sciences, mathematics. It is the exceptional student of mathematics who knows why "$+$" is classed as an operation and "$=$" as a relation, or, indeed, why his exercises are called "examples"; or who understands, even at a fairly advanced stage of technical proficiency, just how algebra is related to arithmetic. His training is entirely in techniques and their application to problems; arithmetic, geometry and algebra are related for him only by the fact that their several techniques may converge on one and the same problem; that is to say, they are related practically but not intellectually. The mathematics books used in schools dwell almost exclusively on rules of operation.

The prestige of mathematics is so great that logic, in emulating its method, tended to follow its pedagogy as well. The excellent textbooks of logic that have appeared during the last fifteen years (see the supplementary new list appended to "Suggestions for further reading") tend similarly to emphasize techniques—transformation, inference, consistency-tests, decision-procedures—without detailed explanations of the concepts involved. Now, mathematics has such obvious practical uses that to learn its tricks without understanding their significance is not entirely silly; but may the same be said of symbolic logic? Is the manipulation of its symbols of such practical importance that students should learn to perform logical operations even without knowing or questioning their conceptual foundations? It seems to me that despite its practical uses, which are still coming to light in unexpected quarters, its chief value is conceptual. Through the influence of the various positivistic schools of philosophy, which are certainly the most prominent and perhaps the most promising schools to-day, our scholars and educators are so imbued with methodology that they value the new logic primarily for its codification of the rules of inference. But that is only one of its contributions to human thought, and even to science; method can be overemphasized, and tends to be so in our intellectual life.

Symbolic logic is an instrument of exact thought, both analytic and constructive; its mission, accordingly, is not only to validate scientific methods, but also to clarify the semantic confusions that beset the popular mind as well as the professional philosopher at the present time. "Semantics" (blesséd word!) is in dire need of responsible analysis and skilful handling, and symbolic logic is the most effective preparation I can think of for a frontal attack on the pathetic muddles of modern philosophical thought. It blasts natural misconceptions with every move, not by a process of "debunking," but by purposeful and lucid construction of ideas.

Because this book seeks to present in clear, stepwise fashion the elementary concepts of logic, it cannot encompass as much technical material as other textbooks do. But to-day that is not a serious embarrassment, because it may be supplemented by a standard text. One of the most useful devices now generally taught—the construction of "truth-tables" to test the legitimacy of constructs in a truth-value system—is included in this edition as Appendix C. The reading list for further study has been brought up to date. For the rest, no revisions have been made except to correct errors, especially a major error in Chapter IV, which mysteriously escaped the several readers of the script, and has necessitated a little actual rewriting. Apart from these details, the book is unchanged—a book for the student who has no teacher, or for the teacher who has to meet too many naïve questions for his comfort. As such it is still alone in its class, at least for English readers; and in the belief that there is always a real need for at least one such book, I send my *Introduction* out anew.

July 1952.   S. K. L.

INTRODUCTION

THE first thing that strikes the student of symbolic logic is that it has developed along several apparently unrelated lines: (1) the symbolic expression of traditional logic; (2) the invention of various algebras such as the algebra of logic, and with this the study of postulational technique; (3) the derivation of mathematics from a set of partially or wholly "logical" postulates; (4) the investigation of the "laws of thought," and formal deduction of logical principles themselves. Every worker in the field drifts into one or another of these specialized endeavours. To a novice, it is hard to see what are the aims, principles, and procedures of logic *per se*, and what relations the several branches bear to it and to each other.

Underlying them all is the principle of *generality* which culminates in the attainment of *abstractions*. The several branches of logic are so many *studies in generalization*. The aims of logical research may vary with the interests of different investigators—one may be interested in the validity of Aristotelian logic, another in that of mathematics, a third in the canons of science, a fourth in the relation between mathematics and science or mathematics and classical logic, etc., etc.—but the procedure is everywhere the same: it is progressive systematization and generalization. Likewise, the criterion of success is the same: it is the discovery of *abstract forms*. The latter interest distinguishes logic from natural science, which is in search of general but not abstract formulae, i.e. formulae for concrete facts.

In order to prepare the reader for further study in *any* branch of symbolic logic, I have undertaken to discuss the characteristics of logical science as such, and show precisely how the branches spring from a parent trunk; to lay down the principles governing all symbolic usage, and to introduce him specifically to the most important systems of symbolization. To this end it is necessary for the student to have plenty of exercise in the actual manipulation of symbols. Nothing else can overcome their initial mystery. Symbolic logic, like mathematics, is a technique as well as a theory, and cannot be learned entirely by contemplation.

The book is built around the two great classic feats of symbolic logic: the Boole-Schroeder algebra, and the logistic masterpiece of Messrs. Whitehead and Russell, *Principia Mathematica*. Its chief aim is to prepare the student to understand the thought and procedure of these two very distinct developments of logic, and to see the connection between them. Most introductions to symbolic logic treat them without relation to each other; the student, who has mastered the algebraic symbolism and "postulational" method of Boole and Schroeder and feels reasonably familiar with the algebra as a system, suddenly finds himself at a new beginning, confronted with an entirely new realm of ideation, new symbols, new aims. Pedagogically, the transition is hard to effect. Therefore, this whole book has been planned to show very precisely that "algebra of logic" and "logistic" are all of a piece, and just how, why, and where they have diverged both in appearance and in sense.

The present work endeavours to be both a textbook *of* symbolic logic and an essay *on* that logic. It is essential that the student should learn both to "do" logic, and to know precisely what he is doing. Therefore the exposition of method is interspersed throughout with discussion of the principles and general import of the procedure. The actual material presented should enable him, at the end of a systematic course of study, to tackle the monographic literature of symbolic logic, and pursue it either in the direction of mathematics, or of postulational theory, or of logistic. Furthermore, it should in some measure prepare students of philosophy to understand the epistemological problems which arise in contemporary philosophy of nature, as presented by Poincaré, Mach, Reichenbach, Carnap,

Russell, Whitehead, and others. To this end it emphasizes the *principles of logical construction*; the possibilities and limits of formalization; equivalent conceptions, fundamental types of formulae, criteria of clarity, simplicity, generality, and above all, *the difference between fecund and sterile notions*. In this connection it seeks to show the bearing of logic on natural science and philosophy of nature.

Although it is intended as a text for a course in symbolic logic (usually a second course, though it presupposes no previous training) it should also serve as introductory reading for a course in philosophy of nature, or a course of general philosophy for upper classmen, or for graduate students seeking a key to the important monographic literature of symbolic logic and logistic. It aims to take no technical knowledge of logic, science, or mathematics for granted, but to develop every idea from the level of common sense, so that it may be comprehensible and useful also to the interested layman who desires a general discussion of the purpose, approach, technique, and results of symbolic logic.

AN INTRODUCTION TO SYMBOLIC LOGIC

CHAPTER I

THE STUDY OF FORMS

1. THE IMPORTANCE OF FORM

All knowledge, all sciences and arts have their beginning
in the recognition that ordinary, familiar things may take
on different forms. Our earliest experience of nature brings
this fact to our notice; we see water freezing into a trans-
lucent block, or the snow which fell from heaven changing
to water before our very eyes. A little reflection makes us
aware of further changes. Where do snow and rain come
from? From the vaporous masses we call clouds, the white
mists that float in the air, and as the snow or rain descends
those clouds dissolve. They have turned to water, or to
white flakes. Where did the clouds come from? They are
made by some process of transformation from the waters
of the earth. Different forms of the same thing may be so
widely diverse in appearance that it is hard to think of
them as essentially the same substance.

All science tries to reduce the diversity of things in the
world to mere differences of appearance, and treats as
many things as possible as variants of the same stuff.
When Benjamin Franklin found out that lightning is one
form of electricity, he made a scientific discovery, which
proved to be but a step in a very great science, for an
amazing number of things can be reduced to this same
fundamental "something," this protean substance called
"electricity": the force that holds the firmament together,
the crackle of a cat's fur, the heat in a flat-iron, the
flickering Northern Aurora. Electricity is one of the
essential things in the world that can take on a vast variety

of forms. Its wide mutability makes nature interesting, and its ultimate oneness makes science possible. But if we could not appreciate its different forms *as* different forms of one thing, then we would have no way of relating them to each other at all; we would not know why sliding our feet over a rug makes the brass door-knob give off a spark at our touch, or why the lightning has a preference for metal crosses on church-steeples, nor see any connection whatever between these two causal facts.

We have two kinds of knowledge, which may be called respectively knowledge *of* things, and knowledge *about* them. The former is that direct intimacy which our senses give us, the look and smell and feel of a thing—the sort of knowledge a baby has of its own bed, its mother's breast, its usual view of ceiling and window and wall. It knows these objects just as it knows hunger or toothache; it has what Bertrand Russell has called "knowledge by acquaintance" of certain things, a most direct and sensuous knowledge. Yet the baby cannot be said to know anything *about* beds, food, houses, or toothaches. To know anything *about* an object is to know how it is related to its surroundings, how it is made up, how it functions, etc., in short, to know what *sort* of thing it is. To have knowledge *about* it we must know more than the direct sensuous quality of "this stuff"; we must know what particular shape the stuff is taking in the case of this thing. A child may know the taste and feeling of a scrambled egg, without knowing that it is an egg which has been scrambled; in that case, he will not associate it with a boiled egg or an omelette. He does not know that these are different forms of the same thing. Neither does he know that in its raw, fresh, natural state the egg is a pristine form of chicken, and by more distant relationship an incipient chicken-dinner.

The only way we can do business at all with a rapidly changing, shifting, surprising world is to discover the most general laws of its transformations. The very word "transformation" tells us what we are dealing with: changes of form. The growth of science is the most striking demonstration of the importance of forms as distinguished from matter, substance, stuff, or whatever we call that which remains "the same" when the form of a thing changes. Whenever we may truly claim to have a science, we have found some principle by which different things are related to each other as just so many forms of one substrate, or material, and everything that can be treated as a new variation belongs to that science.

2. LOGICAL FORM

Not all the sciences deal with material things. Philology, for instance, deals with the relations among words, and although the production of a word in speech or writing always has a material aspect—involving paper and ink, or movement of speech organs—this aspect is not what interests the philologist. When the word undergoes changes of form, as for instance the word "pater" to "père" and "father" and "padre," this cannot be taken to mean that it changes its *shape*, as an egg changes shape when it is scrambled. The meaning of "form" is stretched beyond its common connotation of shape. Likewise, in the science or art of musical composition we speak of a rondo form, sonata form, hymn form, and no one thinks of a material shape. Musical form is not material; it is *orderliness*, but not *shape*. So we must recognize a wider sense of the word than the geometric sense of physical shape. And indeed, we admit this wider sense in ordinary parlance; we speak of "formality" in social intercourse, of "good form" in athletics, of "formalism" in literature, music, or dancing. Certainly we cannot refer to the *shape* of a dinner or a poem or a dance. In this wider sense, anything may be said to have form that follows a pattern of any sort, exhibits order, internal connection; our many synonyms for "form" indicate how wide the range of this notion really is. We speak of physical, grammatical, social *forms*; of psychological *types*; *norms* of conduct, of beauty, of intelligence; *fashions* in clothing, speech, behaviour; new *designs* of automobiles or motor boats; architectural *plans*, or the *plans* for a festival; *pattern*, *standard*, *mode*, and many other words signify essentially the same thing in specialized usage or subtle variations of meaning. But all these words refer to "form" in that most general sense in which we are going to use it here.

It is this most general sense which we always give to the word in logic. Therefore I shall call it "logical form," to distinguish it from "form" in any more restricted sense, particularly its usual connotation of physical shape.

3. STRUCTURE

"Logical form" is a highly general notion, and like all generalizations, it covers a large number of particular ideas. But if these various particular ideas may all be called by one general name, they must have something—some general feature—in common. But what is common to, say, the form of declensions and conjugations in a language, and the topography of a continent? Both are "forms" in the logical sense. What bridge can be thrown across the gap between such widely diverse notions as the shape of the continent, and the orderly sequence of word-endings in the language? Is there any justification for applying the same name to such different matters?

The bridge that connects all the various meanings of form—from geometric form to the form of ritual or etiquette—is the notion of *structure*. The logical form of a thing is the way that thing is *constructed*, the way it is put together. Any thing that has a definite form is *constructed* in a definite way. This does not mean, of course, that it has been deliberately put together by somebody; forms may be preconceived, or they may be natural, or accidental. The famous "Old Man of the Mountain" in

New Hampshire is an accidental rock-formation, put together like a human profile; a piece juts out just a little, as eyebrows do, then there is a gap like the hollow of the eyes, a large projection, exactly as a nose projects, a straight piece, a fissure beneath it, as the mouth is beneath the lip, another straight piece ending in a projection with a great overhang that resembles the projection of a strong chin and jaw. The outline of the rock is made up like a human profile; the powers of nature—glacier, water, and frost—have accidentally constructed the "Old Man of the Mountain" out of granite; the cliff, which has nothing else in common with human flesh, yet resembles a man by its *form*. Nature is full of most elaborate constructs, from the crude structure of strata in a geological fault to the infinitesimal dynamic pattern of protons and electrons in an atom. One must not make the mistake of associating "structure" always with something *put together* out of parts that were previously separate. A snowflake is a detailed construct of very recognizable individual parts, but these have not been "put together"; they crystallized out of one homogeneous drop of water. They were never separate, and there has been no process of combination. Yet the flake has a structure (in fact, an interesting structure) and is therefore called a natural construct.

Now let us consider a form which is not geometric, i.e., which is not a shape: the form, for instance, of the ordinary musical scale, in the so-called "major mode," do, re, mi, fa, sol, la, si, high do. There are eight notes in this scale, counting the customary repetition of do. But to have a major scale we must have more than the eight notes; we must have them put together in just this particular way. The major scale is *constructed* by letting these notes follow each other in just this order. Supposing we put them together differently, as for instance; do, mi, re, fa, si-la sol, do (high). We have then constructed a perfectly singable melody, but it is not a major scale. It has the notes but not the *form* of the scale. We may group them yet differently, and construct another tune; sol-mi-do (high), si, la-fa, re-do. Here we have the same notes again, but the musical form is not the same; this is a "skippy" tune in waltz-time. The two melodies have every note in common; that is to say, exactly the same ingredients have gone into both. Were these ingredients material things, we should say the two constructs were made of exactly the same substance, and differed only in form. Logically we may say this even though the "substance" is immaterial, being a collection of individual sounds, for order and arrangement among sounds is just as much "logical form" as the arrangement of parts in a physical thing. If we compare these tunes with each other and with the conventional "major scale," we see even in this rudimentary and trivial case how very diverse may be the appearance, the character, the value, of things which are merely different forms of the same given material. This fact should always be borne in mind; often it is hard to believe that a philosopher or a scientist has any chance whatever of reducing widely different things to the same category, because they look and "feel" so incommensurable, but he has found a principle by which he can describe them as two forms of one substance, and we are amazed to see how precisely and usefully he then relates them. Logic is full of such surprises; that is why it sharpens and broadens one's outlook, scientific or metaphysical, upon the whole world.

4. FORM AND CONTENT

So far, we have dealt entirely with the different forms that may be exhibited by the same material, and which may make it look like an essentially different thing in each case. The "material" may not be physical at all; the words "matter" and "substance" are not very fortunate, because they only reinforce our natural prejudice in favour of imagining form as *shape*, and whatever has form, as *stuff*.

Logicians usually avoid this connotation by calling that medium wherein a form is expressed, its *content*. We may say, then, that we have so far considered how one and the same content may appear in several forms.

But equally important is the fact that one and the same form may be exemplified by different contents. Different things may take the *same* form. Consider the example given above (page 25) of *structure* determining form—the great stone face called the "Old Man of the Mountain." There it was pointed out that the cliff had nothing in common with a human face, except the arrangement of its parts, but this arrangement gave it the *form* of a man's profile. A form which is usually expressed in flesh and blood is here articulated in stone; the extraordinary *content* arouses our wonder and perhaps our superstitious imagination.

A very much homelier example of different contents for the same form, one which confronts us repeatedly in practical life, derives from the fact that two suits of the same pattern may be cut of different cloths. In this day of standardization, any number of suits, in any number of materials, exhibit exactly the same form, and if we chose to sew up the paper pattern from which they were cut, instead of leaving it spread out flat, we would have yet another suit made of paper. Likewise, one may think of a bread-pudding, a fruit-jelly, a blanc-mange, etc., all cooled in the same mould; they will, then, all have the same form, but differ in material, or content. There is nothing unfamiliar about the notion that diverse things may follow the same pattern. Everybody takes it for granted, just as everybody grants the fact that one substance may assume various forms.

The form of a suit or a pudding is, of course, a geometric form, a shape; so is the form of a face, whether it is moulded of flesh or of stone. But non-material structures may also have various contents. Suppose we return to our former example of a non-material construct, the C-major scale, and imagine it transposed one half-tone higher, so that it reads: C♯, D♯, E♯, F♯, G♯, A♯, B♯, high C♯. Not a single note in the C♯-major scale figures in the scale of C-natural.* Yet the two have exactly the same form, which is commonly called "*the* major scale." It is a peculiar fact that in music forms are easier to recognize than contents; most people can tell whether a given succession of tones is a major scale or not—they will mark any deviation from the form—but very few can tell whether the given major scale is C, C♯, or any other particular key. A normal ear will apprehend the form, but only persons blessed with so-called "absolute pitch" can identify the content.

Furthermore, two different contents for the same form may vary so widely that they belong to entirely different departments of human experience. Suits of cloth or paper are, after all, equally tangible, *physical* contents for a geometric form. Tones in a major scale are all equally *auditory* contents. However we vary our material, as from C to C♯, D to D♯, etc., our scale is still a *musical* form, and its content is some sort of sound. But why is the standard arrangement of these tones called a "scale"? "Scale" means "ladder." The fact is that ordinary, common sense sees a similarity of *form* between the order of successive tones, each new tone being a little higher than its predecessor, and the successive rungs of a ladder, each a little higher than the one before it. The word "scale" or "ladder" is transferred from one to the other. In this way, what was once the name of a certain kind of object has become the name of a certain *form*. Any series whose separate parts are arranged so that each is either higher or lower than any other part, is a "scale." Thus we speak of "going up in the social scale," or call a certain series of successively "higher" spiritual experiences

* On the piano the two scales appear to have certain tones in common, because E♯ and F, B♯ and C, respectively, fall on the same key; but that is due to the inaccuracy of a "tempered" instrument. On a violin they are distinguishable.

"the ladder of faith," without any danger of being mis-
understood, and being thought to refer to a series of tones,
or a wooden contraption with steps or rungs. Everybody
admits the propriety of our usage, by *analogy*; and analogy
is nothing but the recognition of a common form in different
things.

5. THE VALUE OF ANALOGY

Whenever we draw a diagram, say the ground-plan of
a house, or a street-plan to show the location of its site, or
a map, or an isographic chart, or a "curve" representing
the fluctuations of the stock-market, we are drawing a
"logical picture" of something. A "logical picture" differs
from an ordinary picture in that it need not look the least
bit like its object. Its relation to the object is not that of a
copy, but of *analogy*. We do not try to make an architect's
drawing look as much as possible like the house; that is,
even if the floor is to be brown, the floor-plan is not considered any better for being drawn in brown; and if the
house is to be large, the plan need not convey an impression
of vastness. All that the plan must do is to copy exactly the
proportions of length and width, the *arrangement* of rooms,
halls and stairs, doors and windows. The narrow dash that
represents a window is not intended to look like one; it
resembles the object for which it stands only by its location
in the plan, which must be analogous to the location of the
window in the room.

The dissimilarity in appearance between a "logical
picture" and what it represents is even more marked in the
case of a graph. Supposing a graph in the newspaper conveys
to you the growth, acceleration, climax and decline of an
epidemic. The graph is spatial, its form is a *shape*, but the
series of events does not have shape in a literal sense. The
graph is a picture of events only in a logical sense; its constituents, which are little squares on paper, are arranged
in the same proportions to each other as the constituents of

the epidemic, which are cases of illness. If the epidemic has lasted twenty days, the graph will show twenty vertical columns, and if the third day of the epidemic brought sixty cases of illness, the third column of the graph will show black squares up to sixty. Most of us have no difficulty in seeing an order and configuration of events graphically; yet the only form which the graph and the events have in common is a logical form. They have an analogous structure, though their contents are more incongruous than cabbages and kings.

It is only by analogy that one thing can *represent* another which does not resemble it. By analogy, a map can "mean" a certain place; and obviously it cannot "mean" any place which it does not fit, i.e. which has not a contour analogous to the map. If two things have the same logical form, one of them may represent the other, and not otherwise. Six mice may represent six horses, but even a fairy godmother would have had a hard time making six horses out of five, or seven, mice. Likewise, seven lean cows may mean seven poor years, and seven fat cows, seven years of plenty; but had the cows been all alike they would have lost their significance, for the analogy would have been broken. A rosary of beads may represent the number and order of prayers to be repeated, for the beads can be moved one after another, as the successive prayers are accomplished; if the beads were strung so they could not move, the band might be a necklace or a bracelet, but it could not be a rosary, for it would not represent what the shifting of the prayer-beads is supposed to stand for.

Perhaps the most elaborate structure ever invented for purely representative purposes is the syntactical structure of language. Its content, in itself, is trivial; it is a system of various little sounds, not beautiful and arresting sounds, like the content of musical structures, but rather ridiculous little squeaks and hums and groans. Yet in their arrangement and organization, these noises have such a developed pattern that they constitute a great system, any fragment of which has its logical form, its so-called "grammatical structure." What this structure can represent, is the order and connection of ideas in our minds. Our ideas are not mere fleeting images without definite relations to each other; whenever we are really *thinking*, not merely dozing in a haze of passive impressionism, our ideas exhibit sequence, arrangement, connection, a definite pattern. Some ideas belong together more intimately than others; some lead to others; some arise out of others, etc. It is this pattern which the elaborate pattern of language reflects. Separate words usually (though not always) stand for separate impressions or ideas, and such words are put together to make sentences, which express completed, organic thoughts, or propositions. Because the ideas we want to represent are of this complex sort, language cannot be a mere collection of words, such as a spelling-book might offer. Language must have a more articulated logical form. As soon as we are old enough to apprehend this form (not to *com*prehend it, for that is another matter), we learn to speak; our concerted ideas are reflected in the concerted patterns of sound that we utter. There are many ways of combining the elementary notions in our minds, and the commonest, most general of these ways are reflected in the laws of language, which we call syntax. Syntax is simply *the logical form of our language*, which copies as closely as possible the logical form of our thought. To *understand* language is to appreciate the analogy between the syntactical construct and the complex of ideas, letting the former function as a representative, or "logical picture," of the latter.

Bertrand Russell has given an excellent account of the sort of "form" that belongs to language, and by virtue of which we understand it to mean what it does. I quote the passage chiefly because it shows clearly the distinction of form and content in a sentence, and the relation of that form to *structure*, or arrangement of parts.

"In every proposition and every inference there is, besides the particular subject-matter concerned, a certain *form*, a way in which the constituents of the proposition or inference are put together. If I say, 'Socrates is mortal,' 'Jones is angry,' 'The sun is hot,' there is something in common in these three cases, something indicated by the word 'is.' What is in common is the *form* of the proposition, not an actual constituent. If I say a number of things about Socrates—that he was an Athenian, that he married Xantippe, that he drank the hemlock—there is a common constituent, namely Socrates, in all the propositions I enunciate, but they have diverse forms. If, on the other hand, I take any one of these propositions and replace its constituents, one at a time, by other constituents, the form remains constant, but no constituent remains. Take (say) the series of propositions, 'Socrates drank the hemlock,' 'Coleridge drank the hemlock,' 'Coleridge drank opium,' 'Coleridge ate opium.' The form remains unchanged throughout this series, but all the constituents are altered. Thus form is not another constituent, but is the way the constituents are put together. . . . We might understand all the separate words of a sentence without understanding the sentence: if a sentence is long and complicated, this is apt to happen. In such a case we have knowledge of the constituents, but not of the form. We may also have knowledge of the form without having knowledge of the constituents. If I say, 'Rorarius drank the hemlock,' those among you who have never heard of Rorarius (supposing there are any) will understand the form, without having knowledge of all the constituents. In order to understand a sentence, it is necessary to have knowledge both of the constituents and of the particular instance of the form. . . . Thus some kind of knowledge of logical forms, though with most people it is not explicit, is involved in all understanding of discourse. It is the business of philosophical logic to extract this knowledge from its concrete integuments, and to render it explicit and pure."*

The great value of analogy is that by it, and it alone, we are led to seeing a single "logical form" in things which may be entirely discrepant as to content. The power of recognizing similar forms in widely various exemplifications, i.e. the power of discovering analogies, is logical intuition. Some people have it by nature; others must develop it (and I believe all normal minds can develop it), and certainly all may sharpen the precision of their understanding, by a systematic study of the principles of structure.

6. ABSTRACTION

The consideration of a form, which several analogous things may have in common, apart from any contents, or "concrete integuments," is called *abstraction*. If we speak of *the* major scale apart from any particular key, we are treating it as an abstracted form. If we note what is common to a couple of days, a pair of gloves, a brace of partridges, and a set of twins, we are abstracting a form which each of these items exhibits, namely its numerosity, *two*. If we speak simply of a couple, without reference to any content, or simply of "two-ness" or "two," we are treating of this form *in abstracto*. Or again, if we consider the order in which hours of a day follow each other—always one after another, never two at once following the same predecessor —and then regard the order of inches on a ruler, or rungs on a ladder, or the succession of volumes of the *Encyclopaedia Britannica*, or the sequence of Presidents of the United States, we see at once that there is a common form in all these progressions. They are all analogous, all different contents for a pattern which is a section of the *ordinal number series*: first, second, third, etc. It is easy to see that it is but a short step from the recognition of analogies, or

* "Logic as the Essence of Philosophy" in *Our Knowledge of the External World*, London, 1914.

different contents for the same form, to abstraction, or the apprehension of that form regardless of any particular content.

Most people shy at the very word "abstraction." It suggests to them the incomprehensible, misleading, difficult, the great intellectual void of empty words. But as a matter of fact, abstract thinking is the quickest and most powerful kind of thinking, as even an elementary study of symbolic logic tends to show. The reason people are afraid of abstraction is simply that they do not know how to handle it. They have not learned to make *correct* abstractions, and therefore become lost among the empty forms, or worse yet, among the mere words for such forms, which they call "empty words" with an air of disgust. It is not the fault of abstraction that few people can really think abstractly, any more than it is the fault of mathematics that not many people are good mathematicians. There is nothing in our educational curriculum that would teach anyone to deal in abstracted forms. The only notable abstraction we ever meet is that empty form of arithmetic which is called algebra; and this is taught to us in such a way that most of us can pass a fairly hard examination in algebraic technique without even knowing that algebra is, indeed, the abstracted form of arithmetical calculations. No wonder, then, that we feel unfamiliar with pure forms! No wonder that some philosophers and almost all laymen believe abstraction to be vicious and intrinsically false. Without logical insight and training, they cannot go very far before falling into confusion, and then they blame the abstract nature of the ideas they are trying to handle for their own inability to handle them. Yet these same people are not afraid that a problem in, say, distances and horse-powers will become "purely verbal" if they apply algebra to its solution; that is because they know the manipulation of their algebra, and have learned to choose such forms as actually can be applied.

There is nothing abstruse, esoteric or "unreal" about abstract thinking. As Lord Russell remarks, everybody has "some kind of knowledge of logical forms"; it only needs to be made explicit, conscious, and familiar. And this is what the study of logic is supposed to do. We all deal with pure forms in a practical, intuitive way. Whenever we draw the ground-plan of a house, we not only see the analogy between the plan and the prospective edifice, but we intend to convey the mere form of the house without any indication or thought of the material to be used in building it. When we buy a paper pattern for a dress, we intend to use the form, without mentally committing ourselves to follow the suggestion on the envelope that it be made in blue chiffon or flowered voile. When we compose a tune, we recognize it whether it be sung, played, or whistled, and even if it is transposed into a higher or lower key. It is the form that interests us, not the medium wherein this form is expressed.

7. CONCEPTS

This process of attending only to the form of a thing or a situation, and conveying this "abstracted" form, which we carry out unconsciously as part of our common sense, becomes increasingly important when we pass from mere common sense to scientific thinking. Such abstracted forms are our *scientific concepts*. And because there are an astounding number of analogies in nature, we can form concepts which apply to a very great range of events. In fact, a few powerful concepts can systematize, or perhaps revolutionize, a whole field of observation, experiment, and hypothesis, called "a science."

Consider, for instance, how many motions follow the general pattern called "oscillation." The swing of a pendulum, the swaying of a skyscraper, the vibration of a violin-string over which the bow is passing, the chatter of our teeth on a cold day—all these are examples of the type-form called "oscillation." Now, if we were to define this type-form, we would omit all reference to skyscrapers and fiddle-strings and teeth, and describe it, probably, as "rhythmic motion to and fro," or in some such terms that would connote only the *sort of motion* we are talking about and not the *sort of thing that moves*. Probably, each of us has learned the meaning of oscillation through a different medium; but whether we gathered our first idea of it from the shaking of Grandpa's palsied hands—or from the quiver of a tuning-fork—or from the vibration of a parked automobile with the motor running—however our *mental pictures* may differ from each other, they have one thing in common: they are all derived from some rhythmic motion to and fro. The things exemplifying this *type* of motion are not necessarily alike in other respects; the swaying skyscraper and the vibrating violin-string are certainly not alike in appearance, origin, or purpose. But their motions have the common property of going rhythmically to and fro. This property is the *logical form* of their motions, and so we may call all these motions diverse instances of the same form.

When we consider the common form of various things, or various events, and call it by a name that does not suggest any particular thing or event, or commit us to any mental picture—for instance, when we consider this common form of various movements, and call it by a name such as "oscillation"—we are consciously, deliberately abstracting the form from all things which have it. Such an abstracted form is called a *concept*. From our concrete experiences we form the *concept of oscillation*.

The fact that so many things in nature exemplify the same forms makes it possible for us to collect our enormously variegated experiences of nature under relatively few concepts. If this were not the case, we could have no science. If there were not fundamental concepts such as oscillation, gravitation, radiation, etc., exemplified in nature over and over again, we could have no formulae of physics and discover no laws of nature. Scientists proceed by abstracting more and more fundamental forms (often seeing similarities among the abstracted forms, or concepts, themselves, and thus gathering several concepts into one); and by finding more and more things that fall under certain concepts, i.e. that exhibit certain general forms.

8. INTERPRETATION

The latter of these two procedures, finding applications for concepts, is called *interpretation of an abstract form*. It is a process of looking about for *kinds of things* to which a certain form belongs. If, for instance, we would interpret the abstract concept of "rotation," we would think of the rolling of a wheel, the motion of a heavenly body, the spinning of a top, the whirl of a propeller. Wheel-rolling, globe-turning, top-spinning, propeller-whirling, are all *interpretations* of the form, all *different contents for the abstract concept* "rotation." In one sense, two exactly similar spinning tops might be taken as two contents for one form, but in order to avoid confusion I shall call them two *instances* of one content for the same form. By two contents for a form I shall always mean *two sorts of thing* having the same form, i.e. falling under the same concept. That two *instances* do so goes without saying. There will be further discussion of this usage when we come to the distinction between "concrete" and "specific" elements.

Scientific concepts are forms which are exemplified in some general and important part of reality. The natural sciences all deal with abstract forms, but only with a selected set of them, namely those which will take a special sort of thing for their contents. Physics deals with any forms which may have physical things for their contents. Biology deals with just those forms that apply to living matter. That is to say, the special sciences take cognizance of all those and only those conceptual patterns, or formulae, to which they can give some *interpretation* relevant to their chosen subject-matter. Interpretation is the reverse of abstraction; the process of abstraction begins with a real thing and derives from it the bare form, or concept, whereas the process of interpretation begins with an empty concept and seeks some real thing which embodies it. In the sciences as in ordinary life, we are interested in forms only in so far as they are the patterns of certain things that concern us. Most of the abstract concepts we employ are handed down to us—in language, like all our simple adjectival and adverbial concepts; or by deliberate training, like our common knowledge of mathematics, mechanics, and so forth. We learn them as they apply to certain things; we learn number by counting things, shapes by fitting objects together, qualities by comparing various articles, rules of conduct by gradually collecting and judging instances of good and evil. The easiest way to teach a formula is to present several instances and point out their common formal properties. But this is not the easiest way to discover *new* patterns, which no one points out to us. There are, essentially, two ways in which new forms of things are discovered: (1) by abstraction from instances which nature happens to collect for us (the power to recognize a common form in such a chance collection is scientific genius); (2) by interpretation of empty forms we have quite abstractly constructed. The latter way is usually the easier, because if we know a great variety of possible forms, we have at least an idea of what we are looking for. Technical inventions are discoveries of this sort; the inventor rarely, if ever, propounds a new principle, i.e. a new fundamental concept of physics, but cleverly combines the principles he has learned into a new interesting pattern; he may then construct a physical thing, or *actual model*, of that pattern. His abstract form—the calculation he makes on paper—is a mathematical *theorem* from purely conceptual principles; his application of it to the realm of physics is an *interpretation*; and his model is an *instance* of this interpreted special form (and of the principles it combines). He is concerned essentially about interpretations, and his abstract work is all performed for the sake of finding physically interpretable forms.

9. THE FIELD OF LOGIC

But if we would hold aloof awhile from any special science and really gain insight into the great storehouse of forms which may be interpretable physically, or psychically, or for any realm of experience whatever, we must consider abstracted patterns as such—the orders in which any things whatever may be arranged, the modes under which anything whatever may present itself to our understanding. This sounds like an utterly impossible and elusive task; to a casual observer it certainly seems as though there must be as many incommensurable forms in the world as there are different kinds and departments of experience. But, happily for our restricted intellects, this is not the case. Many things which look utterly unlike in experience—far more unlike than the motions of skyscrapers and of violin-strings, or tops and planets—are really made up in very similar ways, only it requires a good deal of practice to see this. "Orderliness and system," said Josiah Royce,* "are much the same in their most general characters, whether they appear in a Platonic dialogue, or in a modern text-book of botany, or in the commercial conduct of a business firm, or in the arrangement and discipline of an army, or in a legal code, or in a work of art, or even in a dance or in the planning of a dinner. Order is order. System is system. Amidst all the variations of systems and of orders, certain general types and characteristic relations can be traced." The tracing of such types and relations among abstracted forms, or concepts, is the business of logic.

* "The Principles of Logic" in Windelband and Ruge's *Encyclopaedia of the Philosophical Sciences*, vol. i, p. 81 (further volumes did not appear).

10. LOGIC AND PHILOSOPHY

What is the use of a science of pure forms? The use of it becomes apparent when we consider what just one branch of this science, pursued for its own sake, has added to human knowledge—I mean the branch of logic which we call mathematics. It has made all the quantitative sciences possible by showing us what relations *may* hold among quantities, i.e. by telling us what to look for. Some mathematical truths probably were discovered in the course of practical application, but by far the greater number, and among them all the more subtle and elusive (and, ultimately, most useful) mathematical relations, were found by people who gave their undivided attention to the study of abstract mathematical forms. Now, what mathematics is to the natural sciences, logic, the more general study of forms, is to philosophy, the more general understanding of the world. The aim of philosophy is to see all things in the world in proportion to each other, in some order, i.e. to see reality as a system, or at least any part of it as belonging to some system. But before we can find order and system, we must know something about them, so as to know what we are looking for, or we shall not recognize them when we find them. Systematic patterns, however, are so much easier to study *in abstracto*, without the confusing irrelevancies of any particular case, that although every science may be said to deal with this topic, logic is the science of order *par excellence*. Philosophy and science deal with interpreted patterns; it is not hard to see that this work is greatly facilitated by a thorough command of the abstract science of forms. In the case of philosophy especially, logic is a well-nigh indispensable tool. It illuminates problems that have been obscure for hundreds and even thousands of years, by showing us a possible new formulation of some thoroughly muddled question; it does away with innumerable notions that are merely different names for one and the same concept; it reveals inconsistencies in our most cherished thoughts, and suggests remarkable generalizations of ideas that seemed quite local in their application.

Logic is to the philosopher what the telescope is to the astronomer: an instrument of vision. If we would become astronomers, we must learn the use of the telescope—not impatiently, chafing to get at more important work, but systematically, finding a certain intrinsic interest in the mysteries of the instrument itself. Great scientific discoveries have often rewarded men who laboured over slight improvements of their instruments. The same is true for logic; if we try to learn it in a cursory fashion, grudging the time and thought we would rather put on metaphysical problems, constantly wondering whether we have not acquired enough logic for our purposes, we shall never see the world in its clear light. We must work with a genuine interest in our restricted, abstract subject if we want it to lead us naturally to philosophical topics, as indeed it will—to problems of epistemology, metaphysics and even ethics. Logic applies to everything in the world; but we must understand its powers and difficulties thoroughly before we can use it. A telescope does not of itself find the object we wish to see, nor does it show us any thing at which we direct it, unless we know precisely how to adjust the focus —that is to say, unless we are truly familiar with the instrument. Logic, likewise, becomes useful and important to the philosopher only after he has really grasped its technique. Any technique seems hard to the novice because at first he is clumsy in his ways; just as a learner at the typewriter feels that his work is made needlessly hard by the exactions of the touch-system, so the beginner in symbolic logic is apt to think the use of symbols is a silly device to make thinking more difficult. But as the typist soon learns to appreciate the tremendous advantage of a method that dispenses with sight, so to the logician the use of symbols soon becomes an inestimable aid in reasoning. Therefore we should try from the very beginning to operate with symbols, not to write long sentences first and then translate them into the required symbolism. Clear expression is a reflexion of clear concepts; and clear concepts are the goal of logic.

SUMMARY

The first step in scientific thinking is the realization that one substance may take many *forms*. Many unlike things may be "understood" as dissimilar forms of the same material. To understand a thing is not merely to know, have sensory knowledge of it, but to have knowledge *about* it, to know how it is made up and what other forms it might take.

"Form" does not necessarily mean "shape." "*Logical form*" means "*structure*," or the way a thing is put together. The many synonyms for "form" show that we use it in a highly general sense. "Structure," again, does not mean a deliberate putting together, or even any actual consecutive combination of parts that first are given separately. It means an orderly arrangement of parts, that may be found in nature as well as in artefacts.

A construct is not necessarily made out of physical substance. Therefore "form" should be distinguished not from "matter" but from "*content*." The content of a logical form may be psychical, musical, temporal, or in some other way non-physical, just as well as physical.

Two things which have the same logical form are *analogous*. The value of analogy is that a thing which has a certain logical form may be *represented* by another which has the same structure, i.e. which is analogous to it. The most important analogy is that between thought and language. Language copies the pattern of thought, and thereby is able to represent thought. To understand language requires some apprehension of logical form.

Abstraction is the consideration of logical form apart

from content. The reason why people distrust abstractions is simply that they do not know how to make and use them correctly, so that abstract thought leads them into error and bewilderment. Abstraction is perhaps the most powerful instrument of human understanding.

Abstracted forms are called *concepts*. Because nature is full of analogies, we can understand certain parts of it in the light of a few very general concepts. All things to which the same concept applies are analogous. Scientists attempt (1) to find many forms for a given content; (2) to abstract a common form from diverse contents, and so form *concepts*; (3) to apply their concepts to more and more kinds of thing, i.e. find new contents for their abstracted forms.

Finding possible contents for an empty form is called *interpretation*. The sciences deal only with forms which may be interpreted for their special subject-matter.

Logic deals with any forms whatever without reference to content. A knowledge of forms and their relations greatly facilitates any study of their possible applications. Logic is a tool of philosophical thought as mathematics is a tool of physics.

QUESTIONS FOR REVIEW

1. What is meant by "transformation"? Why is this notion important for science?
2. What is the difference between knowledge *of* a thing and knowledge *about* it? Do you think a dog has both kinds of knowledge?
3. What is a "logical picture"? How does it differ from an ordinary picture?
4. What is a "construct"? Is it always something that has been put together? Is a cloud a "construct"?
5. What is meant by "content"? What is its relation to form, to "stuff"? May two forms have the same content? May one form have different contents?
6. What is meant by calling two things "analogous"? What is the importance of analogy?

7. Why is the grammatical structure of language important? What, if anything, have the Lord's Prayer and the "Pater Noster" in common? What are their respective constituents? Have they any common constituent(s)?

8. What is abstraction?

9. What is the opposite of "abstraction"?

10. What rôle does abstraction play in science? Do we ever use abstract notions in "common-sense" thinking? Have abstractions practical value?

11. Are scientists interested primarily in abstractions? If so, why?

12. What is the relation of logic to science? Do you think it has any value for everyday life?

SUGGESTIONS FOR CLASS WORK

(AVOID EXAMPLES GIVEN IN THE TEXT)

1. Name three things that may appear in different forms.

2. Give two examples of "logical form" other than "shape."

3. Give an example of a "construct" not deliberately made.

4. Name two things, one material and one immaterial, which are analogous in form.

5. What name would you give to the structure exemplified by (1) a string-quartet, (2) a group of bridge-players, (3) a "good-luck" clover?

6. Give two different interpretations of the abstract concept "progression." To what respective fields of experience (e.g. different sciences) do they belong?

7. Make up a proposition with a different content, but the same form as: "Plato was the teacher of Aristotle."

CHAPTER II

THE ESSENTIALS OF LOGICAL STRUCTURE

1. RELATIONS AND ELEMENTS

In the previous chapter, it was said that the logical form of a thing depends upon its structure, or the way it is put together; that is to say, upon the way its several parts are *related* to each other.

Without adding or subtracting any of the factors in the composition of a thing, we may utterly change the character of that thing by changing the *relations* of the various factors to each other. For instance, consider the three names, "RONALD," "ROLAND," and "ARNOLD"; they contain exactly the same letters, but the relative positions of these letters —that is to say, their mutual *relations* of "before" and "after," or "right" and "left"—are different in each case, and utterly different words result. We may relate these six letters differently yet, and spell the name of an English poet, "LANDOR." What has been changed is not any of the letters, but the relations of "before" and "after" among these letters.

Not only in artificial devices like the letters that spell a word, but in physical things as well, the importance of relations may be seen in the very constitution of objects themselves. Consider, for instance, the character of a coral rock. Its factors are the shells of millions of lilliputian individuals, all in definite relations to each other. Each tiny shell coheres with some other, and that with another, and so forth. Ultimately they all cohere together in an immense lump. So long as their *relations to each other*—i.e. the fact that one is *to the right* of another, or *on* another, or *near* it, *far from* it, etc.,—can undergo no change, they form a solid island. But let some monstrous grinding force change their relations, so that shells which were *to the right* of others are now *to the left*, shells which were *near* each other now are *distant*, and so forth—and what has happened? The rock is no more! Perhaps not a single one of its factors has been destroyed, but if they no longer cohere, and thus keep their spatial relations to each other rigidly unaltered, the rock is destroyed. A mere shifting pile of corals is obviously not a rock. The very nature of the object depended on the *cohesion* of its parts. And cohesion is not itself a factor of the rock, but is a *relation among the factors*.

If you watch a young child playing with blocks, you will see him experimenting with the various relations into which the blocks may enter with one another, and learning to identify the forms which result. He piles one *upon* another, and a third *upon* this, and a fourth *upon* that; by using only the single relation we call "upon," he constructs a *column*. He sets one block *to the right of* another and puts a third one *across* the two; the result is the simplest sort of *lintel*. And so he proceeds, to a wall, a house, a pyramid. He does not change the blocks in any way, he merely changes that all-important thing called structure, by changing the *relations* among his blocks.

Two things of very diverse material may, as I have already pointed out, have the same form. This is because *many different things may enter into the same relations*. Not only blocks may be set one above another, but also boxes, stones, books, or a thousand other things. A column of lines of print is just as much a column as one of bricks, because the same relations hold among the respective parts of both structures. When we speak of "a column" as such, we are quite indifferent to the nature of its material, being concerned only with *things ranged above or below each other*. "Above" and "below" are the essential relations which all columnar structures have in common, and by virtue of which they possess a common form.

Suppose, however, a column to be perfectly homogeneous, made of a single stone or tree-trunk or cement casting.

How can we say, then, that it is made of parts ranged one above the other? It has no parts, in the sense in which a column of blocks or books has parts. There are no dividing lines. What is supposed to be above what? Well, for one thing, the top is above the base. Also, if we draw parallel rings round the column, any such ring will be above or below any other. The rings divide the column into imaginary parts which are ranged in order. We may draw an infinite number of rings, but this relation will always obtain among them. In the previous chapter I pointed out that the elements in a structure need not be physically separate, first existing alone and then brought into combination. They must only be *conceptually distinguishable*; and ideal parts are geometrically distinguishable, though they be set off from each other by artificial, or even purely imaginary, lines. Therefore, even though a column be not composed of pieces set one upon another, it does allow us to conceive of its *possible sections* as ranged in this fashion; and it is simply on the basis of such a conception that we call an upright beam, or an obelisk, or even the air in a chimney or the mercury in a thermometer tube, a column. We can distinguish parts among which the governing *relation* of the column-form holds.

Since the related "parts" of a structure may not be parts at all, but may be physically inseparable qualities, aspects, locations, or what not, just as well as actual ingredients, I shall not refer to them as related *parts*, but as *elements* of the structure. Thus, in a column, whatever is ranged "above" or "below" something else, is an element. Every structure is at least ideally composed of elements. In a musical scale, the elements are tones; in orthography, letters; in penmanship, they would be the height, curvature and slant of lines which compose letters. Note that in this last case the elements are not parts, but merely *abstractable factors*; properties, not portions, of writing. But since these properties may be related to each other, since we may speak of the relative height and width, the spacing, the rounding, etc., of letters, these characteristics may be taken as *elements* in the structure called "a handwriting." Likewise, in judging a musical instrument, say a violin, one considers the proportions among certain attributes of its sound—the timbre, clarity, volume, and so forth—rather than the relations of individual tones to each other. Here the various tone-qualities are the elements of a structure which we call "the tone" of the violin. They are not separable *parts* of anything, but only distinguishable in conception.

Now, the elements alone do not constitute a structure; we must know these elements and also the way they are combined, that is, we must know the *relations* that hold among them. In forming a conceptual picture of a construct, as we do when we "describe" it in language, we must have items in the language-picture to stand for the elements, and also items of language to represent the relations. There are so many ways of relating elements that relations must have names. In fact, one might say that the conveyance of relationships among elements is the real function of language. If our interest centred entirely upon *things*, we would not need the whole system of nouns and adjectives, verbs and prepositions, which we call a "language"; grunts and demonstrative gestures would serve almost all purposes of communication. But relations are not things we can point to; they cannot be known by pure acquaintance; a knowledge of how the elements of a thing belong together is always a knowledge *about* this thing, and requires a logical picture, such as a grammatical word-picture, for its expression. We must have signs for elements and signs for their relationships. And that is just what we have in language. Such words as: "upon," "to the right of," "near," "greater than," are names for relations. They do not denote elements in a construct, but the way these elements are arranged. The same is true of such words as "loves," "hates," "knows," "writes to," "escapes from"; they are expressive of relationships into which certain elements may enter with each other.

2. TERMS AND DEGREE

The elements which are connected by a relation are called its *terms*.

Every relation must have terms in order to become visible to the understanding at all. A relation may be likened to the keystone of an arch, and its terms to the walls, which are combined by the keystone, and at the same time are its sole supports. Thus in a structure involving a relation there must always be elements, too, which serve as terms of the relation; such words as "upon," "loves," "gives," etc., cannot stand alone, but must function in a complex of other words denoting elements.

Different relations require different numbers of terms to support them. The relation "being North of," for instance, requires two terms; we say "Montreal (is North of) New York." On the other hand, the relation "between" requires three terms; we could not say that one term is between another, but should have to introduce another element, and say that the first is between the second and the third. Thus we might say "Cologne is between Paris and Berlin," but we could not say, simply, "Cologne is between Paris" or "Cologne is between Berlin," because "between" is a three-termed relation. "Being North of" is two-termed; for, although we may say "Montreal is North of Albany and New York," what we mean is "Montreal is North of Albany" and "Montreal is North of New York." That is, "between" requires three terms to *complete its sense*, whereas "North of" makes sense with two.

The most elementary characteristic of any relation is the number of terms it requires. If it connects two elements at a time it is said to be *dyadic*, if three, *triadic*, if it has four terms, *tetradic*, and so forth. This numerosity is called the *degree* of the relation.* Some relations, as for instance "among," have no definite degree, but are merely *more than dyadic*, so we may call them *polyadic relations*. "Greatest of," "least of," and all other relations expressed by super-latives, are polyadic. (Some writers call any relation of more than dyadic degree "polyadic," even when it is definitely tetradic, pentadic, etc.; if one deals with relations of very high degree, this usage is obviously justified. But, since we shall deal only with fairly simple structures, I prefer to reserve the expression "polyadic relation" for relations whose terms are of indefinite number.)

3. PROPOSITIONS

The commonest means of expressing a relation among several terms is the *proposition*. Whenever we assert that something is the case, we mention a relation among certain elements. Whether we say "Brutus killed Caesar," or "Abraham was the father of Isaac," or "The winters in Siberia are cold," each proposition asserts that a certain relation holds among certain terms. Any linguistic state-ment of a proposition must contain words for terms and for at least one relation; for the statement is a *word-picture* or "logical picture" of a *state of affairs* (real or imaginary), and a state of affairs is a complex of related elements. If we assert a proposition containing only one relation, such as "Brutus killed Caesar," the number of names for ele-ments that figure in the assertion tells us of what degree the relation must be. By certain conventions of syntax, i.e. by the fact that "killed" is an "active" verb-form, and that "Brutus" stands before and "Caesar" after the relation-sign (here, the verb), we know how the complex of *"Caesar* and *Brutus* in the relation *killing"* is put together.

Any symbolic structure, such as a sentence, expresses a

* This appellation is due to Professor H. M. Sheffer. C. S. Peirce called the property "adinity"—a peculiarly Peircean word.

proposition, if some symbol in it is understood to *represent a relation*, and the whole construct is understood to *assert that the elements* (denoted by the other symbols) *are thus related*. In ordinary language, the verb usually performs both functions; it names the relation and asserts that it holds among the elements. But if, as is often the case, the relation is *named* by a preposition or other kind of word, then an extra verb is required to *assert* the relation. This is the "auxiliary" use of the verb. For example, in "Brutus *killed* Caesar," the verb furnishes both the name of the relation, and the assertion that it holds; but in "the book *upon* the table," the preposition "upon" merely names a relation, without making any assertion; to make the structure a proposition we need an auxiliary word, e.g., the verb "is," to assert that the relation holds between "the book" and "the table." "The book *is upon* the table" is a proposition. The relation is named, and is said to hold between the elements.

4. Natural Language and Logical Symbolism

Unfortunately, in the matter of picturing the exact logical structure of a state of affairs, i.e. in expressing propositions, language is very elusive. In the first place, it does not by any means employ certain kinds of symbols for terms and reserve others for relations. Very broadly speaking, nouns represent elements, and verbs, relations. In a logically perfect language this would always be the case; but in the traditional idioms of the human race, it is not. We use all sorts of word-complexes, all sorts of syntactical devices, to convey now elements, now relations, so that natural language, if we were to take it as a guide, would often lead us into wrong logical analyses. For instance, "wife" is a noun, and in the proposition: "Jones killed his wife," it denotes a term; but if we say: "Xanthippe is the wife of Socrates," the *relation* is "being the wife of." In this case, the noun "wife" *names* the relation, and the verb "is" asserts that it holds between its terms.

To avoid such ambiguity, as well as a great many other difficulties, we replace words by arbitrary symbols—numbers, letters, or other signs—which are not subject to the vagaries of literary grammar and syntax, but present a simplified grammar of logical structure. In such a symbolism, one character stands for one term, another for another term, etc., and *a symbol of different type entirely* represents the relation. Let us suppose that A and B stand for Jones and for his wife, respectively; Then we would not denote the relation of killing by "K," which is another Roman capital letter, but by some radically different symbol. We might use an arbitrary sign, an arrow or a curl, or some different type of letter, or combination of letters. Let us take a combination of lower case Roman letters, "kd." Then the proposition symbolically presented reads:

$$A \text{ kd } B$$

On the other hand, let C stand for Xanthippe and D for Socrates, and the relation "is the wife of" be represented by "wf"; the second proposition is, then:

$$C \text{ wf } D$$

There is no danger of confusing "wife" as a term with "wife" as a relation, if one is called "B" and the other "wf." Our eye shows us the structural difference.

In this symbolism we do not distinguish between verbs, prepositions, adjectives, and nouns which denote relations; for the present, we shall always merely *name* relations, and take the function of the auxiliary verb for granted. A relation symbol placed among symbols for elements shall always have the force of the verb in a sentence, unless otherwise specified; e.g., "between" is a preposition, but if we let "bt" stand for the relation this preposition names, and take A, B, and C for its terms, then

$$A \text{ bt } B, C$$

is to be read: "A *is between* B and C."

Now, ordinary speech is rich in meanings, is full of implicit ideas which we grasp, by suggestion, by association, by knowing the import of certain words, word-orders, or inflections. That is what gives natural language its colour, vitality, speed, its whole emotional value and literary adequacy. A few words can convey very much. But this same wealth of significance makes it unfit for logical analysis. Many apparently simple statements express, in telescoped form, more than one proposition. Thus in "Jones killed his wife" the word which a grammarian would call the direct object does more than a direct object should, namely to denote the element to which Jones stood in the relation of killing; it also conveys that this element stood in the relation "wife" to Jones. In other words, "Jones killed his wife" *means* more than "A kd B," though that is its grammatical form; it signifies

A kd B and B wf A

Here we see how a noun comes to have the same name as a relation; by the grammatical aid of the possessive pronoun "his," it manages to represent a whole proposition. Where propositions are thus telescoped into compact linguistic expressions it is, of course, the easiest thing in the world to miss their logical form completely.

But confusion of elements and relations, and the contraction of several propositions into one, are not even the only charges to be brought against natural language as a revealer of logical forms. The very nature of the relation may be obscured. A dyadic relation may look like a triadic one, as in the example adduced above: "Montreal is North of Albany and New York." Also, two relations of different degree may be expressed in perfectly homologous ways. For example, consider these two statements:

(1) I played bridge with my three cousins.
(2) I played chess with my three cousins.

They seem to present relations of exactly similar structure. But in fact, the relation called "bridge-playing" requires four terms, i.e. it is tetradic, whereas chess-playing is dyadic. Linguistic grammar gives no indication whatever of this distinction. But if we operate with symbols the difference of structure becomes immediately apparent; indeed, the second proposition proves to be ambiguous, for it embodies two different meanings. Let A stand for the speaker, B, C, D, for the three cousins respectively, "br" for the relation "bridge-playing," "ch" for "playing chess." Then the first statement may be expressed:

$$A \text{ br } B, C, D$$

The second, however, means either that the speaker played with each of the three cousins in turn, or that the three banded together as one opponent for a very superior player. Upon the first alternative, three propositions have been collected linguistically into one statement; on the second, one of the *terms* of the relation "chess-playing" is a composite term. But the relation is dyadic, none the less. If we chose the former meaning, the symbolic rendering would be:

$$A \text{ ch } B$$
$$A \text{ ch } C$$
$$A \text{ ch } D$$

For the latter, we should write:

$$A \text{ ch } (B\text{-}C\text{-}D)*$$

But upon either assumption, it is evident that "br" and "ch" are relations of different degree, so that the two propositions which in language seem to differ only by the

---

* The hyphen, which might also be replaced by +, expresses an *operation*, whereby two terms are combined into one; but this subject belongs to a later chapter, so the possibility of uniting B-C-D must here be taken on faith.

denotation of one word actually represent situations of different logical structure. In ordinary conversation, though errors occur through ambiguity, they are not usually of a serious nature; they are righted by explanations and common sense. But when our whole purpose in quoting propositions is the study of their logical forms, then a medium which obscures such essential differences as that between a dyadic construct and a tetradic one is simply inadequate. We must resort to a symbolism which copies the structure of facts more faithfully.

When a relation-symbol stands in a construct, the number of terms grouped with it reveals the degree of the relation. But when it is not actually *used*, but merely spoken of, it is sometimes convenient to have some way of denoting its degree. This may be done by adding a numerical subscript; for example, "kd_2" means that "killing" is dyadic, "bt_3" that "between" is triadic. The upshot of treating the above propositions, (1) and (2), symbolically, is that we find we have relations of different degree, namely "ch_2" and "br_4."

Furthermore, natural language has a strong tendency to let one word embody many meanings. This fallacy, which we exploit in making puns and twisting arguments, seems, at first sight, to be another of those weaknesses of language against which we ought to be guarded by common sense and the vigilance of English teachers. We are supposed to know that

"The morning breaks, and with it breaks my heart,"

involves an amphibolous use of the word "breaks"—a change from one meaning to another, neither of which, in this case, happens to be the "real" (or literal, or primary) meaning. But ambiguity (and with it amphiboly), especially in words denoting relations, is much more general than ordinary, casual reflexion would reveal to us, and in logic at least it may have unsuspected disastrous effects. Few people are aware that they use so common and important a word as "is" in half a dozen different senses. Consider, for instance, the following propositions:

(1) The rose is red.
(2) Rome is greater than Athens.
(3) Barbarossa is Frederick I.
(4) Barbarossa is a legendary hero.
(5) To sleep is to dream.
(6) God is.

In each of these sentences we find the verb "is." But each sentence expresses a differently constructed proposition;

(1) ascribes a *property* to a term;
in (2) "is" has logically only an auxiliary value of *asserting* the dyadic relation, "greater than";
in (3) "is" expresses *identity*;
in (4) it indicates *membership in a class* (the class of legendary heroes);
in (5) *entailment* (sleeping *entails* dreaming);
in (6) *existence*.

So we see that in (1) and (2) it is only part of the logical verb—it serves only to assert the relation, which is otherwise expressed—and in the remaining four cases, where "is" does function as the whole logical verb, it expresses a different relation in every case. It has at least four different meanings besides its use as auxiliary. Our linguistic means of conveying relations are highly ambiguous. But the expression of relations is the chief purpose of language. If we were interested only in *things* and not in their arrangement and connection, we could express ourselves with our forefingers. *Things* are easy to identify; two beings named "John," when actually present, are not likely to be treated erroneously as one person (like the two heroes called "the King" in Gilbert and Sullivan's *Gondoliers*), because it is apparent to every one that there is *this* John and *that* John; but two relations named "is" are very likely to meet with such a fate, because relations become explicitly known—become visible, so to speak—only in discourse. Symbolic expression, through words, diagrams, or other such means, is their only incarnation. So the study of relations is necessarily bound up with a study of discourse. But if the latter obscures and disguises relations, as it often does, there is no escape from error, except by adopting another sort of discourse altogether. Such a new medium of expression is the symbolism of logic. In this ideography, the four propositions wherein "is" really names a relation would not appear to have a common form, but would wear the badge of their distinctions plainly in view:

(3) Barbarossa = Frederick I
(4) Barbarossa ϵ legendary hero
(5) To sleep $\subset$ to dream
(6) E! God

Only by a refined and ever more precise symbolism can we hope to bring logic out of language.

5. Some Principles Governing Symbolic Expression

Since the simplest structures—complexes of one relation and its terms—yield propositions, we may regard propositions as our first material for analysis; and the task to which we immediately address ourselves is *the adequate expression of the forms which those propositions really have,* i.e. the forms involved in their meanings, and not their customary idiomatic renderings. Now, this art of expression cannot be learned by thumb-rule. Symbolic logic is a new science, wherein every student may be something of an innovator, and with exception of a few usages which have become fixed through the classical literature (such as the four signs for different meanings of "is," quoted above), everyone is free to introduce any symbols that serve his purpose. But of course one must have some way of knowing explicitly what each sign stands for, that is, one must know the *interpretation* which is to be attached to it. Therefore it is advisable to state that a given symbol *equals by interpretation* a certain term or relation. This phrase is conveniently abbreviated "= int." Thus, in explaining the symbolism in the four propositions above, I should head my discourse with the glossary:

"=" =int "identical with"
" ε " =int "membership in the class"
" C " =int "entailment"
"E!" =int "there exists"

And in the example of the cousins playing bridge and chess, a complete notation of the propositions (accepting the first alternative for the meaning of "I played chess with my three cousins") would be:

"A" =int "the speaker"
"B," "C," "D" =int "cousins" (respectively)
"br_4" =int "bridge-playing"
"ch_2" =int "chess-playing"

(1) A br B, C, D*
(2) A ch B
     A ch C
     A ch D

The symbols here adopted are arbitrary. We might as well have written 1, 2, 3, 4 for our elements, or α, β, γ, δ; and the relation "br" might have been expressed by a picture of a playing card, and "ch" by a chess-pawn, or any other sign that suggested itself. But certain general *principles of symbolization* should be borne in mind in the selection of logical characters:

(1) Signs for elements and signs for relations should be different in kind.

---

* When a relation is *used*, the subscript is omitted, because the construct itself reveals the degree of the relation.

That is, it would not do to use C and B for the relations, nor be advisable to use even CH and BR, as long as the elements are represented by Roman capitals.

(2) Signs for relations should not strongly suggest relations which are not meant. This principle will be elucidated later, when we classify relations by other properties than mere degree. In effect, it means that one should not represent "above" by a symbol such as ⊙, suggesting "within," or "to right of" by an arrow pointing left, or "br" by a chess-pawn. It is advantageous to choose symbols so that they suggest their meanings; but

(3) Suggestiveness should never be allowed to interfere with logical clarity or elegance.

For instance, if we wanted to state that Chicago lies between New York and Denver, we might well use C for Chicago, and D for Denver, but to use NY for New York would be confusing, because, if we use Roman capitals for elements, the use of *two* letters would suggest some combination of two elements. If we wanted a more suggestive symbolism than A, B and C, we might use C, D and N, or C, D and Y; but not, C, D and NY.

(4) The assignment of arbitrary meanings to signs with traditionally established uses should be avoided. That is to say, one should not use = to mean chess-playing, or ε for "to the right of," because these signs are pre-empted for certain important relations and generally used with those connotations.

(5) Signs should be easy to write and to recognize, and be as compact as possible. A chess-man, unless it were highly conventionalized, would be a poor symbol for "ch" because it would be too elaborate. Also, if we did conventionalize it, we should be careful not to let the resultant figure look like a 2, an i, or any

other symbol, if such a symbol is to occur in our constructs. If a symbol is to appear in print, there are further problems of typographical convenience, but these need not be considered here.

6. THE POWER OF SYMBOLS

An intelligent use of symbolism is of utmost importance in the study of structure; one should try from the beginning to develop definite, consistent, and easy habits of expression. There is something uncanny about the power of a happily chosen ideographic language; for it often allows one to express relations which have no names in natural language and have therefore never been noticed by anyone. Symbolism, then, becomes an organ of discovery rather than mere notation. Consider what a development resulted in the science of mathematics from the introduction of a symbol for "nothing"! It has given us the better part of our arithmetic, columnar addition and subtraction, long division, long multiplication, and the whole decimal system. A child in grammar-school can write, offhand, computations for which a Roman sage would have needed the abacus. This is due simply to our superior symbolism, our nine digits, and o. The revolutionizing of mathematics by the Arabic number system is the most striking example of the aid which a good medium of expression lends to the mind.

SUMMARY

The structure of a thing is the way it is put together. Anything that has structure, then, must have parts, properties, or aspects which are somehow related to each other. In every structure we may distinguish the *relation* or *relations*, and the items which are *related*.

Since these items are not necessarily "parts," but may be qualities, values, or any conceptually distinguishable features, they are called not parts of the structure but *elements*. They may be only ideally distinguishable.

The elements which stand in a relation to each other are called the *terms* of that relation.

Different relations may combine different numbers of terms at a time. Some relations hold always among two terms, some among three, etc. The number of terms which a relation demands is called the *degree* of that relation. Two-termed relations are called *dyadic*, three-termed *triadic*, etc. Some relations have a minimum of more than two, but no maximum, number of terms; they are called *polyadic*.

A symbolic construct, e.g. a combination of words denoting terms and relations, which is understood to assert that the denoted terms stand in the denoted relation, is a *proposition*.

Relations are intangible unless they are formulated in language. Symbolic expression is their only incarnation. Therefore logic is necessarily bound up with language. The simplest logical structures are those expressed by propositions that mention just one relation and its terms. Therefore we shall take such propositions as the most elementary material for logical study.

In a logically perfect language, elements would always be denoted by one kind of word and relations by another; there would be just one word for each element and one for each relation; and the grammatical form would reflect exactly the form of the complex it expresses. In "natural language," however, this is not the case. Its idiom often disguises relations, by (1) using the same word for relations and for elements, (2) telescoping several propositions into one, (3) disguising the degree of a relation, and (4) using one word in several senses.

Because of these shortcomings of natural language, logicians adopt the simpler and more consistent medium of ideographic symbols. In a symbolically expressed proposition the relation is merely *named*, and the fact that it is *asserted to hold* is (for the present) always understood. Since symbols may have meanings arbitrarily assigned, it is necessary to state what each sign *equals by interpretation*.

Ideographic signs may be freely invented or adopted within the limits of the following principles of symbolic expression:

(1) Radical distinction between term signs and relation signs.
(2) Avoidance of false suggestion.
(3) Precedence of logical exactness over any psychological advantages.
(4) Avoidance of traditionally pre-empted signs.
(5) Due attention to distinctness, compactness, and typographical simplicity.

A good symbolism leads not only to a clear understanding of old ideas, but often to the discovery of new ones.

QUESTIONS FOR REVIEW

1. What relations are involved in the constitution of
   (a) a nest of tables, (b) a cluster of swarming bees, (c) a row of fence pickets, respectively?
2. What constituents must a structure have beside relations?
3. What is the chief use of a "logical picture"?
4. What is the most important kind of "logical picture"?
5. What is meant by the terms of a relation?
6. What is meant by the degree of a relation?
7. What is dyadic relation? Polyadic?
8. What is a proposition? What two functions are performed by the main verb in a proposition?
9. Why do logicians use symbols?
10. What dangers can you see in the use of "natural language" to present propositions for logical study?
11. What principles must be observed in the choice of symbols?

SUGGESTIONS FOR CLASS WORK

I. Name a construct whose elements are not physical parts.

II. In the following propositions, underline the words denoting relations:
   (1) "The Assyrian came down like a wolf on the fold."
   (2) "The pen is mightier than the sword."
   (3) "Never trouble trouble till trouble troubles you."

III. In the following propositions, underline the relation and
     state its degree:
   (1) Mary, Margaret, and Jane are sisters.
   (2) James, John, and Jerry are triplets.
   (3) Paris and Berlin are smaller than London.
   (4) The tones C, E, and G form a triad.
   (5) "She dwelled among the untrodden ways."
   (6) "The greatest of these is charity."

IV. Using Roman capitals for terms and symbols of your own
    choice for relations, state the following propositions:
   (1) Jesse was the father of David.
   (2) Keats was younger than Wordsworth and Coleridge.
   (3) New England is Maine, New Hampshire, Vermont,
       Massachusetts, Rhode Island, and Connecticut.
   (4) Sam gave his dog to Rhoda.
   (5) Sam gave his dog a bone.

CHAPTER III

THE ESSENTIALS OF LOGICAL STRUCTURE
(*Continued*)

1. CONTEXT

If you read in the paper a headline: "Lived together ten years without speaking," your imagination promptly supplies suitable terms to the relation which alone is mentioned. A man and his wife, or a mother and her daughter, in short: *someone* and *someone else* must have lived together ten years without speaking. Again, if you open a cook-book at random and read at the head of a page: "these should be rubbed together to a smooth paste," you know at once that "these" must refer to things like flour, shortening, sugar, yolks of eggs, or the like. You may say that you have not the faintest idea *what* is to be rubbed together to a smooth paste, or *who* lived together ten years without speaking; but the mere fact that you say *what* and *who*, respectively, shows that you know something about the missing terms of such propositions. You would feel greatly disconcerted to read that butter and sugar lived together ten years without speaking or that mother and daughter should be rubbed together to a smooth paste. The reason for this is that you have understood the relation and you know, in a general way, what is the range of its possible applications. The same is true, of course, if a certain set of terms is given and the relation left undetermined. If you read, on either side of a blot on the back of a post-card: "We (blot) Niagara," you may not know whether the relation between your friends and Niagara is that they saw the waterfall or that they missed it, liked or scorned, feared or photographed it, but you do know that the lost verb cannot be "married" or "ate" or "strangled." Such relations among such terms would fail to *make sense*. Our thoughts always move within a certain range, a great, vaguely apprehended class of things which we feel could be related to each other, and we look only for relations which might conceivably hold among these things. Such a range of general subject-matter—of terms and relation that may enter together into our thoughts—is called a context. Whatever lies outside a given context is felt to be irrelevant, incapable of adding anything but sheer nonsense.

In ordinary thinking, the context is indefinite, mutable, and tacitly assumed. It grows and shrinks with every turn of the conversation. You hear a bang, and ask: "Who has just come into the house?" And all your thoughts are in terms of *people*, *front door*, and the relations of *closing*, *entering*, etc.; but let the answer be: "No one; that was the cover of the wood-box you heard," and your whole constellation of ideas, your context, has shifted to *wood-box*, *cover*, the relations of *dropping*, *making noise*. The person who gave the answer was thinking in your terms and also in those which his reply presupposes, else he would not have found any sense in your question, and his answer would have been an irrelevant statement, not an answer at all. So the context in everyday conversation is always varying, adjusting itself to the interests of many people and many domains of thought.

2. CONCEPTS AND CONCEPTIONS

But in the sciences, which study the interrelations of elements within certain limited, definite realms of reality, or in logic, which deals with *any* given realm, and studies the possible means of making sense out of its constituents, we cannot do with a vague, indefinite, tacitly accepted context. If we want to build up an elaborate conceptual structure, we must have recognizable concepts, not subjective and incommunicable mental pictures. It does not make any difference what sort of mental picture embodies a concept; all that counts in science is the concept itself.

For instance, it is immaterial whether you imagine "absolute zero" (the temperature of interstellar space in complete absence of heat) as a sensation experienced by someone fantastically floating in a dark void, or whether you imagine it as the lowest mark on a very long thermometer. Two persons, one of whom imagines the void, while the other envisages the mercury-column, may talk perfectly comprehensibly together about the properties of "absolute zero." That is because their mental pictures are merely personal symbols of a concept with which they are both operating. The sensation in the void only *represents* the concept, which is "the first element of the ordered series of all possible temperatures ranged in the relation 'warmer than.' " The lowest mark on the imaginary mercury-column represents the same thing. That is why these two men can talk sensibly with one another.

One might say that, due to psychological factors, the two people have divergent *conceptions* of absolute zero, but are operating with the same *concept*. This difference of meaning between "concept" and "conception" is not rigorously observed in ordinary usage, but neither is it a purely arbitrary technicality; purists in English will agree, I think, that it is better to speak of *"my conception of honour"* than of *"my concept of honour,"* and to refer to *"the concept* 'honour' " rather than to *"the conception* 'honour.' " The distinction between these two terms— "conception" for the mental image or symbol, "concept" for the abstractable, public, essential form—seems to me so convenient that we are justified in adopting it "technically," i.e. as an accepted rule of vocabulary.

3. FORMAL CONTEXT

If we would rule out of our thinking all associated ideas which spring from conceptions rather than concepts, and consequently are the subjective, personal context of our propositions, we must enumerate explicitly the elements and relations to be admitted for consideration. In a scientific discussion of temperatures, the loneliness and silence of the realms where absolute zero obtains are irrelevant; these factors are associated with "absolute zero" only through a picturesque personal conception of that temperature, and are meaningless to the man who imagines a long thermometer with the mercury out of sight. Likewise the astounding length of the imaginary thermometer is irrelevant. "Loneliness," "silence," and "length" are not *logically* connected with the meaning of "absolute zero." If we make our formal statement: "Absolute zero is the first element in a series of all possible temperatures ranged in the relation 'warmer than,'" the only elements are "temperatures," and the only relation is "warmer than." If the man who thinks of the cold void utters this proposition, its *psychological* context probably contains such elements as space, awe, death, or what-not; but the thermometer-man who understands and accepts the proposition knows nothing about these. His *psychological* context contains visual elements The *concept*, however, which the two have in common, and by virtue of which one understands the other, has a different context entirely, which contains as elements only states of temperature, and as relations only the comparative concept "warmer than" and its derivatives ("cooler than," "not warmer than," "of like temperature," are concepts which may be derived *by definition* from "warmer than." See below, chapter vi §1). Everything that can enter into a scientific discussion of "absolute zero" must be constructed within this conceptual frame, which I call the *formal context of the discourse*.

The formal context of any discourse may be agreed upon and expressed; the psychological context cannot. One person may have a fair idea of another's psychological framework—for instance, we know that "death" figures in a different context for a kidnapper's victim who feels a pistol at his back, and for an undertaker whose telephone is ringing—

but we cannot exhaustively state such a context and know all ideas that are relevant to it.

(A) *The Universe of Discourse*

The total collection of all those and only those *elements* which belong to a formal context is called a *Universe of Discourse*. In ordinary conversation, we assume the limitations of such a universe, as when we say: "Everybody knows that another war is coming," and assume that "everybody" will be properly understood to refer only to adults of normal intelligence and European culture, not to babies in their cribs, idiots, or the inhabitants of remote wildernesses. For conversational purposes the tacit understanding will do; but if the statement is to be challenged, i.e. if someone volunteers to produce a person to whom it may be applied, but of whom it is not true, then it becomes important to know just what the limits of its applicability really are. Arguments of this sort have their own technique, by which the opposition marshals contradictory cases—in this example, persons who have no such knowledge—and the asseverator rules them out as "not meant" by his statement. The universe of ordinary discourse is vague enough so that this process can go on as long as the bellicosity of the two adversaries lasts.

Logicians and scientists, however, take no pleasure in casuistry. Their universe of discourse must be definite enough to allow no dispute whatever about what does or does not belong to it. For instance, if an anthropologist makes the statement that everybody is born into some social group, we understand him to mean the baby in its crib and the head-hunter of Patagonia as well as the American ambassador to the Court of St. James, because the universe of discourse of his science is known to include all human beings. Did it not, he would be called upon to state its limits.

We may limit a universe of discourse as much as we like;

so elaborate a structure as a natural science has a very great universe, whereas a lesser construct, say the formal set of rules for playing chess, is limited to 64 elements called "squares," and 32 elements called "men." The chess game does not take in *all* elements called "chess-men"; its universe is limited to 32. In teaching chess to a novice, the first thing one does is to enumerate the elements involved, call his attention to the squares and the men, before one mentions the relations which hold, or fail to hold, among them. Now, this is exactly the way to begin the rigorous analysis of any structure. The universe of discourse must be recognized and expressed. Logicians usually denote it by the letter K, derived from the German *Klasse*, a class, and put in parentheses the notation chosen for its elements. But since we have adopted the practice of using Roman capital letters for elements, I shall use an italic K for the total class of such elements, because this is not itself an element and should have a different kind of symbol.

Suppose we select a very simple universe of discourse, a group of four houses, whose relations to each other we are going to state. We should then introduce our universe as follows:

$$K(A, B, C, D) \qquad K = \text{int "houses"}$$

Here we have an enumeration of just four elements, the symbolic indication that they form a universe of discourse, and the *interpretation* by virtue of which the elements are known to be houses.

(B) *Constituent Relations*

A formal context involves not only elements, but the relations which connect such elements. Obviously one cannot introduce any relation, at random, into any universe whatever; for instance, one cannot say that 2 is older than 3, or that one house is wiser than another. Such statements would be neither true nor false; they would be simply meaningless. We must choose our relations with reference to the sort of elements contained in K.

Now, if we let $K =$ int "houses," there are many relations which "make sense" when taken to function among its elements; we may say of two houses, A and B, that A is *greater than* B, A is *as old as* B, A is *costlier than* B, A is *to the right of* B, and so forth and so on indefinitely. Or of three houses, A, B, and C, it might be said that A is *between* B and C, that A *connects* B and C, that A, B, and C *form a triangle*, etc. Likewise the four houses A, B, C, and D may *form a quadrangle*, or we might say that A is *in the midst* of B, C, and D. All these are possible relations with the given universe of discourse, K. But there is no reason why our formal context should include them all. If we want to describe the spatial arrangement of four houses, the relation *costlier than* has obviously no place in the discussion; neither has *as old as*. Such concepts do not suit our purpose, so we rule them out. In fact, in establishing a formal context, it is a general practical rule *to choose the simplest concepts, and the smallest number of them, that will serve the purpose of the discourse*. Suppose we begin with just one dyadic relation, "to the North of," and symbolize it by "nt_2." This is, then, the *only* relation admitted to the formal context; all propositions must be made solely out of elements A, B, C, and D and the relation "nt."

A relation which belongs to the formal context I call a *constituent relation* of the discourse. It is one of the concepts explicitly assumed as a legitimate constituent of propositions in that discourse. The formal context consists of the universe and all of the constituent relations (in this case, just one), and may be symbolized as follows:

$$K(A, B, C, D) \; nt_2 \qquad K =\text{int "houses"}$$
$$nt_2 =\text{int "to the North of"}$$

Every possible pair of terms from this universe, combined by the relation "nt," yields a proposition; the sixteen propositions which can be made in this wise are called the *elementary propositions* in the formal context K(A, B, C, D) nt$_2$.

4. TRUTH-VALUES

Every combination of elements in a formal context yields a proposition which is either *true* or *false*. But we may not know which it is. If I assert "A nt B," you may understand the proposition, and know, of course, that *either* it is true or it isn't, but you may never know *whether* it is true or false. That is meant by saying you do not know its *truth-value*.

The word "value" has, in common parlance, the connotation of "good," "precious," or (more materialistically) of "having a price." But there is another meaning of the word with which most people are familiar from their schooldays, namely the "value" for an "unknown." Most of us vaguely remember that if a farmer has x sheep, which meet with all sorts of accidents as sheep do in algebra books, so that in the end there are only $\frac{x}{2}$, or ten sheep left, then the *value* of x is 20. It is this sense of "value" that is involved in the term "truth-value," which has nothing whatever to do with the eternal or divine or moral qualities of "truth," but merely with the fact that we have here the property of "true-or-false" and do not necessarily know which. If we decide a proposition is true, we *say it has the truth-value "truth,"* and if it is false, then *its truth-value is "falsity."* "Truth-value" is a very convenient term and is widely used in the literature of logic, but the word "value" must not be taken in any moral or economic sense.

5. RELATED PROPOSITIONS IN A FORMAL CONTEXT

Consider the formal context given above:

K(A, B, C, D) nt$_2$ K = int "houses"
                    nt$_2$ = int "to the North of"

Since nt is dyadic, i.e. combines its terms two at a time, there are sixteen possible ways of combining A, B, C, and D (counting the cases where the same letter stands before and after the relation, as: "A nt A," "B nt B," etc.). Each possible combination by means of "nt" yields a proposition which is either true or false. Without any special information about the four houses in question, can we know the truth-values of any of these propositions?

Well, if "nt_2" is to mean "North of," then certainly no element can have this relation to itself; so we know off-hand that:

A nt A fails*
B nt B fails
C nt C fails
D nt D fails

Here are four truth-values fixed in advance; none of the houses is to the North of itself. To express the fact that a relation fails, i.e. that the proposition in which it functions is not true, it is customary to enclose the proposition in parentheses and prefix to this whole expression the sign $\sim$. Thus, $\sim$ (A nt A) means "A nt A fails," and may be read "A *is not* North of A," or "*It is false that* A nt A." In formal symbolism, then, the four established propositions should be written:

$\sim$ (A nt A)
$\sim$ (B nt B)
$\sim$ (C nt C)
$\sim$ (D nt D)

So the nature of the constituent relation determines the truth-value of four propositions; any other proposition in the formal context, however, may be either true or false. It seems that, to know all the truth-values of the sixteen

* A relation is said to "fail" whenever it is significant, but does not hold among the stated terms.

possible propositions, we would require twelve items of special information.

Now, let us assume just one such item; namely, that "A nt B" is true. Immediately we know the truth-value of not one, but two propositions: we know that

$$A \text{ nt } B$$
and
$$\sim (B \text{ nt } A)$$

The falsity of the latter follows from the truth of the former, as we recognize from our common sense understanding of "nt_2." We know that this particular relation cannot connect two terms in both possible orders. The truth of one proposition *precludes the truth*, or *implies the falsity*, of the other. (Note that to be told "A nt B is *false*" would not give us any knowledge of "B nt A," since both might be false, though not both can be true.)

Suppose, now, we know "A nt B," and are given the further information, "B nt C." At once we realize these two propositions *together* imply that C is also to the North of A. So the *truth* of two propositions determines the *truth-values* of six:

$$A \text{ nt } B$$
$$B \text{ nt } C$$

jointly asserted, assure us of the following facts:

$$A \text{ nt } C$$
$$\sim (B \text{ nt } A)$$
$$\sim (C \text{ nt } A)$$
$$\sim (C \text{ nt } B)$$

So it appears that even in the case of the twelve undetermined propositions, the truth-values that might be assigned to them are not entirely arbitrary and unrestricted. The truth of one proposition *precludes* that of another, or the joint assertion of two propositions *implies* a third. The possible truth-values that could be attached to these twelve constructs are relative to one another.

6. Constituent Relations and Logical Relations

In describing the formal context for this discourse about houses, the only elements to be used were given as A, B, C, D, and the only relation as "nt_2." In merely formulating all the possible elementary propositions in this context, certainly no other constituents were employed. But as soon as the propositions were formulated, it was apparent that some could not reasonably be asserted at all, and even the others could not all be asserted together indiscriminately. Certain ones were dependent upon certain others, by implication, preclusion, and the like. But implication, or even the mere joining-up of two propositions in one assertion, are relations; so there appear to be relations operative in our discourse besides the relation "nt" which is mentioned as a constituent of the formal context.

Such relations, however, hold *among propositions of the discourse*, not *among elements*. The relations which hold among elements form elementary propositions, and are constituents of those propositions, and items in the formal context; the relations which hold among propositions are not constituents of elementary propositions, and are therefore not enumerated as materials of the formal context. I shall call the latter kind *logical relations*, to distinguish them from the *constituent relations* of the discourse.*

The constituent relations vary with the formal context; in every discourse there must be constituent relations, but what these are to be is arbitrary, within the limits of what "makes sense" in the given universe. Logical relations, too, occur in any discourse of more than one proposition; but they are always the same few relations. They are sometimes referred to as the "logical constants" of discourse. They hold among elementary propositions, whatever the constituents of those propositions may be.

* The importance of this distinction was first pointed out to me by Professor Sheffer. The terminology, however, is not his.

The principal logical relations are: (1) *conjunction* of propositions, or *joint assertion*; this is expressed by the word "and," or the traditional symbol ".". Thus, "A is to the North of B, and B is to the North of C," is expressed symbolically,

$$(A \text{ nt } B) . (B \text{ nt } C)$$

(2) *Disjunction* of propositions, the assertion of one proposition *or* the other. This relation is taken, in logic, to mean "one, or the other, or both"; that is, it means *at least one* of the two propositions. For instance, it is always the case that *either* A is not to the North of B *or* B is not to the North of A. Either "A nt B" or "B nt A" must be false; they may, in fact, both be false. So, using the accepted symbol, "V," for "either-or," we may say:

$$\sim (A \text{ nt } B) \vee \sim (B \text{ nt } A)$$

(3) *Implication* of one proposition by another. This covers the notion of *preclusion*, which is the implication by one proposition that another is false. "A nt B" precludes "B nt A," i.e. "A nt B" implies " $\sim$ (B nt A)." The symbol for "implies" is "⊃." Sometimes a proposition is implied by the joint assertion of two or more others. Then you first express the conjunction, bracket the whole expression, and use it as one proposition:

$$[(A \text{ nt } B) . (B \text{ nt } C)] \supset (A \text{ nt } C)$$

(There are various ways of circumscribing, and recasting the appearance, of the logical relations. Instead of "⊃," we might have a symbol for preclusion, since an implied proposition is one whose falsity is precluded, just as a precluded proposition is one whose falsity is implied (as in '(A nt B) ⊃ $\sim$ (B nt A)"). Or we might use and symbolize the notion "neither . . . nor" instead of "either . . . or." But all these relations which may be used in place of ".", "V", and "⊃" really come to the same thing; they express the same *form*, the same state of affairs; so we may as well abide by the ones which are in most general use.)

7. Systems

Two propositions which *cannot both be true* are said to be *inconsistent*. Thus "A nt B" and "B nt A" are inconsistent with each other; one may be true and the other false, and logically it is a matter of indifference *which* is true and *which* is false; or they may both be false (as they would be if the houses stood in the same latitude); but they *cannot* both be true. Likewise,

$$(A \text{ nt } B) \cdot (B \text{ nt } C) \cdot \sim (A \text{ nt } C)$$

cannot be jointly asserted; if $[(A \text{ nt } B) \cdot (B \text{ nt } C)] \supset$ (A nt C), then to assert the truth of the first two and the falsity of the third is inconsistent. To assign inconsistent truth-values to the elementary propositions within a formal context results in a chaotic and absurd discourse.

If, however, we assign a truth-value to every possible proposition, so that each is consistent with all the others jointly asserted, anyone will readily see that this is a systematic description of a certain state of affairs (real or imaginary). It is systematic because the propositions are interrelated, linked to each other by logical relations. *Such an ordered discourse within a formal context is called a system.*

There are innumerable ways of constructing systems. Different constituent relations allow of entirely different combinations of elementary propositions by means of the logical relations; different universes of discourse offer different possibilities of arrangement. In some systems, the several propositions are so closely connected by *implication* that if we know the truth-value of a very few constructs we can assign all the rest unequivocally. The process of reasoning from one truth-value to another among propositions is known as deduction; for instance, from "(A nt B) . (B nt C)" one may deduce "A nt C." A system wherein this is possible, so that a small number of known propositions determines all the rest, is a *deductive system*.

A fair example of such a system may be constructed within the context $K(A, B, C, D)$ nt_2. Suppose you are told that

A nt B
B nt C
C nt D

From the first two in conjunction we deduce "A nt C," since

$[(A \; nt \; B) \; . \; (B \; nt \; C)] \supset A \; nt \; C$
Likewise, $[(B \; nt \; C) \; . \; (C \; nt \; D)] \supset B \; nt \; D$

And if we take this last proposition together with the first, we have:

$[(A \; nt \; B) \; . \; (B \; nt \; D)] \supset A \; nt \; D$

Here are three propositions whose truth is deducible from that of the three given ones. Moreover, each of these true propositions implies that its converse is false:

$(A \; nt \; B) \supset \sim (B \; nt \; A)$
$(A \; nt \; C) \supset \sim (C \; nt \; B)$
$(A \; nt \; D) \supset \sim (D \; nt \; A)$
$(B \; nt \; C) \supset \sim (C \; nt \; B)$
$(B \; nt \; D) \supset \sim (D \; nt \; B)$
$(C \; nt \; D) \supset \sim (D \; nt \; B)$

So, by assuming the truth of just three of the twelve "undetermined" propositions that could be constructed in our context, we have been enabled to deduce all the rest. The three original assumptions were made to establish a *deductive system*.

Its virtues are obvious. Instead of twelve constructs whose truth-values must be arbitrarily assigned, we have only three; a little knowledge of order, relatedness, in short, of *logical structure*, serves us instead of a cumbersome, itemized knowledge of many facts.

Suppose, however, that we assume a different formal context, say a collection of five persons, whom I shall denote as S, T, U, V, and W. The constituent relation is, "likes." I shall express it by the symbol "lk." We have then,

$$K(S, T, U, V, W) \, lk_2 \qquad K = \text{int "persons"}$$
$$lk_2 = \text{int "likes"}$$

Let us assume,

$$S \, lk \, T$$
$$T \, lk \, U$$
$$U \, lk \, V$$
$$V \, lk \, W$$

What may be inferred from these statements? Nothing at all. "Likes" may or not hold both ways between the same elements; (S lk T) . (T lk U) does not tell us whether S lk U is true or false; we cannot even guess whether any one of these persons likes himself, or not. The fact is, that any elementary construct in this context is plausible in itself and is perfectly consistent with every other, or any conjunction of others. If we want to assign truth-values to all the propositions we must make twenty-five separate assignments. Such a system I call *inductive*, in contradistinction from *deductive*. Any system in the given context $K(S, T, U, V, W) \, lk_2$ must be completely inductive; this is due to the character of its constituent relation.

Most systems exhibit a mixture of both types; i.e. some propositions imply others, but there are also some which remain untouched. Such a system may be classed as *mixed*. Most scientific systems are of this hybrid sort; they are partly capable of deductive arrangement, but still contain a large number of facts that could never have been inferred, but are simply known to us as data, arbitrary truths "given" to us by experience. The dream of every scientist is to find some formulation of all his facts whereby they may be arranged in a completely deductive system; and of this desirable type we shall have a great deal more to say in subsequent chapters.

We have now introduced all of the essentials of logical structure: *elements*, and *relations* among elements; *elementary propositions* composed of these simple constituents; relations among elementary propositions, or *logical relations*; *systems*, constructed out of elementary propositions by means of these logical relations. All higher logical structures may be treated as systems or parts of systems.

Summary

Every discourse, no matter how fragmentary or casual, moves in a certain *context* of inter-related ideas. In ordinary thinking this context is indefinite and shifting.

The psychological context of our thoughts is largely private and personal. Two people talking about the same thing may picture it to themselves in widely divergent ways. They have, then, different *conceptions*. But if they understand each other at all, then their respective conceptions embody the same *concept*.

Logic is concerned entirely with concepts, not conceptions. A logical discourse rules out all private and accidental aspects. Its context must be fixed and public. The elements and relations that may enter into its propositions may, therefore, be enumerated in advance. These constitute the formal context of the discourse.

The total collection of elements in a formal context is called the universe of discourse.

The relations which obtain among such elements are called the constituent relations of the formal context.

The combinations which may be made out of the elements in a formal context by letting a constituent relation combine them according to its degree, are the *elementary propositions* of the discourse.

Every elementary proposition has a *truth-value*, which is

either *truth* or *falsity*. "Value" here has nothing to do with the quality of being "valuable."

The propositions constructible in a formal context may be such that they cannot all be true, or cannot all be false; that is, it may be that to fix the truth-values of some of them automatically assigns truth-values to others. The propositions of such a context are interrelated.

The relations which hold among elementary propositions are not the constituent relations mentioned in the formal context, but are *logical* relations.

The logical relations generally used in symbolic logic are *conjunction* (.), *disjunction* (V), and *implication* (⊃). Constituent relations may be freely chosen within the limits of what the universe of discourse admits as "making sense"; logical relations are "constants," the same for every discourse.

A total set of elementary propositions in a formal context, connected by logical relations and jointly assertable without inconsistency, is a *system*.

A system wherein a small number of propositions, known from outside information to be true, implies the truth or falsity of all other elementary propositions, is called a *deductive system*.

A system wherein all truth-values must be separately assigned by pure assumption or outside information is an *inductive system*.

A system wherein some truth-values may be deduced, but others neither imply anything nor are implied, is a *mixed system*.

The essentials of structure are: *elements*, and relations among elements, or *constituent relations; elementary propositions*; relations among elementary propositions, or *logical relations*; and finally, *systems*, the higher forms of structure, composed of related elementary propositions within a logical context.

QUESTIONS FOR REVIEW

1. What is meant by the context of an ordinary conversation?
2. What is the difference between a concept and a conception?
3. What is the difference between "psychological context" and "formal context"? Which is more important in conversation? Which is used in logic?
4. What are the essentials of a formal context?
5. What is a universe of discourse?
6. How may the elementary propositions in a formal context be related to each other?
7. What is the difference between constituent relations and logical relations?
8. What is a system?
9. What are the essential factors of logical structure?

SUGGESTIONS FOR CLASS WORK

1. Give an example of "formal context," expressed symbolically, and state the interpretation in proper form.
2. In the following discourse, underline the constituent relations once and the logical relations twice:

> If we have any desire, then either our desire leads to want or it leads to fulfilment; and fulfilment leads to surfeit; and want leads to pain, and surfeit leads to pain; therefore any desire leads to pain. (Schopenhauer's argument for pessimism.)

3. Express the following statements symbolically, using Roman capitals for elements, symbols of your own choice for the constituent relation or relations, and the customary symbols for logical relations:

   (a) John is older than Tim, and Tim is older than George; therefore John is older than George.
   (b) If New York is colder than Paris, then Paris cannot be colder than New York.
   (c) She loves me—[or] She loves me not
   (d) I am your brother and you are mine.
   (e) Neither the *Washington* nor the *Mauretania* is faster than the *Bremen*.

CHAPTER IV

GENERALIZATION

1. REGULARITIES OF A SYSTEM

In the foregoing chapter we dealt with a system of just four elements; in such a system there are sixteen elementary propositions. When each one of these is either asserted or denied, the system is completely and explicitly stated. In a formal context with a very small universe of discourse this is perfectly practicable, because sixteen propositions are easily perused. Suppose, however, we choose a larger universe, say one of ten elements; for convenience, let us again take a dyadic relation; and let the new formal context be:

$$K(\text{A, B, C, D, E, F, G, H, I, J}) \ fm_2$$
$$K = \text{int "persons"}$$
$$fm_2 = \text{int "fellowman of"}$$

Let the following truth-values be assigned to propositions of the system:

$$\text{A fm B}$$
$$\text{B fm C}$$
$$\text{C fm D}$$
$$\text{D fm E}$$
$$\text{E fm F}$$
$$\text{F fm G}$$
$$\text{G fm H}$$
$$\text{H fm I}$$
$$\text{I fm J}$$

Now, no one can fairly be called his own fellowman: so we may add, at once, ten further propositions of established truth-value:

$$\sim (A \text{ fm } A)$$
$$\sim (B \text{ fm } B)$$

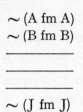

$$\sim (J \text{ fm } J)$$

Furthermore, in the nature of the constituent relation certain implications follow from the nine originally granted facts. Thus, $(A \text{ fm } B) \supset (B \text{ fm } A)$; $(B \text{ fm } C) \supset (C \text{ fm } B)$; and so forth, so that we may assert the implication of the nine converses of the given propositions:

$$(A \text{ fm } B) \supset (B \text{ fm } A)$$
$$(B \text{ fm } C) \supset (C \text{ fm } B)$$
$$(C \text{ fm } D) \supset (D \text{ fm } C)$$

$$(I \text{ fm } J) \supset (J \text{ fm } I)$$

Also, if "A fm B" and "B fm C" are true, then "A fm C" must be true; if A is a fellowman of B, and B of C, then A must be a fellowman of C. This gives us the proposition "A fm C"; so by the same principle, we further relate A to D, to E, to F, etc. Obviously, in a universe of ten elements, this gives us a swarming multitude of statements:

$$[(A \text{ fm } B) \cdot (B \text{ fm } C)] \supset (A \text{ fm } C)$$
$$[(A \text{ fm } C) \cdot (C \text{ fm } D)] \supset (A \text{ fm } D)$$

$$[(A \text{ fm } I) \cdot (I \text{ fm } J)] \supset (A \text{ fm } J)$$

$$[(B \text{ fm } C) \cdot (C \text{ fm } D)] \supset (B \text{ fm } D)$$
$$[(B \text{ fm } D) \cdot (D \text{ fm } E)] \supset (B \text{ fm } E)$$

$$[(C \text{ fm } D) \cdot (D \text{ fm } E)] \supset (C \text{ fm } E)$$

Each proposition to the right of the implication sign is a newly established elementary construct; and each, of course, implies its converse, so we augment the list beginning:

$$(A \text{ fm } B) \supset (B \text{ fm } A)$$
$$\text{etc., etc.,}$$

by:

$$(A \text{ fm } C) \supset (C \text{ fm } A)$$

$$(H \text{ fm } J) \supset (J \text{ fm } H)$$

Altogether, the explicit statement of this system requires 100 assertions.

Many of these assertions, however, look strikingly alike. I have arranged them above in three lists. One contains simple elementary propositions involving just one element apiece; the next contains statements to the effect that an elementary proposition with two distinct terms implies its converse, i.e. the proposition which relates the same two terms in reversed order; the third list consists of pairs of propositions conjoined to imply a third. In each list the several assertions are *analogous*; and by reason of this unmistakable analogy I have not troubled myself to write out each item, but have merely started each column, and let the reader supply what is denoted by dashes or by "etc." We do not have to look very far down any list to appreciate the repetitiousness of the *logical relations* expressed in it; to recognize that, no matter which elements we combine into an elementary proposition, the logical relation of this proposition to its converse is always "$\supset$"; and no matter which three elements we select, if we make two propositions out of them, such that the second term of one is identical with the first term of the second, and relate these two propositions by ".", then this conjunct has the relation "$\supset$" to a third proposition combining the first term of the first with the second term of the second. What the assertions in each list have in common, is (1) the number of elementary propositions involved in them, (2) the number of distinct elements involved in these propositions, (3) the location of identical and of distinct elements, (4) the nature and location of logical relations contained in each total assertion. These regularities stamp all the assertions in any one list with the same logical form, no matter *which* element, or *which* two or three elements figure in any such assertion.

2. VARIABLES

If we wish to express symbolically the logical form of a whole list of propositions, we may do this by using what is called a *variable symbol*. Such a symbol is not a *name* assigned to a certain one of the elements, but means: "A, or B, or C, . . . or J, whichever is chosen for this place." It is called a *variable* because it can mean all the elements in turn; its meaning may *vary* from A to J.

To distinguish such symbols from *specific names*, like A, B, C, etc., I shall use lower case italics for variables. Thus,

$$\sim (A \text{ fm } A)$$

means: "It is false that the element called A has the relation fm to itself"; but

$$\sim (a \text{ fm } a)$$

means, by turns,

$$\sim (A \text{ fm } A),$$
$$\sim (B \text{ fm } B),$$
$$\text{etc., etc.}$$

It may denote any one of the ten propositions involving only one element. Likewise, we might use a construct of two variables to mean, in turn, all propositions involving just two elements. Thus, *"a* fm *b"* may mean, in turn,

A fm B

A fm C

———

B fm C

B fm D

———

But it may just as well mean "B fm A" as "A fm B." The *a* and *b*, respectively, do not mean "A" and "B," but: "the first-mentioned term" and "the second-mentioned term." If "B" is the first-mentioned term, then *a* means "B." If "J" is the second-mentioned term, then *b* means "J."

If, however, two elementary structures are logically related, the whole construct is *one assertion*; and if a variable is given a meaning in one part of that assertion it must keep it throughout. For instance,

$$(a \text{ fm } b) \supset (b \text{ fm } a)$$

may mean: $(C \text{ fm } D) \supset (D \text{ fm } C)$

or: $(B \text{ fm } A) \supset (A \text{ fm } B);$

in the first instance, *a* means C and *b* means D; in the second, *a* means B and *b* means A; but in both cases, *the fact that a certain (first-mentioned) term has the relation* fm *to a certain other (second) term*, implies *that the other term has that relation to the first*. Therefore, no matter how "a certain term" and "a certain other term" are chosen—whether we choose B first and A second, or C first and D second, or what you will—wherever "that first term" and "that second term" recur, we must put in the one we chose first, and the one we chose next, respectively. So we may say that *a variable may mean any element, but whichever it does mean, it must mean that same one throughout the whole assertion.* The variable *a* in $(a \text{ fm } b) \supset (b \text{ fm } a)$ could not mean A in the first case and E in the second. $(A \text{ fm } D) \supset (D \text{ fm } A)$ is a possible meaning for $(a \text{ fm } b) \supset (b \text{ fm } a)$, and so is

(E fm D) ⊃ (D fm E); but (*a* fm *b*) ⊃ (*b* fm *a*) could *not* mean (A fm D) ⊃ (D fm E), because if *a* means A it cannot *in the same total assertion* mean E; it must mean just one and the same thing *in all the logically related elementary propositions of one total assertion*.

This point is very important; once a variable is given a meaning, it keeps it throughout the whole assertion; but it must be remembered that *in another assertion it may have another meaning*. That is, if in

$$a \text{ fm } a$$

we let *a* mean "J," so we have the meaning:

$$J \text{ fm } J,$$

and then say:

$$(a \text{ fm } b) \supset (b \text{ fm } a),$$

the meaning "J" need not therefore be assigned to *a* in this second assertion; we may give *a* and *b* here the meanings E and F, if we choose, or any other pair of elements. But of course, if our choice falls upon E and F, then *a* means E and *b* means F in *both* the elementary propositions connected by "⊃."

3. VALUES

The elements which may be meant by a variable symbol are called its *values*. Here again we encounter the use of "value" in a mathematical sense, not to be confounded with any sort of "worth." A value for a variable is any element which the variable may denote. The entire class of possible values for a variable, i.e. of individual elements it may signify, is called the *range of significance* of the variable.

In the expression "*a* fm *a*" within our formal context, the range of the variable *a* is the entire universe of discourse.

Any element whatever may be substituted for *a*, and the result will be a proposition *which is either true or false*. If an expression involves two variables, as for instance:

$$a \text{ fm } b$$

then the range of this pair of variables is all the *dyads* which can be made in the formal context. Remember that the two terms of a dyadic relation may be the same element; that is, A fm A is dyadic, although the terms are not distinct. In the expression "*a* fm *b*" there is nothing to tell us that *a* and *b* are necessarily distinct; "the first-mentioned element" and "the second-mentioned element" may very well be the *same* element. If the same *variable* occurs in both places, then we *know* that the terms denoted are identical; if different variables occur, we do not know, without further reason, whether their values are identical or distinct.

The proposition "J fm J" is, then, a possible meaning for the variable expression "*a* fm *b*." So is "A fm B," "J fm H," or any other elementary proposition. The entire hundred dyadic combinations which may be made in the formal context fall within the range of "*a, b*"; ten of these compose the range of "*a, a*" in the expression:

$$a \text{ fm } a$$

The process of assigning a specific value to a variable may be called *specification*. This is not the same thing as interpretation; for, when we interpret a symbol, we commission it to mean *a certain kind of thing*, as: "K = int houses" determines that A, B, C, D, shall represent houses, and not trees, or people, or days. Interpretation fixes the *sort* of term involved in the discourse. But if we say: "*a* equals, by specification, the element C" (which may be abbreviated: "*a* = sp C"), this does not tell us that *a* means the *sort* of thing called a house, but *which* house it denotes: the house named C. The range of significance of a variable, then, is the class of all those and only those elements which may be substituted for it by *specification*.

The notion of variables is not peculiar to logic. It is constantly employed in ordinary speech. Every pronoun is a variable, and the rules of specification here expounded are the same rules that were taught to us in school in regard to "antecedents" of pronouns. Take, for instance, the sentence:

I knew you would not do it.

The meaning of such a statement is indefinite until we know the meanings of "I," "you," and "it." If these words are said by one person to another, the two personal pronouns have different values, i.e. different "antecedents"; that is usually the case. But a man who has failed in a high resolve, or resisted a great temptation, might also address himself in this fashion. In that case, the two variables "I" and "you" would denote the same element. Two different pronouns usually but not necessarily have different antecedents. If, however, one says:

You knew *you* would not do it,

then "you" must mean the same person in both cases; for if a variable is once specified, it must keep the same specification throughout the entire statement wherein it occurs; or, in more familiar language, a pronoun must have the same antecedent throughout the entire statement. And this again is simply common sense. Moreover, "you" may mean *any person*; its range is the class of persons. The same thing holds for "I." On the other hand, "it" refers to something else than a person, i.e. it has a different range from the other two variables. In a context where "doing" makes any sense, the universe must contain, *by interpretation*, agents and acts; "it" may become, *by specification*, any one of the acts, whereas "I" and "you" may denote specifically any two of the agents respectively (which may be identical). But the distinction between "personal" variables and "impersonal" variables is a convention of language; in logic, we have no literary way of indicating such restrictions of range.

4. PROPOSITIONAL FORMS

Every proposition in a formal context is *either true or false*. We may not know which it is; but we may rest assured that it is one or the other. An expression like:

$$a \text{ fm } b$$

on the other hand, may be true with one set of values and false with another; in our system, it is true whenever the two values are distinct and false when they are identical. In another system a construct made with variables might not even follow such simple rules; for instance, in the context $K(A, B, C, D)$ nt_2, "a nt b" might mean a true or a false proposition even when the values of a and b were distinct.

The expression "a fm b" (to return to our latest formal context) is, in itself, *neither true nor false*. And that means that *it is not a proposition at all*. It is only the empty form of a proposition, which has to be filled in with specific elements in order to yield a proposition. It is, in fact, a *propositional form*, a variable whose values are propositions.

In most books of symbolic logic, notably the classic *Principia Mathematica* of Messrs. Whitehead and Russell, such an expression which has the form of a proposition, but contains at least one variable term, is called a *propositional function*. The name is not very fortunate; it has no clear connotation for logicians who do not happen to be conversant with mathematics. Its origin is obvious enough, if we remember that the great founders of symbolic logic—Boole, Frege, Schroeder, Peano, Whitehead, Russell, to mention only some of the most important—were primarily mathematicians, to whom the empty logical form and its specific propositional values naturally suggested the mathematical "function" and its numerical "values." So the variable whose values are propositions came by the name of "propositional function," and is generally so denoted in the literature. But the term "function" has so many meanings (see chap. xiii, p. 319, note) that I shall use the clearer, if less popular, name "propositional form," which avoids a great many confusions.*

The sentence: "I knew you would not do it," is a genuine propositional form; as long as no values are assigned to the pronouns, it is neither true nor false. Even if we assign a value to one or two of the three pronouns, the expression as a whole keeps its variable character; only when *all* its terms are fixed it acquires truth-value, i.e. becomes a proposition. Thus, we may say:

(1) I knew you would not do it.
(2) I, George, knew you would not do it.
(3) I, George, knew you, John, would not do it.
(4) I, George, knew you, John, would not cheat at cards.

Only (4) is a proposition; all the others are propositional forms with different numbers of variables, i.e., in different stages of *formalization*.

Let us carry this over from the pronouns of natural language to the a, b, c, etc., which are the pronouns of symbolic language.

In describing the system

$$K(A, B, C, D, E, F, G, H, I, J) \text{ fm}_2$$

* In a dissertation, "The Logical Structure of Meaning" (unpublished paper in the Radcliffe College Library), I first adopted this terminology ten years ago. Since then Professor Sheffer has independently arrived at the same practice, and some of his disciples have recently used it in print; so I do not feel unjustified in employing it throughout this book.

we have ten propositions about elements in relation to A:

$$A \text{ fm } A$$
$$A \text{ fm } B$$
$$A \text{ fm } C$$

$$A \text{ fm } J$$

In these propositions the second term varies from A to J. Suppose, then, we use a variable in its place, and write:

$$A \text{ fm } a$$

This is a propositional form of one variable. It is neither true nor false; one of its *values* is a false proposition, whereas all the others are true ones.

Now, there is also a list of propositions of the form "B fm a," and one of "C fm a," and "D fm a," etc. So long as only one element is formalized we need ten propositional forms to enumerate all the possible elementary propositions of the discourse. But when we align these in a list:

$$A \text{ fm } a$$
$$B \text{ fm } a$$
$$C \text{ fm } a$$
$$D \text{ fm } a$$

$$J \text{ fm } a$$

it is clear that the first element, too, could be formalized, that we could write:

$$b \text{ fm } a$$

and let the two terms vary over the entire range of both, i.e. over all possible dyadic combinations within K. There are one hundred values for this propositional form of two variables. Ten of these values are false propositions and ninety are true.

The propositional form "A fm a" is in one sense a value for "b fm a," but not in the genuine sense in which

"A fm E" would be. "A fm *a*" is related to "*b* fm *a*" by *partial specification*; it still remains a propositional form; and I shall call it a *restricted propositional form*, because the specification of one element restricts its range to propositions of the given first term. A restricted propositional form might be called an *ambiguous value* for the unrestricted form. But all these names are mere conveniences; the thing to remember is that *as soon as we replace a single term in a proposition by a variable, we have a propositional form* which has as many values as there are values for that variable; and *the more elements we "formalize," the greater becomes the range of the entire propositional form.*

5. THE QUANTIFIERS (*a*) AND (∃*a*)

A propositional form is neither true nor false; but if we know that all the values for a certain form are true propositions, then why may we not save ourselves the trouble of writing out all those propositions, when we wish to describe our system, and merely write the *form* and let it "mean" all its values in turn?

Well, the mere statement of the form does not tell anybody that its values are all assertable in the system. The form alone is not a proposition, and does not assert anything. But we may adopt a device to express that a propositional form *holds for any value of its variables*, i.e. that no matter how the terms are specified, the resultant proposition is true. Let us take the form:

$$\sim (a \text{ fm } a)$$

This is the *form* of the assertion that a certain element does not have the relation "fm" to itself. It is not itself an assertion, but its values are. And however we choose *a*, the resultant assertion is true; that is, the form

$$\sim (a \text{ fm } a)$$

holds for every value of *a*.

To express this fact, we use the symbol "(a)," which may be read: "for any value of a," or more briefly if less precisely: "for any a." Whenever this symbol is prefixed to a propositional form, it means that no matter what element we substitute for a, the proposition which results is true. Thus,

$$(a) : \sim (a \text{ fm } a)$$

is read: "For any a, it is false that 'a fm a.'" This is as much as to say:

$$\sim (A \text{ fm } A)$$
$$\sim (B \text{ fm } B)$$
$$\sim (C \text{ fm } C)$$
etc., etc.

In this way the form may indeed be used to express all its values collectively.

Now, let us take a propositional form of one variable, which does not hold for all values of that term. The only way we can construct such a complex of a single variable in our system is to use a restricted propositional form, i.e. to use one specific term and formalize the other. Let us take the form:

$$A \text{ fm } a$$

This holds for every value of a except A; "A fm A" is false. But one case wherein it fails destroys the right to say it always holds. All we may say for it is that it sometimes holds. The accepted symbol for "sometimes," or better: "for some value or values of a," is (∃a). Hence,

$$(\exists a) : A \text{ fm } a$$

means: "For some value or values of a, 'A fm a' holds." Or, briefly: "For some a, 'A fm a.'"

It is a good practical rule, in logic, not to say more than is essential. In this respect logicians are very prudent. If we always let a symbol mean the *least* it can possibly claim to mean, there is little danger of letting irrelevant meanings creep in. Now, the most modest way to say "sometimes" is, "at least once." So the best reading of ($\exists a$) is: "for at least one value of a," or: "There is at least one a, such that . . ." The last version seems to me the best; when we come to more complicated structures its advantages will become clear. So,

$$(\exists a) : \text{A fm } a$$

had best be read: "There is at least one a, such that 'A fm a.' "

If a propositional form has two variables, we are interested, of course, to state that it holds for some or for all *pairs* of elements. Consider, for instance, the propositional form:

$$a \text{ fm } b$$

This is not true for all values of the couple a, b, because it fails whenever the two elements are identical. We may only say, then,

$$(\exists a, b) : a \text{ fm } b$$

"There is at least one a, and at least one b, such that 'a fm b.' "

No *elementary* propositional form of *two* variables, in our system, holds for all possible pairs of values. If we resort to *logical* propositional forms, however—i.e., to such as contain a logical relation among elementary constructs— we shall find some that always hold. For instance, it is always true that *if* a fm b holds, *then* b fm a also holds; in other words, the complex proposition

$$(a \text{ fm } b) \supset (b \text{ fm } a)$$

holds, no matter how we choose a and b. So we may say:

$$(a, b) : (a \text{ fm } b) \supset (b \text{ fm } a)$$

"For any a and any b, 'a fm b' implies 'b fm a.' "

The symbols (a) and $(\exists a)$ are called the *quantifiers* of the term a. They indicate what part of the total range of a yields true propositions of the given form. (a), which means "for any a," is called the *universal quantifier*, because it lets the form hold for every element in the universe, i.e. makes it *universally true*. $(\exists a)$, "there is at least one a, such that . . ." is the *particular quantifier*, for it refers the form only to particular choices within the universe.

Sometimes the two quantifiers are combined in quantifying a single form. For instance, we might encounter:

$$(a)\ (\exists b): a \text{ lk } b$$

$$(\exists a)\ (b): a \text{ lk } b$$

Now, since a is no specific element and b is no specific element, does it matter which quantifier—the universal or the particular—is mentioned first? If you read the two statements aloud, there will at once appear a very obvious difference. The first says:

"For any a, there is at least one b such that 'a lk b.'" In other words, for every person a there is at least one b whom a likes (it may be himself). The second, however, asserts: "There is at least one person, a, such that for any person b, 'b lk a'"; that is, there is at least one a whom everybody likes.

With the relation lk_2 both statements are possible (though the second is highly improbable), but suppose we took the relation fm.

$$(a)\ (\exists b): a \text{ fm } b$$

is true if there is more than one man in the world; but

$$(\exists a)\ (b): a \text{ fm } b$$

cannot be true, because (b) makes b refer to any man whatever, including the first term of the relation, so we would have by implication:

$$(\exists a).\ a \text{ fm } a,$$

which is false

The proper use of quantifiers requires close attention to the sense we wish to make. For instance, if we wished to say: "Everybody has some secret which he will not tell to anyone," the form of the proposition (using "→" for "telling"), is:

$$(a) \ (\exists b) \ (c) : \ \sim (a \rightarrow b, c)$$

"For any a, there is at least one b such that, for any c, a does not tell b to c." Try to read the quantifiers in some other order, and the change of meaning will immediately be apparent; there will be some secret that no one will tell anyone, or some person who won't tell anybody anything, or someone whom nobody will tell a secret, etc. But the sense of the original statement will not be reproduced.

6. GENERAL PROPOSITIONS

If a propositional form of one variable is said to hold or to fail for all values in the range of significance of that variable, this is a statement about the form. Such a statement is either true or false; that is, either it is true that

$$(a) : \ \sim (a \ \mathrm{fm} \ a)$$

or it is false. But anything that has truth-value is a proposition; so we have here not an empty form to be filled in with values, but a proposition *about* an empty form and its possible values. We do not assign values to a by specification, and thus make a true or a false proposition; we say that *if* certain values are assigned to a (in this case, any whatever in its range), *then*: "a fm a" will be false. And this is supposed to express a *fact* of our system. Yet "$(a) : \ \sim (a \ \mathrm{fm} \ a)$" is not the same sort of proposition as the elementary constructs made with "fm" in our universe of discourse; "a" is not the name of an element. In dealing with propositional forms, we regarded it as a symbol of variable meaning, standing for all the elements *in turn*; but when we prefix the quantifier (a) to $\sim(a \text{ fm } a)$, we no longer mean just $\sim(A \text{ fm } A)$ or just $\sim(B \text{ fm } B)$, or any specific proposition. The expression (a) means *all* of these at the same time, yet not as one class, but severally. It means simultaneously $\sim(A \text{ fm } A)$ and $\sim(B \text{ fm } B)$ and $\sim(C \text{ fm } C)$ . . . and $\sim(J \text{ fm } J)$. It is, then, a *general term*; it means not first this element and then that, but *any* one, no matter which.

The expression "$(a) : \sim(a \text{ fm } a)$" is, therefore, a *general proposition*, because it makes an assertion about the elements of K, in general. It does not have to be "filled in" with certain values in order to be true or false; "For any a, a is not his own fellowman" is true, and expresses a general condition.

The same thing may be said of forms preceded by the particular quantifier. Such a statement as: "$(\exists a) : A \text{ fm } a$" states a *general fact* about elements in relation to a given element, A. At first it may seem as though $(\exists a)$ must be less general than (a); but this is not so; the difference is merely that, whereas (a) makes reference to *any* element in the entire range of a, no matter which, $(\exists a)$ refers us to *some* element in that range, but—again—*no matter which*.

An example from ordinary thinking may make this clearer. Suppose we let four elements, A, B, C, D, represent four people, on a desert island, a mountain-top, or other isolated place where they constitute the whole population. Let A mean a person named Smith. Now, Smith has been robbed. Let "rb" stand for "robbing." The officious radio promptly reports to the world:

$$\text{"}(\exists a) : a \text{ rb A!"}$$

"Somebody in the party robbed Smith!"

This is a perfectly general statement. The "a" is not a variable, for the statement is supposedly *true*. Without the quantifier, "$a \text{ rb A}$" would be merely a propositional form, because "a" would have no meaning. To broadcast "$a \text{ rb A}$"

would be like saying "He robbed A" without naming anyone. But "$(\exists a) : a$ rb A" declares a *general condition* of the party, namely that somebody in it robbed Smith. It does not name any specific person as the robber; there may have been more than one; but this we know, that there is at least one person such that this person robbed Smith. And a means "this person, or these persons, whoever that may be."

So long as any real variable remains in a structure, that structure is a propositional form; but if every variable has a quantifier, *the completely quantified propositional form is a general proposition.* Now, a proposition may be not entirely general; it may contain some general and some specific terms, like the example above:

$$(\exists a) : a \text{ rb } A$$

We must generalize both terms:

$$(\exists a, b) : a \text{ rb } b$$

"There are at least two terms, a and b, such that 'a rb b' holds." Both of these statements are general propositions; but one is only partly generalized, and the other completely so.

7. The Economy of General Propositions

Now let us return to the system of ten persons and the constituent relation "fm_2." We were given, originally, nine specific propositions; all others followed from our knowledge of the general ways in which the relation "fm" operates. The nine specific propositions are all *instances* of the general fact that $(\exists a, b) : a$ fm b. But they cannot be *replaced* by this general proposition, because the instances, successively surveyed, show that in fact every element of the system is sooner or later given a different mate, and this is a circumstance which no general statement can tell us; for, if only five of the specific instances were given, the general proposition $(\exists a, b) : a$ fm b would still be true and in no wise affected, but our knowledge of the system would be seriously impaired. So, if we do not want to alter or curtail our given data, we must keep the original nine propositions. We start then, as before, with the context

$$K(A, B, C, D, E, F, G, H, I, J) \text{ fm}_2$$
$$K = \text{int "persons"}$$
$$\text{fm}_2 = \text{int "fellowman of"}$$

And the nine "given" propositions:

A fm B
B fm C
C fm D
D fm E
E fm F
F fm G
G fm H
H fm I
I fm J

But how about the implications of these facts? Here we had lists of logical propositions, such as:

(A fm B) ⊃ (B fm A)
(B fm C) ⊃ (C fm B)
etc., etc.

Here, clearly, what holds for one pair of terms holds for all:

$$(a, b) : (a \text{ fm } b) \supset (b \text{ fm } a)$$

This one general assertion takes the place of nine specific ones. Similarly,

$$[(A \text{ fm } B) . (B \text{ fm } C)] \supset (A \text{ fm } C)$$

is an instance of a universal proposition:*

$$(a, b, c) : [(a \neq c) . (a \text{ fm } b) . (b \text{ fm } c)] \supset (a \text{ fm } c)$$

* Note that the general proposition must *state* a fact which the special instance *shows*—namely, that the first term ≠ the third term.

This saves the whole list of derivations of A fm C, A fm D, A fm E . . . B fm D . . . to H fm J. The converses of these derived propositions, by the way, are already provided for by the first logical statement. Finally, the fact that "fm" cannot relate a term to itself may be stated universally:

$$(a) : \ \sim (a \text{ fm } a)$$

So it may be shown that, whereas a statement of the system in entirely specific terms requires one hundred separate assertions, a *general* account involves just twelve —nine specific and three general propositions. And that is certainly a considerable saving in paper, ink, and human patience!

8. THE FORMALITY OF GENERAL PROPOSITIONS

Suppose we adopt a new universe of discourse, which I will denote by K^1(L, M, N, O, P, Q, R, S) fm$_2$

$$K' = \text{int "creatures"}$$
$$\text{fm} = \text{int "fellowman of"}$$

Now, of every two creatures it is true or false that one is the other's fellowman; it is true if the two elements are distinct, and both are human; and otherwise it is false. That is to say, "*a* fm *b*" is *significant* with any two elements of K', but not necessarily *true* for them. If we had enough specific propositions, we could, of course, exhaustively describe the system. But even if we have no specific propositions at all, we know something about the conditions which obtain in it; for instance:

$$(a) : \ \sim (a \text{ fm } a)$$
$$(a, b) : (a \text{ fm } b) \supset (b \text{ fm } a)$$
$$(a, b, c) : [(a \neq c) . (a \text{ fm } b) . (b \text{ fm } c)] \supset (a \text{ fm } c)$$

That is to say, we know *how the relation "fm" operates in this* universe *if it operates at all*. In other words, we know nothing about the universe of discourse except that its elements are "creatures," not worlds, propositions, or historical events. We do not know whether any two elements are identical or distinct; they may be all one and the same creature. Also, if they are distinct, there may be only one human creature among them, or none at all, in which cases the propositional form a fm b would be false with all its values, i.e. it would be true that

$$(a, b) : \sim (a \text{ fm } b)$$

But, on the other hand, there may be two or more men. These might be L and M, or L and O and S, or any two, three, four . . . up to the entire eight elements. Suppose there are "some." Do we need a specific proposition to assure us of this, i.e. do we need to select any *specific* elements, say S and R, or L and P, and assert "S fm R" or "L fm P"? No; *which* ones they are makes no difference whatsoever; it is enough to know:

$$(\exists a, b) : a \text{ fm } b.$$

"There are at least two elements of which it is true that one is the other's fellowman."

This is enough to assure us that the relation obtains somewhere in the system. But we need not commit ourselves even to this assertion.

So it appears that a good deal may be known about the system without the introduction of any specific propositions. And what we know about the elements in K' without any specific information, we know also about K; and we would know it of *any* system in a formal context where "fm" was significant. Why, then, must we enumerate *specific elements* at all? Are we bound to any *certain* elements, or even any certain number of them? So long as we assert only general propositions, we have no occasion to call elements by their names. Why, then, introduce these individual names, when they are immaterial to the discourse—when all we need to know is that there is a collection of elements among which the relation functions in certain ways?

Clearly, all we require is a K of "some elements," such as "a first, a second, a third . . . an nth element." But these are not named. Therefore we no longer have elements A, B, C, etc., but quite generally "some element, a" "some other element, b," etc., and write our *generalized universe of discourse*:

$$K\,(a, b, c \ldots)$$

In a formal context with such a universe, specific propositions are no longer possible. If we assert:

$$(a): \sim (a \text{ fm } a)$$

this proposition does not deal specifically with an element called a in the universe. "$(e): \sim (e \text{ fm } e)$" means exactly the same thing as "$(a): \sim (a \text{ fm } a)$." It is merely a matter of mathematical elegance to use a where only one general term is needed, a and b for two, and so forth.

Consider the following three systems, expressed entirely in general terms, and note the different conditions which may be stated in general propositions:

I. $K(a, b, c \ldots) \text{ fm}_2$ $K =$ int "creatures"

                                  fm $=$ int "fellowman of"

   1. $(a): \sim (a \text{ fm } a)$

   2. $(a, b): (a \text{ fm } b) \supset (b \text{ fm } a)$

   3. $(a, b, c): [(a \neq c) . (a \text{ fm } b) . (b \text{ fm } c)] \supset (a \text{ fm } c)$

   4. $(a) (\exists b): a \text{ fm } b$

II. $K'(a, b, c \ldots) \text{ fm}_2$ $K' =$ int "creatures"

                                  fm $=$ int "fellowman of"

   1'. $(a): \sim (a \text{ fm } a)$

   2'. $(a, b): (a \text{ fm } b) \supset (b \text{ fm } a)$

   3'. $(a, b, c): [(a \neq c) . (a \text{ fm } b) . (b \text{ fm } c)] \supset (a \text{ fm } c)$

   4'. $(\exists a) (b): \sim (a \text{ fm } b)$

   5'. $(\exists a, b): a \text{ fm } b$

III. $K''(a, b, c \ldots)$ fm$_2$ K'' =int "creatures"

                                          fm =int "fellowman of"

$1''$. $(a) : \sim (a$ fm $a)$

$2''$. $(a, b) : (a$ fm $b) \supset (b$ fm $a)$

$3''$. $(a, b, c) : [(a \neq c) . (a$ fm $b) . (b$ fm $c)] \supset (a$ fm $c)$

$4''$. $(a, b) : \sim (a$ fm $b)$*

In the first system, proposition 4 asserts that every creature has a fellowman; every creature in this universe, then, must be human. In the second, $4'$ asserts that there is at least one creature which is not any other's fellowman; this means that either it is not a man, or else no other creature is. The latter alternative, however, is denied by $5'$, which says that there are at least two men. Hence there are some men in this universe, and at least one creature which is not a man. In III we learn from proposition $4''$ that no two creatures are fellowmen, i.e. that there cannot be more than one man in K''.

Among these three systems there is an obvious similarity; the first three propositions are identical in all three cases. These propositions describe the *general nature of* fm$_2$, and since fm$_2$ is assumed in each system, its description occurs in each. To this extent a system is always affected by the character of its constituent relation (or relations). The other propositions—4, $4'$ and $5'$, and $4''$—describe the nature of the three respective universes. Such statements, regarding the arrangement of elements in a universe, are the only items that may vary, and thus produce different systems, when the same interpretations are given to the formal context. (The information here given about the universes K, K' and K'' is meagre, because more detailed descriptions in general terms would require a technique which belongs to subsequent chapters of this book. But much more definite and specialized statements are possible, without any mention of specific elements.)

* Note that the assertion of $4''$ makes $1''$ unnecessary; for $1''$ is simply a case of $4''$, namely the case where a and b are identical, and is therefore implicit in $4''$.

If, now, we take the first system, wherein every creature has some fellowman, i.e. every creature is a man, and specify the elements of K (a, b, etc.) to be the ten persons of our original discussion, then these ten persons in the relation "fm" furnish an *instance* of a certain kind of system. The United States Senate is another instance, having a different number of specific terms, but exactly the same conditions The people inhabiting Paris are another (we are taking "fellowman" to mean, as it naturally does, fellow-*human*, not necessarily *adult male*), and the two authors of *Principia Mathematica*, though they represent the minimum number of K-elements, are yet another instance. All the actual groups of people here named are constituted in the same way, i.e. any one of them answers to the description given in terms of $K(a, b, . . .)$ fm$_2$. Each group is a very simple specific system, and *each one of these systems exemplifies the same form. It is this form which may be expressed in general, without mention of any specific elements*. So it may be said that, as long as we have a specific K, our general propositions are merely an economy, i.e. they serve to say in small compass what could also be said in a great array of specific statements; but as soon as we generalize the elements of K, our general propositions express the formal properties of any such system. Here, the general propositions are more than an economy; they are a means of *formulating universes of a certain sort*. They convey *principles of arrangement*, rather than specific *facts*. In system I we have a formulation of *any* group whose elements are creatures, in the relation "fellowman," where all the creatures are human; in II, the arrangement of any group containing at least two men, and at least one non-human creature; in III, that of any group containing not more than one man (which applies to such as contain no man). These generalized systems are the respective descriptions not of three groups, but of three *kinds* of group.

A general account of a system describes its form. Since

it is the form, not the specific instance of it, that concerns logicians, we shall henceforth deal entirely with generalized universes of discourse, and therefore with general propositions as *descriptions of systems of certain kinds*, not as shorthand renderings of whole lists of specific facts, describing specific systems. Therefore, we are through with Roman capitals for elements; all elements from now on will be denoted by lower-case italics, and all elements in propositions hereafter must be quantified. There are no more "variables," i.e. words (or letters) of unassigned meanings, and no more "values," or specific meanings assigned to "variables." Logic deals only with general terms.

9. QUANTIFIED TERMS IN NATURAL DISCOURSE

Just as pronouns are the "variables" of natural language, so there are words which serve the purpose of quantified terms. They are commonly called by the rather misleading name of "indefinite pronouns," and are: something, anything, somebody, anybody, nobody, nothing, none. A sentence about "somebody" or "something" expresses a general proposition which would be preceded by $(\exists a)$; "anything" or "anyone" is quantified by (a). "Nothing" is symbolically rendered by the universal quantifier before a negative proposition, but for a negation with the particular quantifier there is no special word. We use "something" together with "not." This little irregularity in the expression of logical forms is quite characteristic of natural language; it is one of the things that make language a poor medium for logical analysis. Yet it has been incorporated, in the traditional logic which derives from Aristotle, in the four types of proposition:

A	All S is P
E	No S is P
I	Some S is P
O	Some S is *not* P

Anyone conversant with symbolic expression must be struck immediately by the fact that in "E" the "$\sim$" is incorporated in the quantifier, whereas in "O" it is not, so that "A" and "E" seem to have different quantifiers, which is not the case, and "E" and "O" seem to be different propositions, which is not true either. When we replace the verbal quantifiers by symbolic ones and express "not" by "$\sim$," the true pattern of these propositions about "S" (which alone is generalized, "P" being either specific or variable) becomes visible:

$$
\begin{array}{ll}
\text{A} & (s) : s \text{ is P} \\
\text{E} & (s) : \sim (s \text{ is P}) \\
\text{I} & (\exists s) : s \text{ is P} \\
\text{O} & (\exists s) : \sim (s \text{ is P}).
\end{array}
$$

Wherever, in ordinary language, we meet an "indefinite pronoun," we have a general proposition (unless some personal pronoun without antecedent makes the sentence a propositional form). To find the logical structure of such a proposition, replace the "indefinite pronoun" by a general term, i.e. a properly quantified "variable," and express negation, if there be any, by "$\sim$" (note that the negation sign *never* precedes the quantifier). This will show that, although there are many "indefinite pronouns," there are really only two kinds of quantification; all general terms of language may be rendered by the use of (a) and $(\exists a)$. So it appears that language, which (as we saw in a previous chapter) often gives complicated relations a false appearance of simplicity, may also sin in the opposite direction, and needlessly complicate structures which, when expressed with greatest rigour and economy, are found to be genuinely simple and clear.

Summary

When a system is completely stated, its propositions may be listed in such a way that each list shows a marked internal regularity. That is to say, the propositions may be listed so that each list assembles all the propositions of a certain *form*.

Here we may introduce a new type of symbol, which is not employed to *name* an element, but to denote *in turn* all the elements in a collection. Such a symbol is called a *variable*. It has no fixed meaning, but may mean any of a given number of things. The totality of terms from which it may select its meaning is called the *range of significance* of the variable.

An element which is "meant" by a variable is called the *value* of that variable. The range of significance, then, is *the class of possible values* for a variable. Once a certain value is assigned to a variable term, this value must be kept throughout the total assertion wherein the term occurs, and must be substituted wherever the same variable appears (several elementary propositions connected by a logical relation constitute one total assertion). But the same variable occurring in independent constructs need not have the same value every time.

A proposition is either true or false. But a construct containing a variable whose value is not fixed is neither true nor false. It may yield a true proposition with one value and a false one with another. It is only an empty *form* of several propositions, and is therefore called a *propositional form*.

If a propositional form is known to yield true propositions with any values that may be assigned to it, then the form *plus this information* may be used to represent the whole list of propositions which are its possible values. The symbol denoting "true for all values of a" is (a). This is called the *universal quantifier*. A propositional form preceded by the universal quantifier signifies that all values for this form are true propositions; i.e. that the relation expressed in the form holds among any terms. Where more than one variable occurs, there must be more than one quantifier.

If only some values of a variable in a form yield true propositions, this fact is expressed by the *particular quantifier*, ($\exists a$). This is read: "There is at least one a, such that . . . "

Where different quantifiers precede the same form, quantifying different variables within that form, great care must be taken to give them their proper order, as differences of order often make differences of sense.

A completely quantified propositional form is a *general proposition*.

In describing the properties of a specific system, general propositions serve as an economical substitute for long lists of specific ones. But their usefulness goes beyond mere economy; for they describe what is, in fact, true of all systems which are *like* the given, specific, one. General propositions may describe the properties of a certain *kind* of system.

When they are used in this way there is, of course, no mention of specific terms, because no specific collection "K" is under discussion. The universe of such a discourse is a collection of elements *in general*; any elements so interpreted and so related are under consideration. We pass, then, from specific universes to "$K(a, b \ldots)$." The general universe has merely "a certain number" of terms; the general propositions describe (1) how the relation functions among such terms if it functions at all, and (2) whether it holds for all, or merely some, or no terms of the universe. Such a generalized discourse conveys a principle of arrangement, and presents a logical pattern of which many different specific systems are instances.

We have discussed two procedures in the use of symbolism, which must not be confused, namely: (1) *interpretation*, the assignment of meanings (*con*notations) to symbols. The opposite of interpretation is *abstraction*, of which more will be said in later chapters. (2) *Specification*, the assignment of values (specific *de*notations) to variables. The opposite of specification is *generalization*, with which we have dealt in the present chapter.

Natural language also has its symbols for quantified

terms; these are the so-called "indefinite pronouns." But there are more linguistic forms than necessary, and their grammatical use is somewhat arbitrary; the symbolic expression of general propositions is simpler than their rendering in ordinary speech.

QUESTIONS FOR REVIEW

1. What is meant by saying a completely stated system shows "regularities"?
2. What is a "variable"? How does it "mean" any term, or terms, in a specific universe of discourse?
3. What is the "range of significance" of a variable?
4. What is meant by a "value"?
5. When a term in a proposition is replaced by a variable, what sort of construct results?
6. What is a "quantifier"? How many quantifiers are there? How are they expressed?
7. What is the meaning of the "universal quantifier"? Of the "particular quantifier"? How would you express the fact that a certain dyadic relation *never* holds in a given group of terms?
8. What is a general proposition?
9. Does a general proposition have truth-value? Does a propositional form have truth-value?
10. How may a general proposition be used in a formal context with a universe of specific terms?
11. Have general propositions any use besides that of abbreviating descriptions in a specific system? If so, what other use or uses have they?
12. In a discourse where no specific propositions occur, how is the universe to be expressed?
13. What is the subject of such a discourse, i.e. what does the discourse describe?
14. Do we ever assert general propositions in ordinary conversation? If so, how do we express the quantified terms involved in such propositions?

SUGGESTIONS FOR CLASS WORK

1. Classify the following expressions as (1) specific propositions, (2) general propositions, (3) propositional forms.
   A. "Nobody knows the trouble I've seen."
   B. Yesterday was a warm day.

C. "All Gaul is divided into three parts."
D. Nelson won the battle of Trafalgar.
E. "Every lassie has her laddie."
F. "Charlie is my darling."

2. Express symbolically the propositional forms exemplified by:

A. $1 + 2 = 2 + 1$
   $3 + 5 = 5 + 3$
   $7 + 2 = 2 + 7$

B. New York is greater than Boston.
   London is greater than Paris.
   Paris is greater than London.

C. If Paris is greater than London, then London is not greater than Paris.
   If London is greater than Paris, then Paris is not greater than London.
   (Suggestion: ">" is the usual symbol for "greater than.")

3. Find two sets of values for which the following propositional form holds, and two for which it fails:

a is West of b and b is West of c.

Express in general propositions that it sometimes holds and that it sometimes fails.

4. Try to express the following general propositions symbolically:
A. Nobody is everybody's friend.
B. Nothing can come out of nothing.
C. Some people are twins.
D. Everybody has relatives.

5. Express symbolically a system consisting of six streets of a certain town, as follows: Oak Street, Ash Street, Cedar Street, High Street, Front Street, Exeter Street. The constituent relation in the context is "parallel to." Using your own symbol for this relation and the traditional symbols for logical relations, state the following propositions:

Oak is parallel to Ash.
Cedar is parallel to Oak.
High is parallel to Oak.
Front is parallel to Ash.
Exeter is not parallel to Oak.

Draw all possible consequences. Keeping within this specific system, state as many propositions as possible in general terms.

CHAPTER V

CLASSES

1. Individuals and Classes

A specific proposition always concerns a certain subject, which could be pointed out and given a proper name. It is about *this* or *that* subject; *this* boy James, *this* house called A, *that* place, *that* poem. Such a subject, whether it be a person, place, thing, or what-not, is termed an *individual*. Anything is an individual if it may be indicated, without any description, by pointing and saying "this"; and individuals are the terms of specific propositions.

Completely general propositions, on the other hand, never mention individuals. They may *apply* to specific subjects, but that is a very different matter. If the famous proposition "all men are mortal" is applied to Socrates, then Socrates figures in a specific proposition, which describes an *instance* of the general fact asserted by the general proposition. "All men are mortal" entails "Socrates is mortal" by *specification*; that is what we mean by saying it "applies to Socrates."

Sometimes an application is so obvious or so important that the general proposition from which it is made is unconsciously taken for a specific one. This is especially apt to be the case where there is only one instance of the expressed condition. For example, in the fable of Reynard the Fox, a complaint is brought that "some animal has killed a lamb." This is a general proposition. But the guilty fox, feeling that it *applies* to him, cries out: "Your honour, it was *not* I!" and realizes too late that no accusation was made—no proposition *about him* was ever asserted—and he has needlessly given himself away by applying the statement to himself.

2. MEMBERSHIP IN A CLASS

What a general proposition does mention is *a member, or members, of a certain class*. "Any man is mortal" means that any member of a certain class, namely the class of men, is mortal. "Some animal has killed a lamb" asserts that at least one member of the class of animals has killed a lamb. Logic does not deal with specific men or animals; it can *apply* to individuals if they are members of a class, but it can actually *mention* them only as members, not as individuals. We cannot say in logic, "Reynard killed a lamb," meaning by "Reynard" an individual known by personal acquaintance; we can only say,

$(\exists x) : x$ is named Reynard and x killed a lamb.

But this tells us only that *at least one member of a class* is named Reynard, and has killed a lamb. It still leaves us with "at least one," not with "this one." The fact that *this fox* killed a lamb, that *this* is Reynard, goes beyond the sphere of logic; it requires sense-experience, to furnish a specific individual to which one may *point*.

But the fact that such individuals may be members of classes makes it possible for logic, which deals only with "some, or all, members of a class," to apply to individuals. Otherwise there would be no traffic whatever between logic and life. The relation of *class-membership*, therefore, is one of prime importance. For hundreds of years it has been confused with the *relation of part to whole*, and this circumstance has led to some of the most intricate metaphysical problems known to philosophy. The confusion we owe in large measure to the officious ubiquity of the little word "is"; and its removal, to the fact that an Italian mathematician and logician, PEANO, recognizing the difference between "is" and "is a," honoured the latter relation with a special symbol, "ϵ," the Greek letter epsilon (from "$\epsilon\sigma\tau\iota$"). By means of a distinct notation, the relation of class-membership may at last be clearly distingished from identity, inclusion, entailment, or any number of other relations named "is," with which it has traditionally been confounded. Thus, to express briefly and concisely that Reynard is a member of the class "fox," we shall write:

$$\text{Reynard} \ \epsilon \ \text{fox},$$

which may be read "Reynard is a fox," if we bear in mind that "ϵ" really means "is a member of the class," and do not confuse it with other sundry meanings of "is." Likewise, we may write

$$2 \ \epsilon \ \text{number}$$
$$\text{A} \ \epsilon \ \text{house}$$
$$(\exists a) : a \ \epsilon \ \text{house}$$

The relation of membership in a class must be distinguished from that of a *part* to the *whole* which it helps to compose. A class is not a composite whole, as a little reflection upon examples will show. Suppose, for instance, that the class of 1938 in a college enters with one hundred members, and this class pledges a graduation gift of $500 to the college. Now, let 20 members of the class drop out in the course of its four academic years, and fifteen new members join during that time; is the pledge still valid? The membership of the class has changed; is the class which gave the pledge in 1934 still there to redeem it in 1938? If we were to treat a class as a whole composed of its members, then in 1934 there was no class of 1938. Then a class of persons would mean no more than "those people"—depending for its import on our actual acquaintance with certain individuals. But, obviously, we mean more than that. We know what we mean by the class "fox" without knowing how many foxes there are, and it remains the same class, whether Reynard gets shot, or no. We know what we mean by "mankind," which is a class, although obviously we do not know all its members. But if its members were the parts of which the class were composed, then we could not know the class without knowing how many members it had, and recognizing them individually, as we must know individually *who* is meant by the demonstrative phrase "those people over there." There is nothing permanent about such a collection; the phrase is meaningless as soon as the people disperse. If this were indeed the nature of classes, then the meaning of a class-name such as "mankind" would change with every birth and every death.

But if a class is not the sum of its members, what else is it? If the relation ϵ is not that of a part to the whole, what else is it? Before we can answer these questions we must consider how classes are characterized and distinguished from each other.

3. CONCEPTS AND CLASSES

A class is usually referred to as "the class of so-and-so's," i.e. the class whose members have a certain character. Having this character, being a so-and-so, is what marks a thing as belonging to a class. A man, for instance, belongs to the class of politicians if and only if he is a politician. "Being a politician" is the character which determines his membership in the class of politicians.

But different people have different ideas of what it means to be a "politician." So long as we let these vague ideas, or personal conceptions, determine what "politician" means, few people will always agree with each other as to whether Mr. So-and-so is a politician or not. Here it becomes a matter of importance to *define the concept* represented by various conceptions of "politician," and to abide by the bare concept, in deciding the membership of a class. We cannot enumerate the class of "college students" if we are not agreed as to what characterizes a "college," and what are the conditions of being a "student" in such an institution. We must fix the concept before we can decide on the propriety of applying it to this or that individual; and it is the application of a concept that marks an individual as a member of a certain class.

A "class" may be described, then, as a collection of all those and only those terms to which a certain *concept* applies. If we collect all the individuals to which the concept "being a fox" applies, we form the class of foxes. If we would form the class of prime numbers, we must indicate all the items to which the concept "prime number" applies. We may say, then, that a class is the *field of applicability* of a concept; in traditional logic, this field is called the extension of the concept.* We may not know just what this field includes, but we can refer to the field *in general*, i.e. to the field whatever it includes. We may talk about the extension of the concept "politician," without knowing how great or small that extension is. That is why the notion of a *class* is not a collective *specific* notion, but a *general* one; for we may speak of "the extension of the concept 'politician,' *whatever this includes*," and that is the same as "the class of politicians."

4. "Defining Forms" of Classes

What does it mean to say that Socrates is mortal? It means that at some time, Socrates must die. If "Socrates must die" is true, then Socrates belongs to the class of mortals. Also, if "Plato must die" is true, Plato is a member of this class; and "Apollo must die," if it were true, would relegate Apollo, too, to the class of mortals. But "Apollo must die" is false; therefore Apollo is not a mortal.

Now, all these propositions exemplify the same form:

$$x \text{ must die}$$

All their subjects are values for "x." With some the resulting proposition is true, with others false. All those with which it is true are mortals, all those with which it is false are not

---

* The *extension*, or field of applicability, is traditionally opposed to the *intension*, or complete definition, of a concept. Further elaboration of these notions may be found in any standard Logic.

mortals. Therefore the criterion for being a member of "mortals" is, to be a *true value for x* in the propositional form "*x* must die." The class of mortals is the whole collection of true values of "*x*" in this form. The form, then, may be said to *define* the class, since it furnishes the criterion for membership; therefore it is called a *defining form of the class* "*mortals*."

The defining form of the class "mortals" is "*x* must die"; of "mankind," "*x* is human"; of "carnivora," "*x* eats flesh"; of "politicians," "*x* engages in politics." In every case, the class in question is the *range of applicability of the concept* expressed by its defining form. This concept is called the *class-concept*, or sometimes the *class in intension* (see footnote above).

We may now answer the questions: What is a class, if not the sum of its members? and: What is ϵ, if not the relation of a part to a composite whole? A class is the extension of a concept, whatever that extension may comprise. The relation ϵ, of membership in a class, is the relation of falling under a concept. The class is not a fixed collection; it is defined by a propositional form, not by its specific members. If we understand the class-concept, we are acquainted with the class, even if we have never seen a single individual that belongs to it. Since concepts are abstractions, and classes are based on concepts, we may regard a class as a logical construction, a purely conceptual entity. Therefore a member of a class, being a concrete individual, cannot be a *part* of it in any literal sense; the relation "ϵ," or "membership," is a peculiar and subtle one.

5. CLASSES AND SUB-CLASSES

Despite their abstract character, however, classes may have parts—logical, not physical parts. For instance, the class of sheep may be divided into black sheep and white sheep. But "black sheep" is a class, and so is "white sheep"; the class "sheep," then, is divisible into at least two other classes. These are called *sub-classes* of the original class.

Since we are no longer talking about individuals, A, B, C, etc., we may put the Roman capital alphabet to a new use; and I shall henceforth let these letters denote *certain classes*. Individuals are only mentioned in general now, but classes are specified, in that we speak of the class of men, the class of sheep, and so forth. Therefore, capitals shall now represent classes, and lower-case italics, as before, stand for variables whose values are individuals, or (if quantified) for *individuals in general*.

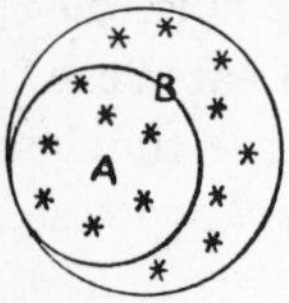

FIG. 1

If a certain class, A, is a sub-class of B, then every individual which is a member of A is also a member of B. If A is the class of white sheep, and B, sheep of all sorts, then A is a sub-class of B; every member of A is also a member of B, i.e.: every white sheep is a sheep. This may be expressed in a general proposition:

$$(x) : (x \in A) \supset (x \in B)$$

The class A is entirely *included* in the class B. A diagram (Fig. 1) may show this more clearly. The large circle represents B, and all the asterisks that fall within it are "sheep," members of B; the smaller circle is A, and all the asterisks within it are "white sheep," members of A. Obviously they are all members of B as well. A lies wholly within B; it is therefore called a sub-class of B. If it had a single member that did not belong to B, i.e., were it not entirely *included*, it would not be a sub-class of B.

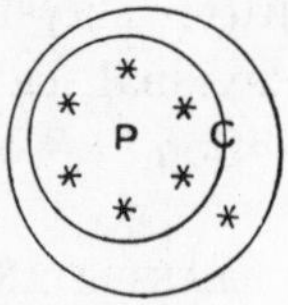

FIG. 2

By way of another example, let the class C, in Fig. 2, be the class of "royal children" in the old fairy-tale, *The White Swans*. There were seven royal children, six boys and one girl; all the boys were turned into swans by enchantment, to be redeemed by their faithful sister. Now, let P represent the class of princes. Every prince is a royal child, a member of C. In other words, $(x) : (x \in P) \supset (x \in C)$.

But there is one member of C that is not a member of P;

that is the sister. C, then, is greater than P, and includes P as a proper part. P is a sub-class of C.

6. The Notion of a "Unit Class"

Suppose there were six princes in the story, and also six princesses; then we could form not only the sub-class "princes," but another sub-class, "princesses." Let us call this latter class S, and describe it as a sub-class of C by the general proposition:

$$(x) : (x \in S) \supset (x \in C)$$

Obviously there would be such a class not only if there were six princesses, but also if there were four, or three, or if there were only two. The number of members in the class is immaterial, so long as every such member of S is also a member of C.

But in the fairy-tale there was only one princess. May we, then, claim to have a *sub-class* "princesses"? Yes, indeed; for the class of princesses is the extension of the *concept* "princess," and if this extension happens to include only one element, then that element is the sole member of the class. A class which has only one member is known as a *unit class*.

At first the notion of a unit class may seem a little difficult, because most of us operate with a *conception* of "class" based on the fancy of collecting individuals into a group. We cannot very well imagine ourselves collecting one princess into a group. But this is merely one of those extraneous personal conceptions, pictorial helps for the intellect, against which we must guard in logic. The *concept* of "class" involves no process of collecting individuals. It involves only the notion of a propositional form and the field of its applicability; and of course some form might have only a single application, its variable might have only a single value that would yield a true proposition.

As a matter of fact, the idea of a unit class is not peculiar to logic, nor unfamiliar to men of affairs. A committee of one is a unit class; it is a "committee" despite the fact that it has only one member, and its rights and duties are those of an *appointed body of persons*, not simply of an individual. A so-called "corporation sole" is another case of a unit class. It functions exactly like a corporation of several members, except that all its offices devolve upon one and the same member. Again, if we count the number of families in a population, each family is a class of persons; in the case of a completely unattached individual, perhaps a stranger in the land, we have a family of only one member—a unit class. All these examples are homely and popular, and illustrate how often we *use* a logical construction in practical life which looks new and odd on paper.

How may we express in formal terms that a certain class, A, has only one member? We cannot enumerate its membership, because specific individuals are not named in logical discourse. So it is necessary to state in *general propositions* that there is just one member (whatever individual that may be). Now, "just one" means "no less than one," or: "at least one," and also "no more than one," or: "at most one." The first condition is easy to express:

$$(\exists x) : x \in A$$

That there is at most one, however, can be expressed only by asserting that *any other one* is identical with the one already mentioned. But another general proposition cannot refer to the *same* element mentioned above, because x in one general proposition need not mean the same thing as in another; so it is necessary to conjoin two propositions, one stating that there is a member of A, the other that *any* member of A is identical with that one: thus we have the conjunctive statement,

$$(\exists x) \, (y) : (x \in A) \, . \, [(y \in A) \supset (y = x)]$$

"There is at least one x, such that, for any y, x is an A, and if y is an A, then y is identical with x."

This limits the membership of A to some one element, x.

The conventions of language are very well adapted for expressing the condition of sole membership. When we wish to denote an individual as such, we use a *name*, without any article; but when an element is to be mentioned as member of a unit class, we employ the definite article, "the," and use a word (or words) for the class-concept in the singular. "The" indicates that *all* members of the class are meant. "The sons of Charlemagne" denotes all three members of that class, and if, unknown to history, there were more than three, the unknown ones are logically included in the denotation. "The city-states of Greece" refers to *all* members of the class "city-states of Greece"; i.e. it means collectively *all* true values for the form:

$$x \ \epsilon \ \text{city-state of Greece}$$

If, then, we combine "the," which indicates that *all* members of a class are meant, with the grammatical "singular number," which signifies that *not more than one element* is denoted, this combination expresses exactly the logical condition for sole membership: the whole membership of the class, yet only one element. So, to entitle a book: "The Laws of Thought," implies that it contains *all* laws of thought; that any value for x with which "$x \ \epsilon$ law of thought" becomes true, is treated in the book. The plural form of "laws" means that there is more than one such law. But if we speak of "*the author* of 'the Laws of Thought,'" this refers to just one person, though not to a specific one; for "the" means that "author" refers to *all* values, collectively, for y, in the propositional form:

$$y \ \text{wrote "The Laws of Thought"}$$

and the singular form of "author" signifies that there is only one such value. Everybody understands the indications of syntax in his own language; everyone knows that "*the* author" refers to one person who is the sole writer of a certain book; but it takes a little reflection to realize that the combined use of "the" and a singular noun conveys: "*all* members, and *at most one*, of the class in question."

7. THE NOTION OF A "NULL CLASS"

The word "the" means more than "all"; it also expresses the fact that *there is at least one element* in a certain class. If we speak of "The wife of King Arthur," we mean (1) that we refer to the *whole* extension of the concept "wife of King Arthur," and (2) that at least one element falls under this concept. So "the" really means "all, and at least one." The singular noun "wife" then adds, "at most one." The total combination conveys: "there is *just one x*, such that *x* is a wife of King Arthur." But suppose that King Arthur had remained celibate; would the form: "*x* ε wife of King Arthur" define no class? Would the concept "wife of King Arthur" have no extension?

If we know what *sort of thing* we mean by a noun or a descriptive phrase, then there is a class of things defined thereby, for a "class" is exactly the same thing as a "sort." Now, there may be no wife of King Arthur; then there is simply *nothing of that sort*. That is the same as to say there is no element which is a member of that class. The class, therefore, is said to be empty, or to be a *null class*.

If a class is empty, or "null," then "all its members" means none at all. If King Arthur were unmarried, then "All wives of King Arthur are named Mary" would simply mean the same thing as "No wives of King Arthur are named Mary." "All wives of King Arthur" makes sense, even if the King is a bachelor, for "all" refers to the total extension of a concept, and may so refer even when this extension covers no elements.

Of course we are not likely to make remarks about "all the wives" of someone who is not known to be married;

but sometimes we come across important propositions, expressed universally, that may refer to an empty class. In city parks one often sees signs that read: "All persons picking flowers, etc., will be prosecuted." This statement is true even when there happens to be no such person, i.e. when the class of flower-pickers, etc., is empty.

But obviously, we could not say: "*The* persons picking flowers will be prosecuted," if we do not know that there are any. We cannot refer to "*the* wife of King Arthur" if he is unmarried. "The" connotes existence as well as universality. It combines the senses of (x) and $(\exists x)$ into: "all, where there is at least one." And in doing this it offers another example of the way several logical conditions may be telescoped into one modest little word (sometimes even into a mere word-ending) by the genius of natural language.

8. The Notion of a "Universe Class"

Suppose, in a given universe of discourse, we form a class A such that "$x \in A$" holds for all values of x, i.e. such that

$$(x) : x \in A$$

This is not difficult to do. If we resort to the simple system expounded in the previous chapter, of houses in the relation "nt," we may form the class of "houses which are not to the North of themselves." Obviously this class comprises all elements in the universe of discourse, since

$$(x) : \sim (x \text{ nt } x)$$

It is therefore called a *universe class*.

In ordinary language, any statement about "everything" concerns a universe class. "Everything is mutable" asserts that the class of mutable things contains all elements in the universe, i.e. that

$$(x) : x \text{ may change}$$

Also, every statement about "nothing" may be expressed as a statement about a universe class, because what is true for nothing is *false for anything*. Thus, "Nothing is created from empty space" means that anything you like is *not* so created:

$$(y) : \sim (y \text{ is created from empty space})$$

Note that the opposite of this characterization, i.e. the form:

"x is created from empty space"

defines a null class. Likewise in the system of houses, where

$$\sim (x \text{ nt } x)$$

defines a universe class, the positive form: "$(x \text{ nt } x)$" defines a null class. These two forms are always correlative; and because this is the case, we do not need a quantifier for "no x," but can get along with "all x" and the *denial* of the form that characterizes an empty class. To say that *everything* lacks a certain property, is the same as to say *nothing* has it. Formally, then, assertions about a null class are always expressed as denials about a universe class; and we define a universe class whenever we make a universal statement about the elements in a universe. For instance, if our universe contains "creatures," and we say:

$$(x) (\exists y) : x \text{ fm } y$$

then the class of "creatures having a fellowman" is a universe class. But even when the statement is particular, but involves a universal condition, a universe class is defined; for instance, in a system discussed in Chapter III the constituent relation was "liking," and "a likes b" was expressed as "a lk b." We might very well assume that there is one person who likes everybody (including himself), i.e.

$$(\exists a) (b) : a \text{ lk } b$$

This is a particular proposition, because its first quantifier is particular; but it expresses as universal the condition of "being liked by *a*," and the class of "elements liked by *a*" is a universe class.

9. IDENTITY OF CLASSES

One class is said to include another if every member of the latter is also a member of the former. "Royal children" includes "princes," because every member of "princes" is a member of "royal children." It is natural to assume that the included class is smaller than the including one.

Suppose, however, that we form a class, "Passengers on the first trip of the *Mayflower*" (call this class A), and another class, B, "Founders of Plymouth." We have here two very different defining concepts. But it so happens that every passenger on that famous trip was one of the Founders of Plymouth, so A is included in B; and also, every founder of Plymouth was a passenger on the *Mayflower's* first trip, so is not B included in A? By the definition of "inclusion," which we have adopted and by which we must abide, this is exactly the case. The two classes are *mutually inclusive*, for they have the same membership. They differ only in their definitions, or, as logicians say, they differ in *intension*. Their *extensions*, however, are exactly alike.

If we relate classes to each other by their intensions, then "Passengers on the first trip of the *Mayflower*" and "Founders of Plymouth" have nothing to do with each other. But if we relate them by their extensions, then these two have the closest of all possible relations—they are *identical*. The extension of A is the extension of B; so we say, the two class-concepts *define the same class*.

It is much more practical to take classes in extension, i.e. as exemplifications of a concept, than in intension, or as pure meanings. The first and strongest reason is that a completely extensional treatment gives us a simple principle of relating classes to each other, namely the principle of *common membership*. If we depend upon intensional relations, then most concepts have nothing to do with each other at all; and a systematic ordering of concepts becomes an impossibility, except in very small compass. For instance, in the example given above, "Passengers on the first trip of the *Mayflower*" and "Founders of Plymouth" have nothing whatever in common if we take them intensionally; to a person knowing the respective meanings of these phrases, i.e. *understanding* the concepts expressed, but not knowing anything of their applicability, they would reveal no relationship whatever. It is only because their *extensions* coincide that we can say: "The passengers on the first American trip of the *Mayflower are* the founders of Plymouth." The concepts as such offer no clue to each other; their only relatedness lies in the fact that they determine the same class. This fact is too valuable to be neglected or despised by logicians; so, when they are faced with a choice, whether to treat classes as extensions or as intensions (pure concepts), they usually decide in favour of the former.

Another reason for dealing with classes in extension is, that a class in extension is described by a *general proposition*. A systematization of pure concepts might be aesthetically gratifying, but would have absolutely no relation to the systematization of mundane facts, which we call "science." General propositions, however, occur in science; and *the systematization of general propositions* is the great contribution of logic to the concrete sciences. But general propositions, which are quantified propositional forms, always refer to members of a class, for it is only of such that we can say "all" or "some." Obviously only propositions about *extensions* can be quantified; there is no sense in prefixing "all" or "some" to the *meaning* of "house" or of "founder of Plymouth."

Two defining forms, then, may define one and the same class. That is what is meant by saying, two classes which have the same membership are identical, or two mutually inclusive classes are identical. Formally, "A includes B" means "$(a) : (a \epsilon B) \supset (a \epsilon A)$;" and "A includes B and B includes A," i.e.:

$$(a) : (a \epsilon B) \supset (a \epsilon A) \cdot (a \epsilon A) \supset (a \epsilon B)$$

may be expressed by the simple equation,

$$A = B$$

10. The Uniqueness of "1" and "0"

Now let us return once more to a simple and familiar system, to study a further condition of its logical structure. I assume once more the system $K(a, b \ldots)$ fm, of creatures in the relation of "fellowman." Suppose our universe to be composed of human beings; then

$$(a) (\exists b) : a \text{ fm } b$$

The class of "creatures having a fellowman," then, is a universe class. Let us call it by a special name, the number "1," to connote "wholeness" or "totality." It includes everyone of the K-elements. Furthermore, it is a general proposition of the system that

$$(a) : \sim (a \text{ fm } a)$$

No creature is its own fellowman; therefore the class of "creatures which are not their own fellowmen" is another universe-class, which I will call "1'," for it also includes all the K-elements. These two classes, then, are identical, for they have exactly the same membership. It is not hard to see that *all* universe-classes within a formal context are identical. So, instead of speaking of "a universe class" in the context $K(a, b \ldots)$ fm, we may speak of "*the* universe class" in this context. This class, the class including everything, may be defined by various propositional forms; but whatever concept we may use to form it, it is still the one unique class, which is commonly called "1."

That all universe classes in a context are identical is easy to grasp, because we can review their membership in imagination. But suppose that in the same context we form the class of those creatures which are fellowmen to themselves; since there are *no such creatures*, this class, which I call "o," is empty, is a null class. Its extension is zero (hence the appropriate symbol o). Now, consider the class of all those creatures which have no fellowmen at all; in a universe where "$(a)\ (\exists b) : a$ fm b" holds, that class must also be null. Call it o′. Its extension also is zero. The extensions of o and o′ are, therefore, the same; and *all null classes are identical*. This is not so easy to visualize in one's mind as the identity of all universe classes, yet a little reflection makes it acceptable; there is only one class "nothing." The difficulty lies in thinking of any null class in extension, since it has no elements.

One genuinely logical problem presents itself, however, in this connection: if o = o′, then it is, of course, defined by the defining form of o′, which is:

$$(b) : \sim (a \text{ fm } b)$$

(Note that this expression remains a *form*, although b is a general term; the fact that a is not quantified leaves it a variable, so the expression reads "a has no fellowman," which is a propositional form.) But it is also defined by the form:

$$a \text{ fm } a$$

To have no fellowman and to be one's own fellowman are incompatible conditions; how, then, can they define the same class?

The answer is, that the null class is the one and only class which may have incompatible properties, and more than that, *it is the class which has all incompatible properties, which all absurd combinations of concepts define*. It is the class of round squares, secular churches, solid liquids, and fellowmen without fellowmen. For to any of these we must say there is no such thing. The class of round squares is null, the class of secular churches is null, etc., etc. It is, indeed, rather hard on the imagination to suppose that all round squares are all secular churches, and also all round squares are all married bachelors; but imagination is no measure of logical possibility or fact, and besides, no one is called upon to imagine that there *is a* round square which is a married bachelor or a secular church. It is comforting to know that there is none. There is, however, *the Null Class*; and since it is defined by all forms that have no true values, it most conveniently saves us from having to deal with all sorts of structures that might look just like defining forms but define no class. Such forms define the null class.

Common sense considers a class as a finite selection of elements, including more than one and less than all the elements of the universe from which the selection is made. Ideas such as that of a class with only one member, or with all possible members, or no member at all, are unfamiliar. Yet we use them constantly, and in just the way logicians recommend. Even the commonest of common-sense philosophers would agree that all statements about "everything" are about the *same* "everything"; that there may be committees of one, and that in country schools the graduating class may have one member; and that "nothing" = "nothing" no matter by what concept we describe it. All that logic demands of us is the explicit admission that "everything," "nothing," and the committee of one or the modest graduating class *are classes*. If only this is conceded, we demand no more stretches of imagination and conception, for the whole system of classes and of relations among them, which is the topic of the next chapters.

Summary

Specific propositions deal with individuals. An individual is anything that might be pointed out, indicated by "this," or given a proper name. General propositions deal with *some or any member of a class*, and refer to individuals only indirectly, i.e. by *applying* to them. A general proposition expresses a *general condition* in a class; a specific proposition quotes an *instance* of such a general condition.

The relation of a member of a class which contains it is not that of a part to a whole. "Is part of" and "is a" are distinct relations. The latter is symbolized by "ϵ."

A class is determined by a *concept*, known as the *class-concept* for that class. The concept may be expressed through a *propositional form*, which is called the *defining form* of the class in question. A propositional form always contains a variable (for the present we have restricted our study to defining forms of one variable). Every value for this variable with which the form yields a true proposition is a member of the class defined; so, *the membership of the class consists of all true values for the variable in the defining form.*

The *meaning* of a concept is called its *intension*, the *range of applicability* its *extension*. A class, then, may be defined as the extension of a concept. If we speak of a class by merely naming its class-concept, we are considering the class "in intension"; if we speak of it as a group of things exemplifying the concept, we treat it "in extension." Thus, "the class 'fox' " is named in intension, "the class of foxes" in extension.

If all the members of one class are also members of another, then the first class "in extension" is included in the second. This does not mean that their intensions have anything in common. The class which is included is called a sub-class of the other.

Since we are never to name *certain individuals* any more, the capital Roman alphabet is released from its original service and may be put to the new use of naming *certain classes*.

To say a class A is included in a class B, one may use a general proposition about *members* of A and B respectively, and say:

$$(x) : (x \in A) \supset (x \in B)$$

Since a concept may be such that it applies to only one thing in the world, there may be classes of only one member. In natural language, "the so-and-so," where a singular noun is used, denotes a sole member of a class. The member must not be confused with the class; for the member is an individual, but the class is the extension of a concept. A class of just one member is called a unit class. The formal statement that a class, A, is a unit class, requires the joint assertions that there is a member of A, and that *every* member of A is this member.

If a concept has no application, i.e. if the variable in the propositional form expressing the concept has no true value, then the form defines a *null* class.

If a concept applies to every element in a formal context, then its extension is a *universe class*.

Two classes, A and B, which have the same membership are *mutually inclusive*; for, in this case,

$$(x) : [(x \, \epsilon \, A) \supset (x \, \epsilon \, B)] \, . \, [(x \, \epsilon \, B) \supset (x \, \epsilon \, A)]$$

So by the definition of "inclusion," A is included in B, and B is included in A. Their two class concepts have the *same* extension, i.e. their two defining functions *define the same class*. Two mutually included classes are identical.

This shows that a class may have more than one defining function.

Since all universe classes in a formal context have the same extension, namely "everything," all such classes are identical; so we may speak of *the* universe class in a formal context.

The same holds for all null classes; their extensions are all alike, namely "nothing," so all null classes are identical, and we may speak of *"the* null class."

The null class is defined by any form that has no true values. It is the extension of any concept that has no application. Hence, all pairs of incompatible concepts, combined in one defining form, define the null class.

QUESTIONS FOR REVIEW

1. How do specific propositions differ from general ones?
2. In what way can general propositions have any bearing on individuals at all?
3. Is a class identical with the things in it?
4. How are classes related to (1) concepts, (2) propositional forms? What is (1) a "class-concept," (2) a "defining form"?
5. What is a "class in extension"? A "class in intension"? Give examples.
6. What is a unit class? How does one express in logical symbolism that a class, A, is a unit class?
7. What is a universe class? A null class? How does one express formally that A is a universe class? That B is a null class?
8. What is a sub-class?
9. What is meant by "inclusion" among classes? By "mutual inclusion"? How is mutual inclusion expressed in logic? What is meant by saying two classes are identical?
10. How many universe classes may be formed in a given formal context? How many null classes? How many unit classes?
11. How many defining forms may belong to one class? How many classes may one form define?
12. What class is defined by "$x \epsilon$ living mammoth"? By "x nt x"? By "$x = x$"?

SUGGESTIONS FOR CLASS WORK

1. Express in logical symbolism:

> Fido is a dog.
> Fido is a dog and not a cat.
> No dog is a cat.
> Every dog is an animal.
> Collies are a kind of dog.

2. Form three sub-classes of humankind. Name each one in extension and in intension, and cite (1) the class-concept, and (2) the defining form. Express symbolically, for each class, that it is a sub-class of the given class.

3. Express symbolically:

> There is just one Pope.
> George VI is the King of England.
> Everything must perish.
> The king can do no wrong."

4. (*a*) Give two examples of unit classes.

   (*b*) Express two propositional forms defining the same class (not the null class).

   (*c*) Express two propositional forms defining the null class.

CHAPTER VI

PRINCIPAL RELATIONS AMONG CLASSES

1. THE RELATION OF CLASS-INCLUSION

In the previous chapter, I pointed out that it is advantageous to regard classes in extension, because from this point of view they exhibit relations to one another which their mere intensions, i.e. the meanings of their class-concepts, do not allow us to infer. The only relation introduced in that chapter was that of *class-inclusion*. Since classes are logical constructs, not physical things, "class-inclusion," of course, does not mean just the same thing as "inclusion" of (say) one box in another; it is used in a special sense. Just what this sense is, we know from the definition: "A is included in B" *means*

$$(x) : (x \in A) \supset (x \in B)$$

The relation between A and B, which we express directly by the word "inclusion," is here described indirectly, in terms of *class-membership*; inclusion figures as a logical relation between two cases of class-membership. That is a perfectly adequate but very complicated rendering of the close and simple connection between A and B. If the words: "A is included in B" may be taken to *mean* the state of affairs described in the formula, then certainly we may as well employ a symbol to express the relation *directly between* A *and* B, and stipulate that this expression is to be *equivalent* to the longer description in terms of ϵ. The traditional symbol used for this purpose is $<$. It is the mathematical sign for "is less than," originally adopted with the idea that the included class must be "less than" the including one. We have seen that this need not be the case, since two identical classes include each other; but, barring this one case, the suggestion of the sign is not bad, so we may follow

common usage in letting $<$ stand for "is included in."
Thus,

$$A < B$$

is read: "class A is included in class B," or: "A is included
in B," and is known to mean:

$$(x) : (x \in A) \supset (x \in B)$$

"Every member, x, of A is also a member of B."

These two expressions are *equivalent* to each other *by definition*; we have *defined* $<$ in terms of x, $\in$, and $\supset$. Wherever
we find one expression we may substitute the other if we
like, for they mean the same thing. Now, "equivalence
by definition" is a relation between propositions, and a
relation between propositions is called a logical relation;
so we have here a new logical relation, which I shall denote
by "$\equiv$df," "is equivalent by definition to."* Whenever
the use of a new symbol is defined in terms of an older
convention, it should be formally introduced as equivalent
by definition to the old; so we shall now define the expression
"A $<$ B" as follows:

$$\text{"A} < \text{B"} \equiv \text{df "}(x) : (x \in A) \supset (x \in B)\text{"}$$

The introduction of new symbols by definition is a very
important device in logic, for it often saves us from typographical complications that threaten to become perfectly
unreadable, and allows the eye to glance with ease over
very complex structures. But it must always be borne in
mind that a defined symbol does not carry a new idea; it
is a concentrated rendering of an old idea, and its meaning
could be expressed with equal accuracy, only not with the

* In *Principia Mathematica* this relation is expressed by
"$\ldots = \ldots$ def," as in: "$p \supset q . = . \sim p \lor q$ def." But the use of a
split symbol for a simple dyadic relation seems to me unfortunate,
as also the use of "$=$," meaning *equality of terms*, for *equivalence of
propositions*. So I use the sign of *logical equivalence*, "$\equiv$," and
combine it directly with the modifier "df."

same dispatch, by the exclusive use of old symbols. *It is a mere shorthand.* Nevertheless, in dealing with anything as intangible as logical structures, our whole ability to recognize these structures at all may hang upon the possibility of symbolizing them in a way which eye and mind can readily follow. Where symbols are our only tools, the importance of a "mere" symbol, even of a "mere shorthand," may be momentous. Also, a defined symbol may have psychological advantages that were lacking to the terms in which it was defined. This is certainly true of the symbol $<$; it is easier to think of "sub-classes of a given class" than of "members of classes which (members) are also members of a given class." Sub-classes may be visualized, as in the diagrams used with § 5 of the foregoing chapter. A complex structure of ϵ-propositions is hard to envisage by any diagram.

2. CONSEQUENCES OF THE DEFINITION OF "$<$"

In using a defined symbol such as $<$, and giving it a familiar name, like "inclusion," one always runs a little risk of dragging into the discourse some personal conceptions and other irrelevant suggestions attached to the symbol or the word. But in logic, the symbol stands for a strict concept, namely its definition, and nothing else; this fact may place some peculiar restrictions upon the use of the word by which we render it. For instance, if "one class is included in another" means "every member of one class is a member of the other," then it follows that every class is included in itself; for certainly, every member of a class is a member of that class. The proposition

$$A < A$$

looks strange to common sense, but is perfectly acceptable by the definition of $<$; and shows us at once that the technical use of a word may be broader than its ordinary use.

Another and more obvious result of the definition is that every class which can be formed within a formal context is a sub-class of 1. Since 1 contains all the elements in the universe, every other class must be included in it; and we have seen that it includes itself, because every class is self-inclusive. So, if we wish to characterize the universe-class in terms of $<$ instead of ϵ, we may say that it is the class which includes all classes. Clearly, no other class can have this property; for if there were another class having this property, say 1', then 1 would include 1', by its characterization; and by virtue of the same characterization 1' would include 1, so we would have

$$(1' < 1) . (1 < 1')$$

a case of mutual inclusion; and that means identical membership; so $1 = 1'$.

Mutual inclusion, like self-inclusion, is an idea unfamiliar to common sense, but sanctioned by the logical definition of $<$. The more sanctions our definitions will grant, the more powerful is the defined relation, and the broader will be the uses to which we can put it in sorting out, comparing, and ordering the classes that may be formed within a universe.

In fact, the notion symbolized by $<$ is so far-reaching that all relations of classes in extension may be expressed by it. The fundamental principle by which classes are related is that of common membership; of their having *all*, or *some*, or *no* members in common. This gives us five possible types of inclusion: (1) Mutual inclusion or identity of classes. (2) Complete inclusion of a lesser in a greater class. (3) Partial inclusion of one class in another, or "overlapping" of two classes. (4) Complete inclusion of two or more classes in one greater class, or "composition" of a class out of lesser ones; and (5) Complete mutual *exclusion* of classes. All these cases may be visualized in diagrams, where the classes are depicted as circles, whose areas signify the extensions of class-concepts. Suppose two classes, A and B, to have the same extension; the circles representing them will exactly coincide, so the diagram for type 1 is a

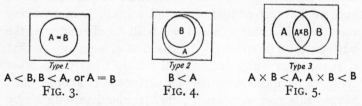

Type 1.
A < B, B < A, or A = B
FIG. 3.

Type 2
B < A
FIG. 4.

Type 3
A × B < A, A × B < B
FIG. 5.

single circle. The second type, complete inclusion of a lesser in a greater class, we have already discussed, and pictured (chap. v, § 5), but its diagram is given here for the sake of completeness. Type 3, however, is new, and merits special attention.

3. PARTIAL INCLUSION OR CONJUNCTION OF CLASSES

Two classes, A and B, neither of which includes the other, may yet have some members in common. In this case the circles representing them would *overlap*, though neither falls completely within the other. It is not true that $(x) : (x \in A) \supset (x \in B)$, nor that $(x) : (x \in B) \supset (x \in A)$; but it *is* true that $(\exists x) : (x \in A) . (x \in B)$. There is at least one individual which is a member of A *and* is a member of B.

The class of those elements which are members of A and also members of B is called the *product of A and B*, and is symbolized by A × B. Two classes which have members in common are said to be *conjoined*; so the operation expressed by × is called *conjunction*.

The defining function of the class which is the product of A and B, i.e. the defining form of the class A × B, is

$$(x \in A) . (x \in B)$$

Clearly, then, every member of A × B is a member of A, so A × B is a sub-class of A; and by the same principle, A × B is a sub-class of B. Moreover, since the class A × B is defined by the form just mentioned, *everything* that is both an A and a B must belong to A $\times$ B; so we may assert the general proposition:

$$(x) : [(x \in A) . (x \in B)] \supset (x \in A \times B)$$

In terms of $<$, we may say that $(A \times B < A) . (A \times B < B)$. Its members are all those elements which have the properties both of A and of B.

Like most logical concepts, the product of two classes is simply an explication of a very common practical notion. Whenever we characterize an individual by more than one trait, we class it under two or more class concepts, i.e. we put it into a class which combines the defining functions of two other classes. A *red apple* belongs to the class of red things and the class of apples, i.e. the class defined by

$$(x \in \text{red thing}) . (x \in \text{apple})$$

a *female dog* is of the class "females $\times$ dogs," it is both a female creature and a dog. Or, to deal with more interesting classes, let A stand for the class of "Englishmen" and B stand for "Socialists." Not all Englishmen are Socialists—we cannot assert that B *includes* A—nor are all Socialists Englishmen, so we cannot say A includes B; but we can form the class of "English Socialists," and this is the "overlapping" of the circles in the diagram of type 3, A $\times$ B. Obviously, "English Socialists" is a sub-class of "Englishmen," and also of "Socialists." It is the *product* of the two classes, "Socialists" and "Englishmen."

4. JOINT INCLUSION, OR DISJUNCTION OF CLASSES

Two classes may be related to one another by a third class. If we take two classes, A and B, together as one class, this new class contains everything that *either* belongs to A *or* belongs to B; so it is called the *sum of* A *and* B, and is expressed, just like a mathematical sum, as A + B. Its defining form is

$$(x \in A) \lor (x \in B)$$

So we may assert the general proposition,

$$(x): [(x \in A) \lor (x \in B)] \supset (x \in A + B)$$

"It is true for any individual that *if* either it is an A, or it is a B, *then* it is a member of A + B."

In the accompanying diagram for type 4, the whole area enclosed in the dotted line represents the extension of A + B. Obviously, if anything is an A, then it is an "A or B," so A is a sub-class of A + B; and likewise, B is a sub-class of the sum of A and B. Moreover, if A and B happen to overlap, so that there are elements belonging to

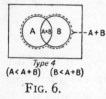

Type 4
(A < A + B)   (B < A + B)
Fig. 6.

A × B, these belong to A, and therefore to A + B; and also to B, and therefore to A + B. What is *both* A and B is doubly sure to belong to at least one of them. So the existence of A × B need not trouble us; A × B goes in with A and B to compose the sum of them, A + B. Two classes which compose a third are said to be *disjoined*; and the sign + is known as the *sign of disjunction*.

If you tell the cook to throw out all the apples which are either over-ripe or wormy, you are talking about the class "Wormy apples + over-ripe apples." This is a disjunction, or sum, of two classes. The cook presumably understands that if any of the apples are *both* over-ripe *and* wormy, she is to throw them out, too; she takes for granted that "Wormy × over-ripe" < "wormy + over-ripe." There may be no apples that have both defects, or a few that have, or they may all be wormy and over-ripe; your order has covered all three cases.

Disjunction of classes may enter into very important

definitions. Consider, for instance, what is meant by a *native citizen of the United States*. There is a class of persons born of American parents. They may be born in China, or Holland, or the Congo, or in the United States, but they must be born of American parents. Let us take A in the diagram of type 4 to stand for this class. There is also a class of persons born on American soil. These may be born of Russian, or Chinese, or English or any other parents, perhaps of American parents; but they must be born on American soil. We will let B represent the class of such persons. Now, there is a third class, that of native Americans, to which belong all people who are *either* born of American parents *or* born on American soil. Native Americans are all persons belonging either to A, or to B, or to both. Obviously, very many of them belong to both—are born on American soil, of American parents. The class of native Americans is the class A + B. It is the disjunction, or sum, of A and B, persons born of American parents and persons born on American soil. The area within the dotted line represents this class.

Logically, nothing is changed if we assume two such classes to be entirely distinct, i.e. to have no members in common. For instance, Parliament—the class of Parliamentarians—is the sum of two mutually exclusive classes, the House of Commons and the House of Lords; every member of Parliament is a member *either* of the House of Commons *or* of the House of Lords, and no one belongs to both. If we let A stand for the class of Commons and B for that of Lords, then "Parliament" is the class A + B. Whenever we write an expression like A + B, it must be understood to mean, "Either A, or B, or both, in case anything is both."

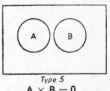

Type 5
A × B = 0
FIG. 7.

Two classes are mutually exclusive if their product is the null-class, i.e., in the case of A and B above, if

$A \times B = 0$. There are *no* individuals who are both Lords and Commons; the class of such persons is zero. Also, there are no carnivorous cows; if A means "carnivora" and B means "cows," then $A \times B = 0$. This is the fifth type of inclusion-relation, shown in the figure on p. 141: complete mutual exclusion.

5. THE PRINCIPLE OF DICHOTOMY: A AND -A

Whenever we form a class within any universe of discourse, then every individual in that universe must either belong to the class, or not belong to it. If our universe is "houses" and we form the class of "two-storeyed houses," then every house falls either within or without this class; for, every house either has two storeys, or it has not. If it has not two storeys, it may have one, or one and a half, or three, four, . . . *n* storeys, but it is a "not-two-storeyed" house. If our universe is "creatures," and the sub-class "cats," then every creature is a cat or a non-cat, whether the latter be dogs, men, or microbes.

This is simply the ancient and honourable method of classification introduced by Aristotle, the division of a universe, known as the *fundamentum divisionis*, into *what is* A and *what is not* A. Suppose we let the universe =int "creatures"; the *universe class* 1, in this universe is the class of "all creatures." Now, let A stand for "cats." Then

$$(x) : (x \in A) \lor \sim (x \in A)$$

"For every x, either x is an A or x is not an A." So there is a class for the defining form "$x \in A$," and another for the defining form "$\sim (x \in A)$." The latter depends for its extension entirely on A, for it takes in, by definition, anything that A leaves out, since obviously nothing can both be and also not-be a cat. This class is called *the class not-A*, and is usually written -A. Since everything in the universe belongs either to A or to -A, the universe class must be the sum of A and -A; i.e.,

$$1 = A + -A$$

It does not matter what class we form, if this class takes in less than the whole universe, there is a remainder in 1; and if we call the class (say) C, this remainder constitutes the class of not-C, or -C. If D = int "dogs," then

$$1 = D + -D$$

"Creatures" = "dogs + not-dogs"; also, we know that "creatures" = "horses + not-horses," "mosquitoes + not-mosquitoes," "men + not-men." The divisions may cut across each other, as "male" and "not-male" (in a universe limited to bi-sexual creatures, not-males are females) cuts across the division between men and not-men, dogs and not-dogs. (See the accompanying diagram.)

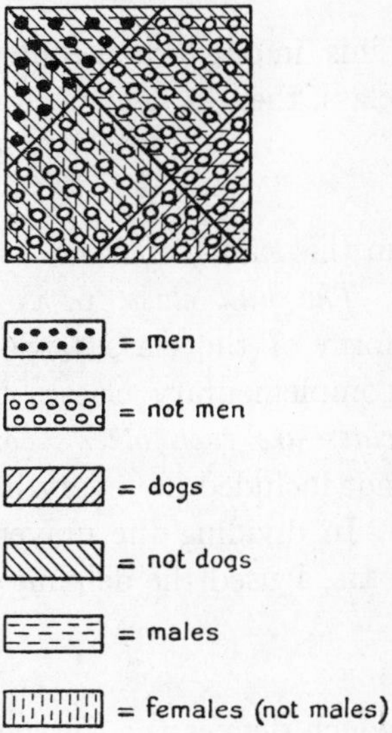

= men

= not men

= dogs

= not dogs

= males

= females (not males)

Fig. 8

Every class creates a *dichotomy*, or "division-in-two"; for every class, say N, defined by a form "$x \in N$" automatically determines a class with the following form,

$$"(x \in -N)"$$

Two classes which have no members in common, but divide the universe between them (A and -A, N and -N, etc.) are called *complementary classes*, for each needs the other to complete the universe. Each is the complement of the other.

So far we have dealt with classes having some members, but less than the entire universe. The complement of a

class, however, was said to be determined by *negating the
defining form*; and this definition does not tell us anything
about the membership of the class. If a defining form of a
class can be negated, then the class has a complement.
Now, this may *always* be done. Suppose we take the defining
form,

$$x \in \text{creature}$$

This, in our formal context, defines the universe class. What
class, then, is defined by

$$\sim (x \in \text{creature})$$

in this same context?

The null class, o, is defined by negating any defining
form of the class 1. So it follows from our definition of
complementary classes that *the universe class and the null
class are each other's complements*. Every element that is
not included in "everything" is "nothing."

In dividing the universe of creatures into cats and not-
cats, I used the defining form

$$x \in \text{cat}$$

which defines the *class of cats*; and this in turn was seen to
determine the *class of not-cats*. But suppose I had started
with the form:

$$x \text{ is unfeline}$$

this would have defined *first* the class of not-cats. Let us
call that class A. Now, the only class defined by

$$\sim (x \text{ is unfeline})$$

is the class of feline creatures, i.e. cats. Therefore, if "not-
cats" is A, "cats" is -A. Which class is A and which is -A
depends on which we choose to express by a defining form.
Positive and negative concepts have nothing to do with
this. Male and female are equally "positive" notions, but

in a universe of bi-sexual organisms they are complements; if "females" is (say) B, then "males" is -B, and *vice-versa*. The complement of any named sort of thing is "something else," and this need not be a "negative" or "privitive" or otherwise less-favoured sort. If we name the latter first, the original class becomes the "negated" element.

6. THE IMPORTANCE OF DICHOTOMY: NEGATION

Two complementary classes not only divide the universe between them, but are also mutually exclusive. This follows immediately from the nature of their defining forms: one form is the denial of the other. Consequently, no element in the universe can be a true value for both forms, i.e. no individual can belong to both classes. No creature can be a cat and not be a cat; if A =int "cats," then $A \times -A = 0$. Whatever is a cat and not a cat, is nothing.

The significance of dichotomies in the universe is that it makes a *negative* statement, such as:

$$(\exists x) : \sim (x \in A)$$

equivalent in meaning to another, which is *positive* in form:

$$(\exists x) : x \in -A$$

That is, the *denial* of an individual's membership in a given class may be replaced by an *assertion* of its membership in another class; since it must belong to one class or the other, a denial of the form "$x \in A$" is equivalent to an assertion of the form "$x \in -A$"; and as it cannot belong to both classes, the assertion of one proposition is as good as a denial of the other. In this way, *all negative propositions about class-membership may be replaced by positive propositions*, namely by assertion of membership in the complementary classes.

If we wish to combine classes either by conjunction or disjunction, we need positive statements about their memberships. We cannot relate, say, cats (C) and dogs (D) through the concept $<$ at all, if all we know is

$$(x) : (x \in C) \supset \sim (x \in D)$$
$$(x) : (x \in D) \supset \sim (x \in C)$$

Since there is nowhere a common element, $<$ cannot be introduced between C and D. But if $\sim (x \in D)$ is equivalent to $(x \in \text{-D})$, and $\sim (x \in C)$ is equivalent to $(x \in \text{-C})$, then

$$(x) : x \in C \supset (x \in \text{-D})$$

which is equivalent by definition to:

$$C < \text{-D}$$

and likewise, of course,

$$D < \text{-C}$$

Here the relation of type 5 is also expressed in terms of $<$, or class-inclusion. The principle of dichotomy gives us two great liberties in logical expression: (1) it allows us to turn negative statements into positive, or positive into negative ones, to suit our purposes of arrangement and calculation; and (2) it lets us express the case of complete exclusion as an inclusion. In the following chapter, the advantage of such alternatives in expression will become more and more apparent. At present I can point out only how the reduction

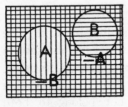

FIG. 9.

of *all* inter-class relations to $<$ makes for neatness, and that the replacement of a negative defining form by the positive form that defines the complementary class makes this reduction possible. Diagrammatically, we have now two classes, A and B, each of which lies entirely *in the complement* of the other; for if everything horizontally striped is -A, and everything vertically striped is -B, A is vertically striped and only vertically; B is horizontally striped but only horizontally; and everything else is striped both ways. Everything that is *neither* A *nor* B is *both* -A *and* -B, i.e. it is -A $\times$ -B. Note that there is no area representing A $\times$ B; one of the weaknesses of diagrammatic expression is that it cannot represent o.

7. The Ubiquity of the Null Class

One reason why o cannot be represented by any diagram is the very odd but perfectly logical fact *that the null class is included in every class*. Every extension includes "nothing." This is frankly not a common-sense notion, yet with the common-sense ideas we have so far employed to establish relations among classes, this somewhat surprising proposition may be demonstrated in several ways. It follows from what has so far been granted; and, being thus within the law, it must be accepted.

The easiest way of demonstrating it takes us back to the discussion of the null class in the previous chapter (§ 10), where it was said that the null class is the class which has all incompatible properties. It is the class of things which, for instance, are cats and not-cats:

$$x \in A . x \in -A$$

defines the null class.

So we may say that

$$(x) : (x \in o) \supset (x \in A) . (x \in -A)$$

But if o is thus included in A *and* in -A, it must *at least* be included in A, and *at least* in -A. So o is included in every class which is a member of a complementary pair; and since every class has a complement, every class includes o. So we may add, somewhat belatedly, to our list of consequences from the definition of $<$: whatever class we call A,

$$o < A$$

The null class is ubiquitous; it is included in every class.

8. Complements of Sums and Products

Every class which may be formed in a given universe has a complement; this must apply, then, to sub-classes of any given class, or to composite classes, as well as to those which we name by a simple letter. I have already shown that it applies to 0 and 1.

If two classes have elements in common, or, to speak graphically, if they "overlap," then the common part, or the *product* of the two, is another class. If our classes A and B are "soldiers" and "brave men" respectively, then there is a Class C, "brave soldiers," a sub-class of soldiers and of brave men. This class C is the product of A and B, that is,

$$C = A \times B$$

But if we have a class C, we must also have -C; therefore there must be a class

$$-(A \times B)$$

This class -(A × B) includes everything that *is not both brave and a soldier*. A diagram (Fig. 10) will show this clearly.

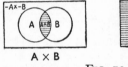

A × B   -(A × B)

FIG. 10.

-(A × B) includes all the A which is not B, since this is not *both* A and B; all the B which is not A, for the same reason; and everything that is neither A nor B.

The sum of two classes, say the same A and B, is likewise a class within the universe. There is a class D which includes all soldiers, brave or not, and all brave men, soldiers or not. This is the sum of A and B:

$$D = A + B$$

But if D is a class, then there is a -D which is its complement; that is, there is also a class

$$-(A + B)$$

The class of men who are *not* "either brave or soldiers."

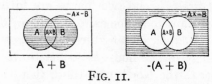

A + B   -(A + B)

FIG. 11.

This class is the complement of the sum A + B.

Since the *complement of any class is a class*, we may combine not only our original classes, A and B, to form sums and products, but also A and -B, B and -A, and every such combination will yield another class. There is a class A × -B, and an A + -B; -A × B and -A + B; and of course these have complements: -(A × -B), -(A + -B), -(-A × B), -(-A + B). The easiest way to grasp all the possible combinations and the dichotomies they create is by the use of diagrams (Fig. 12).

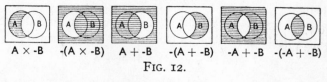

A × -B   -(A × -B)   A + -B   -(A + -B)   -A + -B   -(-A + -B)

FIG. 12.

It is excellent practice to draw the circles A and B, choose some arbitrary combination of A, B, -A, -B, and shade the proper portions; then in another diagram shade the remainder, or complement. The shaded portion always represents a single class.

9. EQUIVALENT EXPRESSIONS

Suppose we turn back to a simple deductive system,

$$K(a, b \ldots) \, nt_2 \qquad K = int \text{ "houses"}$$
$$nt = int \text{ "to North of"}$$

Granted propositions:

1. $(a) : \sim (a \, nt \, a)$
2. $(a, b) : \sim [(a \, nt \, b) . (b \, nt \, a)]$
3. $(a, b, c) : [(a \, nt \, b) . (b \, nt \, c)] \supset (a \, nt \, c)$

The conditions here laid down are (1) that no house is to the North of itself, (2) no two houses are to the North of each other (which is the same as to say that *if* one is to the North of the other, *then* that other is not to the North of the first), and (3) if one house is to the North of another, and that other to the North of a third, then the first is to the North of that third. These three conditions are obvious facts to anyone who knows the meaning of "nt."

Now, suppose we single out some element, call it x, and say there is at least one (perhaps more than one) house to the North of x; we have then the general proposition,

$$(\exists x)\,(\exists y) : y \text{ nt } x$$

The condition of being North of x may apply to any number of individuals in K. But a condition which may or may not apply to one, or to several, individuals, is a *class-concept*.

$$y \text{ nt } x$$

where x is a certain element, is a defining form, and defines a *class*, call it A_x, of "houses North of x." Consequently,

$$(y) : \text{``}y \text{ nt } x\text{''} \equiv \text{df ``}y \in A_x\text{''}$$

We have defined A_x so that henceforth "y nt x" shall be equivalent to "$y \in A_x$."

Now, suppose there is such a term y, i.e. A_x is not o, and that we take *a certain* y in A_x; then certainly,

$$(z) : (z \text{ nt } y) \supset (z \text{ nt } x)$$

By the third of our granted general propositions, any house North of y must also be North of x; that is, the above condition implies that $z \in A_x$, because it is North of y. But "any term North of y" refers us to a *class* of "houses North of y." Let us call this class B_y. Therefore

$$(z) : (z \text{ nt } y) \supset (z \text{ nt } x)$$

may also be written:

$$(z) : (z \in B_y) \supset (z \in A_x)$$

"Any house, z, that is 'a house North of y' is also a 'house North of x.'"

These two statements are equivalent. Wherever we may use one, we may also use the other, and the choice rests only upon our personal preference or practical convenience.

But the statement:

$$(z) : (z \in B_y) \supset (z \in A_x)$$

asserts that any member of B_y is also a member of A_x; and this is known to be equivalent, by definition, to a yet simpler expression:

$$B_y < A_x$$

The class of "houses to the North of y" is included in the class of "houses to North of x."

So we have three expressions for the same fact, in the context $K (a, b \ldots) \text{nt}_2$; one of these is formed entirely of the original terms and relations, the other two are worded by means of *defined terms* (A_x, B_v), and *defined relations* (in one case $\in$, in the other $<$). The meaning, however—the actual state of affairs referred to—is the same in all three of these propositions:

1. $(\exists x, y) (z) : (z \text{ nt } y) \supset (z \text{ nt } x)$
2. $(z) : (z \in B_y) \supset (z \in A_x)$
3. $B_y < A_x$

For the first one reads:

(1) "There are two houses, x and y, such that any house z which is North of y is also North of x." Obviously, then, y is either identical with or North of x.

The second reads:

(2) There are two classes, "houses North of x" and "houses North of y," such that any house in the latter class is also in the former. Hence any house North of y must be North of x; which is statement (1), just given above.

The third one reads:

(3) There are two classes, "houses North of x" and "houses North of y," the latter of which is included in the former. This, again, means simply that every house in the latter is also in the former class; and that is statement (2), which has been found equivalent to (1).

To have so many different ways of saying the same thing may seem like looking for trouble, like confusing the issue with more symbols than necessary, and overloading one's mind with vocabulary at the expense of clear concepts. But *the power of recognizing equivalent expressions is the test of clear apprehension.* All ingenuity, all skill in logical thinking requires this ability to *re-express* the same pattern in simpler and more manageable ways. The real import of such a concept as "class-inclusion" is understood only if we can connect this concept with other concepts, as here we connect it with "nt" and "⊃" or with "ϵ" and "⊃," so that we may *use the concept* where the particular terminology is lacking; just as we were taught in school to turn fractions into decimals and *vice-versa*, so as to have always the most convenient method of reckoning at our disposal. It does us no good to draw circles and express inclusions if our material is given in terms of individuals and a constituent relation, unless we can pass from the elementary propositions of that context to classes and < by means of ϵ. The intelligent use of *equivalent forms* is the touchstone of logical insight.

An example of this general fact is the way the notion of "exclusion" may be turned into one of "inclusion" by the well-aimed definition of "complements." Without the *defined notion* of "-A," we would always be left with the one case of class-relationship that could not be expressed in terms of <. But by this device, the relation < has at once become universally useful, has been empowered to express *every* pattern of classes, every combination that the graphs can show (and even more, e.g. o < A). Anyone who is ambitious to *use* the principles of symbolic logic should acquire the habit of translating "defined" symbols into their defining terms, of passing freely from one type of expression to another, without losing sight of the fundamental meaning that inspires all our logical formulations, and holds them in check with the reins of common sense.

SUMMARY

The main reason for taking classes in extension rather than in intension is that the former allows us to use the relation of class-inclusion. "A < B" $\equiv$df "$(x) : (x \in A) \supset (x \in B)$." Where the meaning of "<" is defined in other terms, for instance in terms of x, $\in$ and $\supset$, the expression "A < B" is merely shorthand for the longer expression on the other side of the sign "$\equiv$df."

If the definition thus given is really taken seriously, it follows that (1) A < A, (2) A < 1, (3) 0 < A, for any class called A. Wherever a symbol is defined, all consequences of the definition must be accepted even though they violate the ordinary sense of the word by which we have named the symbol.

The relation < as here defined serves to express *all* relations of classes in extension. There are five types, or degrees, of inclusion: (1) Mutual inclusion, or identity; A = B. (2) Complete inclusion of a lesser in a greater class, A < B. (3) Partial inclusion of one class in another, or overlapping; the overlapping part, or *product of* A *and* B, is called, A $\times$ B. (4) Joint inclusion of two classes in a greater class, or composition; the two classes A and B, *disjoined* to form a greater one, are called the *sum of* A *and* B, or A + B. (5) Complete mutual exclusion of A from B, or A $\times$ B = 0.

Whenever we form a class in a universe of discourse, the universe thereby is divided into two (perhaps very unequal) parts; namely, *what is in the class* and *what is not in the class*. The latter part, or remainder, forms another class correlative to the given one, known as its *complement*. If the class is called A, its complement is -A, called "not-A." Its defining form is: $\sim (x \epsilon A)$.

This division of a universe into A and -A, B and -B, etc., is called *dichotomy*.

The advantage of the principle of dichotomy is that by forming a class such as -A, we may turn negative statements about the membership of A into positive ones about the membership of -A. For instance, in type 5, the fact that A is entirely *excluded* from B could not be expressed with $<$ because there was no *inclusion*. But if everything excluded from B thereby belongs to -B, then "A is excluded from B" may be written with $<$, as: A $<$ -B. The notion of complementary classes, i.e. the use of -A, -B, etc., makes it possible to express *all* relations among classes (in extension) in terms of $<$.

The diagrams cannot picture the class o. This class is included in every possible class. There are several ways of demonstrating this fact; the simplest proof is, that o is the common part of every class and its complement, and the "common part" is contained in both classes.

Since the sum of two classes is another class, and every class has a complement, such a sum, e.g. A $+$ B, has a complement, -(A $+$ B); likewise every product has a complement; and the complement of any class may enter into further sums and products, so that *any* combination of areas in a diagram represents a class, and whatever is left of the diagram is the complement of that class.

Relations among classes may be expressed either with $<$ or with ϵ. If we know how membership in a certain class is defined, we may further reduce ϵ-propositions to propositions in the terms of the definition. This gives us several alternative ways of expressing the same fact. It is very important to cultivate skill in recognizing *equivalence* in different propositions, because a statement fits into a certain context only if it is formulated in terms of that context, but our information may come to us in a very different form. If we operate with the notion of "inclusion," then information about the "exclusion" of one class from another does us no good unless we can turn it into a case of "inclusion." The translation of an idea from one formulation, i.e. one kind of expression, into another requires practice; but it is a test of our real comprehension of the idea.

QUESTIONS FOR REVIEW

1. How is "A < B" defined in terms of *membership*?
2. What is meant by saying two expressions are *equivalent*?
3. What are the principal relations among classes?
4. If A =int "honest men" and B =int "musicians," what is meant by: A × B, A + B, B < A?
5. What is a dichotomy?
6. What is meant by calling two classes, A and B, "complementary"? If A is "horses" and B its complement, what class is B? How is the complement of A usually expressed?
7. Has o a complement? Has 1 a complement?
8. What are the logical advantages of forming a class -A?
9. How may *exclusion* of A from B be expressed in terms of <?
10. Has the sum of two classes a complement? If so, how is this written?
11. How is o expressed in a diagram? How is 1 represented?
12. What is meant by "equivalent expressions"? Can you give an equivalent expression for: C = A × B?
13. What is the purpose of introducing equivalent expressions?

SUGGESTIONS FOR CLASS WORK

1. Express in terms of ϵ:

   A < B
   A × B ≠ o
   A = B
   A + B = C

2. Express the *defining forms* of the following classes:

   White swans.
   Non-combatant men.
   Musicians or actors.
   Musicians who are actors.

3. Express in two ways (i.e. with ϵ and with $<$ or $=$):

 There are no unicorns.
 "Children" are boys and girls.
 No men are gods.
 All men are animals.

4. Express with ϵ, with $<$, and by a diagram (i.e. with circles) the relations of "married men" and "white men" in a universe of "all men."

5. In the following diagrams, shade the portions representing the class named under each one:

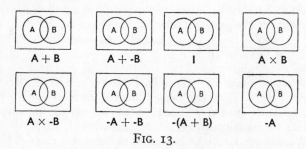

 A + B **A + -B** **I** **A × B**

 A × -B **-A + -B** **-(A + B)** **-A**

FIG. 13.

6. In the system cited in § 9, try to define the following classes:

 (1) Houses *on the same latitude* as x.
 (2) Houses to the *South* of x.

7. Express in two alternative ways:

 There are some houses North of x.
 All houses North of a certain house x are on the same latitude with a certain house y.

CHAPTER VII

THE UNIVERSE OF CLASSES

1. RELATIONS AND PREDICATES

The system of houses, which served as an example in the previous chapter, was based upon a general K of individuals (houses) and a dyadic relation. All elementary propositions in such a system have to be expressible in terms of *two elements*. In order to construct a class, such as A, we must select some fixed element, *m*, which shall serve as one end, or one pole so to speak, of the relation, while "being the other end" is the class-concept for the class we want to form. Every class, then, is relative to some given element, since the defining form of the class must be a dyad. Had we started with a triadic relation, such as "between," we should have had to fix *two* elements to generate a class; e.g. "the class of terms between *a* and *b*," or "the class of terms not between *a* and *b*."

Ordinarily, however, we do not invoke relationship to a given term in order to form a class; we form such classes as "white houses," "two-storeyed houses," etc., without reference to any given term. What sort of formal context does this require? What relation functions among the elements of our universe to generate a class of "white houses"? If there is no relation among the elements of the universe, such as "nt_2" or "bt_3," how can we have any elementary *structures* of terms, i.e. elementary propositional forms in the given context, to define classes of elements?

The answer rests upon a concept which is usually the first thing we meet in approaching logic: the concept of *predicates*. Traditional logic begins with terms and their predicates, rather than with terms in relation; but I shall now try to show why "symbolic" logic, or the study of structures, is better begun with relations, and how the notion of predicates fits into it.

Every relation, as was shown in a much earlier chapter, combines its terms two, three, four, . . . n at a time; this numerosity of its terms, called its "degree," is its most fundamental characteristic.

The lowest degree we are acquainted with is 2. A relation, it appears, must be at least dyadic, must affect at least two terms at a time. But suppose, just by way of using all possibilities, there were a relation which affected only one term at a time, so that every term in the universe either had it or failed to have it; it would always give rise to a proposition, but to a proposition of only one term. "Being white" has the properties of such a relation; any term, a, has it or does not have it, but since there is no second term we cannot say that a has this relation *to* any other. *Such a relation of "monadic" degree is called a predicate.*

There is considerable disagreement among philosophers and logicians as to whether it is "fair" to call a predicate a monadic relation, or whether it is something utterly different from relations. I cannot see that our judgment one way or the other in this matter makes any difference. Let us agree that "relation" is one thing, and "predicate," "quality," or whatever we choose to call it, is another; all that I wish to call attention to is that predicates figure in logical systems exactly *like* relations of a single term— they have all properties that a monadic relation would have. They characterize one term at a time, hold or fail for every element in a single universe, give rise to propositions of one term when used with a specific or generalized element, and to propositional forms when used as a variable. Such propositional forms serve as defining forms of classes. What more or what less could a monadic relation do? Our treatment of predicates, then, follows the pattern adopted for relations; and we may say, according to our philosophical inclinations, either that predicates are relations of a single term, or that all relations have two or more terms, but predicates function *instead of* monadic relations in a system.

The use of predicates, however, is characteristic and limited; for predicates do not *connect* terms directly with each other. If we use "wt" for the predicate "is white," and say "$(\exists a)$: wt a," this does not connect a with anything else, as does the proposition: "$(\exists a, b)$: a nt b." A system $K (a, b \ldots)$ wt, would have to be entirely *inductive*; we would have to be told for every element, a, whether "wt a" holds, or "$\sim$ (wt a)," for the ascription of a property to one element does not so much as mention any other. Such properties as "holding only one way," "holding only for distinct elements," "connecting an element with itself," etc., which come in question for genuine relations, are meaningless where there is but a single term.

The only important use of predicates in a logical structure is *classification*. Their great significance lies in the fact that *they generate the simplest type of defining form*, namely a form requiring no "fixed" element (specific or general), but containing only one element, the variable whose values constitute the defined class. Thus the propositional form

$$\text{wt } x$$

"x is white," defines the class of white things, without any mention of a term to which such "white things" are related. Predicates are the most economical, most natural, and most usual means of classification. When we think of, say, a sub-class in the universe of "houses," we may indeed think of "houses North of x," but we are more likely, in ordinary discourse, to think of "brick houses," "white houses," "colonial houses," etc., without reference to any *relation among* houses. That is to say, where our main purpose is classification, we are more likely to start with a formal context containing *elements and predicates* than with a relation-pattern in the strict sense.

Because the sole business of predicates in logic is to

define classes, I have not introduced them into this discussion until, in due course, the argument had proceeded
from elements-in-relation, via propositions, forms, and
general propositions, to classes. In a study of structures,
genuine relations are more essential than predicates, which
present merely a special case. But now we have come to
that case: the case of the simplest kind of defining form for
a class.

For the same reason, namely the intimate connection of
predicates with classes, so-called "Aristotelian" or "traditional" logic *begins* its discourse with a consideration of
subjects (terms) and predicates; for the older logic is a logic
of classes. Its fundamental concepts are "individuals,"
"classes" in common-sense conception, and a relation "is,"
which is sometimes taken to be ϵ, sometimes $<$, and sometimes $=$. Since this logic takes the existence and precise
conceivability of classes for granted, it naturally deals with
predicates, the instruments *par excellence* for distinguishing
classes, before it considers true relations; and because I
have here presented classes as *constructions* in a formal
context, I have begun with true relations, the instruments
of elementary construction, and considered predicates as a
special case with a special function.* The chief advantage
of this latter treatment is that it does not sustain the distinction of *kind* between so-called "subject-predicate" propositions and "relational" ones, but assigns to the former
their exact place in a wider field of logic.

2. Classes as Indispensable Constructs in a System

Since predicates may be treated as "monadic relations,"
there is no particular difficulty in assuming a formal context
wherein such predicates take the place of constituent rela-

* An analogous contrast may be traced throughout the two views
of logic; the older one tends to reduce relations to predicates, until
it ends in such doctrines as the "internality of relations"; the present
view tends to treat predicates as relations, and ends by making the
predicate a pragmatic fiction called the "monadic relation."

tions. Suppose we use the familiar universe of "houses," but, instead of "nt_2," use "wt_1." We may say of every house that it is white, or that it is not; that is, the two propositional forms we can make with "wt" and one element are:

$$wt\ x$$
and
$$\sim (wt\ x)$$

We may quantify these as we like; since there is only one element to quantify, we have just four possible general propositions

$$(a) : wt\ a$$
$$(a) : \sim (wt\ a)$$
$$(\exists a) : wt\ a$$
$$(\exists a) : \sim (wt\ a)$$

Furthermore, we may combine such forms by logical relations, and manipulate the quantifiers, to say that there is just one element which is white, or just two, just three, etc.* But beyond this we can make no structural distinctions by predicative general propositions. For *all a predicative proposition can do is to classify an element*, and *all that its generalization does is to delimit the class*.

This fact would reduce predicates to a very trivial position, were we always limited to just one in every system. So far we have dealt entirely with systems of only one constituent relation, because a relation of dyadic or higher degree furnishes enough complication all by itself. But of course it is possible to have several relations in a system; we might assume a context:

$$K(a, b, c \ldots)\ lk_2, br_2, md_3 \qquad K = int\ \text{"persons"}$$
$$lk = int\ \text{"likes"}$$
$$br = int\ \text{"is a brother of"}$$
$$md = int\ \text{"mediates between"}$$

* The method of expressing in general terms "there is just one such-and-such" was given in chapter v. "There are just 2" may be expressed similarly, as follows:

$$(\exists x, y)\ (z) : x \neq y \ . \ [(z = x) \lor (z = y)]$$

Higher numerosities may, of course, be similarly expressed.

The possible combinations of propositions in such a context would reach a staggering figure, yet their relations, though complex, would be perfectly definite; a system so constructed should be logically irreproachable.

Where the constituent relations are represented by predicates, it is not at all impracticable, even for a novice in the art, to manipulate more than one. Let us assume two predicates instead of one with our given K; we have, say,

$$K(a, b \ldots) \text{ wt, bk} \qquad \begin{aligned} K &= \text{int "houses"} \\ \text{wt} &= \text{int "is white"} \\ \text{bk} &= \text{int "is of brick"} \end{aligned}$$

The elementary propositional forms in such a context are:

$$\text{wt } a$$
$$\sim (\text{wt } a)$$
$$\text{bk } a$$
$$\sim (\text{bk } a)$$

Since there is but one element in such a form, it is completely generalized by a single quantifier; and as each form may take either one of the quantifiers, there are eight elementary general propositions:

1. $(a): \text{wt } a$
2. $(a): \sim (\text{wt } a)$
3. $(a): \text{bk } a$
4. $(a): \sim (\text{bk } a)$
5. $(\exists a): \text{wt } a$
6. $(\exists a): \sim (\text{wt } a)$
7. $(\exists a): \text{bk } a$
8. $(\exists a): \sim (\text{bk } a)$

Certain ones of these general propositions cannot be asserted together: thus 1 and 6, 2 and 5, 4 and 7, 3 and 8, are contradictory pairs; 1 and 2, or 3 and 4, may be jointly asserted only in the trivial case that K is empty, i.e. that there are no houses. But, barring contradictions and jokes, we may have any selection of these elementary propositions;

and what is more, any individual must be determined in two ways, namely, in respect of *both* predicates. A system with two predicates requires *compound propositions* for each generalized term; that is, it is not enough to know that some houses are white and some are brick, but we must know whether any of the white houses are *also* brick, etc. So we have the further possibilities:

9. $(a): (\text{wt } a) . (\text{bk } a)$
10. $(a): (\text{wt } a) . \sim (\text{bk } a)$
11. $(a): \sim (\text{wt } a) . (\text{bk } a)$
12. $(a): \sim (\text{wt } a) . \sim (\text{bk } a)$
13. $(\exists a): (\text{wt } a) . (\text{bk } a)$
14. $(\exists a): (a) \text{ wt } . \sim (\text{bk } a)$
15. $(\exists a): \sim (\text{wt } a) . (\text{bk } a)$
16. $(\exists a): \sim (\text{wt } a) . \sim (\text{bk } a)$

Here again there are, of course, certain contradictories; in fact, the increase of determinations has greatly heightened the chances of contradiction. Of the four universal propositions, only one can be true; and if one is true, then the only particular proposition that can be true is the one that exhibits the same form. If, however, none of the universal propositions is true, then all the particular ones may be true together. These facts may be easily apprehended by common sense, by considering some imaginary house under the various possible rubrics.

There are other characterizations to be made for a single element, by asserting certain logical relations between the two predications. Thus, any house may be "either white or brick," "either white or not brick," etc. This gives us a third list of eight possible general propositions:

17. $(a): (\text{wt } a) \lor (\text{bk } a)$
18. $(a): \sim (\text{wt a}) \lor (\text{bk } a)$

---

24. $(\exists a) : \sim (\text{wt } a) \lor \sim (\text{bk } a)$

But if we have made our choices among 9–16, all the truth-values in 17–24, as well as in all possible propositions related by ⊃, will be found already determined.

At present I shall leave this very important logical fact to the slip-shod corroboration of common sense, and merely adduce it to explain why we need not carry out the enumeration of general propositions about a single term beyond proposition 16.

Suppose we make a choice of consistent general statements in our universe

$$K\,(a, b\,.\,.\,.)\ \text{wt, bk}$$

Let us assume:

13. $(\exists a): (\text{wt }a)\,.\,(\text{bk }a)$
14. $(\exists a): (\text{wt }a)\,.\sim(\text{bk }a)$
15. $(\exists a): \sim(\text{wt }a)\,.\,(\text{bk }a)$
16. $(\exists a): \sim(\text{wt }a)\,.\sim(\text{bk }a)$

These are very powerful propositions; the four of them together determine the truth-value of all other possible propositions of one term, as anyone may prove to himself who cares to juggle combinations and contemplate the sense of any resultant assertion. But what sort of *pattern* do our "accepted facts" present? Not a single element has been related to another. What *connection among houses* has been established by introducing two predicates into our universe of discourse?

The only pattern which emerges is one of *classifications*. The two predicates have given rise to four propositional forms,

$$\text{wt }a$$
$$\sim(\text{wt }a)$$
$$\text{bk }a$$
$$\sim(\text{bk }a)$$

each of which defines a class; and the general propositions of our system declare that each of these classes has members (note that propositions 5–8 are implicitly given in 13–16), and that certain of them have members in common. So, instead of thinking in terms of "some element" and its predicates or lack of predicates, we may shift our conceptual outlook to the contemplation of four specific classes and their relations to one another. *The only connection among elements which can be established by predicative propositions is common membership in a class.*

In a context where predicates figure in place of constituent relations, the formal arrangement of elements always falls into a pattern of class-distinctions and cross-classifications, and it may fairly be said that the construction of classes is the first step in dealing with such a context. The first thing we do is to pass from *general elementary propositions in logical relations* to *classes in class-relations.* The transition is effected by definition:

$$(x) : \text{"wt } x\text{"} \equiv \text{df "} x \in W\text{"}$$
$$(x) : \text{"bk } x\text{"} \equiv \text{df "} x \in B\text{"}$$

This changes our "assumed" propositions to:

$$(\exists a): (a \in W) \cdot (a \in B)$$
$$(\exists a): (a \in W) \cdot \sim (a \in B)$$
$$(\exists a): \sim (a \in W) \cdot (a \in B)$$
$$(\exists a): \sim (a \in W) \cdot \sim (a \in B)$$

By a further definition, familiar from the previous chapter, namely: "$\sim (a \in B)$" $\equiv$ df "$a \in \text{-B}$," we may simplify the statements to:

$$(\exists a): (a \in W) \cdot (a \in B)$$
$$(\exists a): (a \in W) \cdot (a \in \text{-B})$$
$$(\exists a): (a \in \text{-W}) \cdot (a \in B)$$
$$(\exists a): (a \in \text{-W}) \cdot (a \in \text{-B})$$

What is the point of changing "wt a" into "$a \in W$"? It is a transitional step to the much easier, briefer, and more natural statement of the whole system *in terms of classes, and classes alone*. For, by all the expositions of a former chapter, we know that

$$\text{``}(\exists a) : (a \; \epsilon \; W) \; . \; (a \; \epsilon \; B)\text{''} \equiv \text{df ``} W \times B \neq 0\text{''}$$

Consequently the four propositions assumed for our system may be written as statements about the *specific classes* W, "white houses," and B, "brick houses," as follows:

$$W \times B \neq 0$$
$$W \times -B \neq 0$$
$$-W \times B \neq 0$$
$$-W \times -B \neq 0$$

The economy of symbolic expression here is obvious; but another advantage presents itself in the fact that we may now resort to *diagrammatic expression*, which is a tre-

Fig. 14

mendous aid to logical insight. Graphically, our propositions assert that W and B overlap ($W \times B \neq 0$), yet neither is entirely included in the other ($W \times -B \neq 0$ and $-W \times B \neq 0$), and they do not, between them, exhaust the universe-class ($-W \times -B \neq 0$). Here is the whole system in a form so simple, so visible, that all its relations may be intuitively grasped—the height and ideal of logical explication.

3. Classes as "Primitive Concepts" in a System

The admirable simplicity of statement which has thus been reached is bought, however, at the price of elaborate definitions. The clear and economical propositions, that express the whole system in a handful of symbols, rest upon a tedious process of translation and re-translation. Before we ever assert the fundamental facts that certain classes are not empty, i.e. not equal to 0, we have to construct the notion of "class" and of "equal to 0." Our whole formal context has to be reformulated before we can begin to say the simplest thing.

But a formal context in which the simplest thing cannot be said is not a well-chosen context. What is the use of introducing individuals and predicates if we are not going to talk about them? Why start with a *general universe of houses*, if our real concern is the interrelationship of *specific classes of houses*? Our propositions prove to be, in the end, all specific; they are about parts of W and B, and the fact that those parts are unequal to the class o. We started out bravely with a general K, only to drop it completely out of sight; and with wt_1 and bk_1, never to mention them again. The only relation we finally assert is $=$, which is shorthand for mutual *inclusion*, for a double use of $<$ between two classes. Now, could not all this preliminary labour of restatement be avoided? Is it necessary to drag in the forms "wt a" and "bk a" at all, to reveal the structure we want to see?

Every system rests upon a certain number of *primitive concepts*, terms and relations which are not defined, but simply taken for granted; their meaning is given by *interpretation* only. In the context with which we started, these primitive concepts were "houses"—undefined elements, whose meaning was assigned by interpretation—and two predicates, wt_1 and bk_1, also supposed to be understood in advance. We may just as well start, however, with primitive elements of another sort, say with a certain number of specific elements which are to mean, by interpretation, "the class of white houses," and "the class of brick houses," and their complements and sub-classes. The relation $<$, which in the old context was defined in terms of ϵ, which in turn was defined by the predicates wt and bk, may now be taken as a constituent relation, to mean, by interpretation, "is included in." So we solve our problem by *assuming an entirely new formal context*, one whose elements are certain classes:

K(B, W, -B, -W, B×W, -B×W, -B× -W, o, I)<
$$K =\text{int ``classes of houses''}$$
$$B =\text{int ``cls* of brick houses''}$$
$$W =\text{int ``cls of white houses''}$$
$$-B =\text{int ``cls of not-white houses''}$$
$$-W =\text{int ``cls of not-brick houses''}$$
$$B \times W =\text{int ``cls of white brick houses''}$$

_____

_____

$$o =\text{int ``cls of no houses''}$$
$$I =\text{int ``cls of all houses''}$$

Ten elements and a dyadic relation will give us 100 specific propositions. Most of these we may assert or deny from our general knowledge of classes: thus, we know

$$B < B$$
$$W < W$$
_____
_____
$$I < I;$$

Also,
$$B < I$$
$$W < I$$
$$-B < I$$
_____
_____

Also,
$$o < B$$
$$o < -B$$
$$o < W$$
_____
_____
$$o < I$$

We know that a class which, by interpretation, *means* the

* "cls" (pl. "clss") is the usual symbol for "class."

overlapping part of two classes, must be included in both of them:

$$B \times W < W$$
$$B \times W < B$$
$$B \times -W < -W$$
$$B \times -W < B$$

But one thing we cannot know is, whether any of the given classes is included in o. Since o is included in every class, any class included in o must equal o, since it provides a case of mutual inclusion; so, to express for any class—let us say, B—that it equals o, it is sufficient to say

$$B < o$$

This guarantees that B is empty. Then any sub-class of B must, of course, equal o, too; any part of the empty class is empty.

Here we must look to our "granted propositions." We are told that $B \times W \neq o$, i.e.

$$\sim (B \times W < o)$$

Neither B nor W, then, can be empty. Also,

$$\sim (-B \times W < o)$$
$$\sim (B \times -W < o)$$
$$\sim (-B \times -W < o)$$

That is to say, there are some white houses of brick, and some not of brick; some brick houses not white; and some houses neither white nor made of brick. Now, these are all the possible conjunctions of predicates, so the description of our universe is completely settled by four arbitrary conditions and the nature of "<." If we wish to form such further classes as $B + -W$, $-B + -W$, etc., their places in the system, i.e. their inclusion-relations with other classes, may all be learned by deduction; but that is a fact which had better be taken on faith in this chapter and explained in the next. The ten classes in K do not comprise all sub-classes of 1 that could be made by juggling B and W; but they are all we need to describe any others.

Here is a much simpler system than that of individuals and predicates: a system of classes and inclusion, which refers *by interpretation* to those very individuals with those very predicates. There has been a shift in our conceptual material; the same classes which in one system were elaborate constructs, are "primitive elements" in the other. The relation $<$, which was defined, in the first system, by logically related elementary propositions, has become in the second system a constituent relation giving rise to elementary propositions. The whole structure is analysed, so to speak, on a different level. No individual can figure in this "higher" pattern, since the undefined, ultimate elements of K are classes, and are above the level of individuals.

This brings us to an important point which is sometimes overlooked in the literature of logic: namely, the radical distinction between K, the universe of discourse, and 1, the universe class. De Morgan, who originated the term "universe of discourse," namely the total collection of terms (or "names," as he calls them), warned against the fallacy of identifying this "universe" with the greatest class that may be formed in it. "Nothing is more easy," he says, "than to treat the supposition of a name being the universe as an extreme case."* John Venn, whose *Symbolic Logic* appeared in 1881, adopts the notion from De Morgan, describes the "universe of discourse" unmistakably as the sort of collection I call *"K,"* and then identifies it with the universe-class, which he calls 1.† So he introduces precisely that confusion against which De Morgan cautions

* A. De Morgan, *Formal Logic* (1847), edited and republished by A. E. Taylor, London, 1926.

† J. Venn, *Symbolic Logic*, London, 1881, ch. viii passim.

him; and any number of writers, especially in elementary treatises, have followed him in this practice.

The ground of their error is that they are concerned sometimes with *classifying individuals* and sometimes with *relating classes to each other*. In a K of individuals, the greatest class we can form out of these individuals happens to coincide with K. But when we are relating classes to each other, the greatest class, 1, is not K, but is an element in K, just like any other class. If we take any element in the context $K(B, W, B \times W \ldots 1) <$, say B, the relation of B to 1 is, $B < 1$; but its relation to K is $B \in K$. Likewise, $1 \in K$, but $1 < 1$; $K < K$, or $1 \in 1$, would be nonsensical. So the identification of 1 with K, the "universe class" with the "universe of discourse," rests upon a fallacy which is not apparent in a system of *individual* elements, but is immediately visible when we deal with a K whose elements are *classes*.

4. THE GENERALIZED SYSTEM OF CLASSES

We have passed from a system of individuals and predicates, a general $K(a, b \ldots)$ wt$_1$, bk$_1$, to a system of certain classes and their $<$-relations, a specific $K(B, W \ldots 0, 1) <$. This takes us back to an earlier stage of logical study, back to a system expressed in lists of analogous, specific propositions (cf. ch. iv); only there our terms were such-and-such persons, and now they are such-and-such classes. But the same canons of generalization, which led us from

$$\sim (A \text{ fm } A)$$
$$\sim (B \text{ fm } B)$$
$$\overline{}$$
$$\overline{}$$
$$\sim (J \text{ fm } J)$$

to the general proposition:

I $(a) : \sim (a \text{ fm } a)$

allows us to pass from

$$(B \times W < B) . (B \times W < W)$$
$$(-B \times W < -B) . (-B \times W < W)$$

to the general fact that, if x and y are *any* two classes, then

II $(x, y) : (x \times y < x) . (x \times y < y)$

Likewise, the whole list of propositions about the specific class o,

$$o < B$$
$$o < W$$
$$o < -B$$
$$o < -W$$

$$o < -B \times -W$$
$$o < o$$
$$o < 1$$

might be dispensed with by generalizing the second term of any such proposition, and substituting the partly generalized proposition,

$$(a) : o < a$$

Analogously, of course, we may eliminate another long list by introducing a general assertion about the specific term 1,

$$(a) : a < 1$$

But in *any* universe whose elements are classes there is one class having the logical properties of "the class of no houses," i.e. an empty class; and this class is included in every class in the universe. Also, in any such universe there is one "greatest class," analogous to "the class of all houses," and this includes every class in the universe. So we may say that any K whose elements are classes contains a 0 and a 1. We could therefore employ two completely general propositions:

III $\qquad\qquad (\exists 0)\ (a) : 0 < a$

"There is at least one class, 0, such that, for any class a, 0 is included in a,"

and: IV $\qquad\qquad (\exists 1)\ (a) : a < 1$

"There·is at least one class, 1, such that, for any class a, a is included in 1,"

then $\qquad\qquad (a)\ 0 < a$
and $\qquad\qquad (a)\ a < 1$

would *exemplify* these general propositions for the specific system here described.

All the propositions so far stated are true for *any* system whose elements are classes. The only statements about $K(B, W \ldots 0, 1) <_2$ that have not been taken care of are the four "granted propositions," which were characterized, above, as four *arbitrary* conditions. They do not follow from the nature of classes as such, nor from the meaning of $<$; therefore not every K whose elements are classes must needs exhibit them. Yet even these conditions are not peculiar to the *specific* system of "the class of white houses," "the class of brick houses," etc., with which we are dealing; there may be other universes of classes wherein they obtain, i.e. wherein two classes and their two complements are such that none of the resulting products are memberless. The condition in itself may be expressed quite generally, as:

$$(\exists a, b): \sim (a \times b) < 0$$
$$\sim (-a \times b) < 0$$
$$\sim (a \times -b) < 0$$
$$\sim (-a \times -b) < 0$$

This is a special condition, but not a specific one; it is exemplified in some systems, but not in others; classes being what they are, and $<$ meaning what it does, these propositions are *possible* in any context of classes and class-inclusions, but not *necessary*.

It appears, then, that any relation of classes in extension may be expressed quite generally, no matter whether the classes were formed by the use of a dyadic or triadic relation, as: "the class of houses North of John Smith's house," "the class of cities between Paris and London," or by a predicate, as: "the class of white houses," "the class of bad boys." Taking together all those propositions which are true for any classes whatever, we may generalize from "the class of white houses" and "the class of brick houses" to "any class" and "any other, or same, class," that is to say, from $K(\mathrm{B}, \mathrm{W} \ldots \mathrm{o}, \mathrm{I}), <$, with its specific interpretations to

$$K\ (a, b \ldots) <$$

with the general interpretation:

$$K = \text{int "classes of individuals"}$$
$$< = \text{int "is included in"}$$

Such a system starts on a different level of logical analysis from any *generalized system of individuals*. The elements, now symbolized in the lower case, are classes *by interpretation*; and the inclusion-relation is therefore the *constituent relation of a general system of classes*. This system, which was developed, at least in its main outline, by George Boole, has become a centre and kernel of mathematical logic. It serves us as an almost perfect example of systematization, being very simple, yet genuinely mathematical; and it has lent itself to such mutations and adaptations that most far-reaching and unexpected ventures in logical theory have taken their start from its few but fertile concepts. Consequently I shall give it extensive consideration, even presenting it in several forms, so that the essential structure of it, the relation of those forms to each other, and the significance of its basic ideas for the whole realm of logic may become visible to a thoughtful student.

5. A Convenience of Symbolism: Logical Punctuation

Before we pass from the simple systems we have so far used as illustrations of structure to the more interesting "Boolean" system, it were well to adopt a convention of symbolism which has proved a great convenience to logicians; that is, to substitute a system of dots, single, double, triple, etc., for parentheses and brackets. When the latter are multiplied they become unwieldy; their shapes have to be varied to help the eye; they always occur in pairs, which means that at the end of a complex expression we are apt to have a series of four or five perfectly useless symbols, such as:)] }]. But if we use dots, these occur only between the expressions that are to be set apart. Their number is easy to apprehend without any variation of type, they take little effort to write, and may be made to serve every requirement of logical punctuation.

The single dot has already been introduced as a sign of logical conjunction. In this capacity it serves to set two propositions apart, and also to express the weakest sort of relation—mere co-existence in a system, or joint assertion. Wherever no other symbol than the dot appears between two propositions, the dot may be read: "and," as in the statement:

$$(a, b) : a \text{ fm } b . b \text{ fm } a$$

If we regard any expression that is not broken up as a simple proposition, then the two elementary propositions here separated by the dot are the natural factors of this statement.

Whenever single dots occur together with a sign of logical relation, however, they represent parentheses, and signify that the expressions they separate are to be treated each as a separate whole. Thus, in the proposition:

$$(a, b, c) : a \text{ nt } b \,.\, b \text{ nt } c \,.\, \supset \,.\, a \text{ nt } c$$

the dots around the implication-sign set apart "a nt b . b nt c" from "a nt c." The implication holds between a compound proposition and a simple one.

Note that the quantifier is set off from the rest of this expression by a double dot. That means that the quantifier is related to the expression as a whole. Double dots are to single dots as brackets are to parentheses; everything in one pair of parentheses is a unit in a structure enclosed by brackets, i.e. (a, b, c) quantifies "a nt b . b nt c . $\supset$. a nt c." But instead of *enclosing* the quantified form we dispense with the end symbol] by dividing the entire form from its quantifier by double dots, which "extend over," or subsume, any single dots in the form.

If we wish to relate two propositions which already contain logical relations other than "and," then the relation between these propositions must be surrounded by double-dots. For instance, to say that if a is North of b or of c, then it is North of d, would read:

$$(\exists a, b, c, d) : .\; a \text{ nt } b \,.\, \vee \,.\, a \text{ nt } c : \supset : a \text{ nt } d$$

Note how the quantifier, which quantifies this whole expression, is set off from it by triple dots. The implication "extends over" the disjunction; the double dots are like brackets, the single dots like parentheses. The triple dots serve as braces, $\{\ \}$. But the entire structure is visually and typographically much simpler than:

$$(\exists a, b, c, d) \left\{ \left[(a \text{ nt } b) \vee (a \text{ nt } c) \right] \supset (a \text{ nt } d) \right\}$$

Wherever a negation-sign occurs, dots indicate how great a proposition is affected by the sign. For instance,

$$(a, b) : \sim .\, a \text{ nt } b \,.\, \supset \,.\, b \text{ nt } a$$

is quite different from

$$(a, b) : .\, \sim : a \text{ nt } b \,.\, \supset \,.\, b \text{ nt } a$$

The first proposition asserts that if a is not North of b, then b is North of a; the other states merely that no implication holds between the two elementary propositions. In the latter case, the "$\sim$" extends over the whole structure, making it negative; and the quantifier extends over the *negative form*. The maximum number of dots always indicates the degree of complexity of the total proposition.

With a little practice, dots become much easier to use than any other sort of punctuation. The subordinate parts of subordinate parts, and so forth, become obvious to inspection. Therefore it is highly desirable to practise this symbolic usage as freely as possible, and to use parentheses only to indicate quantifiers, for which purpose they may well be maintained, or to enclose terms like "$a + b$" or "$a \times b$" when these are to be negated, i.e. to distinguish -$(a + b)$ from -$a + b$. But *propositions are no longer to be enclosed in parentheses, brackets, or braces; dots or groups of dots can serve all purposes of logical punctuation.* This principle should be mastered in theory *and in practice* before we proceed to the actual study of the calculus of classes.

SUMMARY

A class may be formed by varying one term of a relation over its entire *range of applicability* (not its range of significance). Usually, however, no relation in the strict sense (i.e. of dyadic or higher degree) enters into the class-concept. Classes are usually defined by predicates.

A predicate has exactly the logical properties that would belong to a relation of one term, if there could be such a thing. Some people, therefore, regard predicates as "monadic relations," whereas others maintain that predicates exist *in place of* monadic relations because the latter are not thinkable. In practice the distinction is immaterial.

Predicates have just one important use in logic: they are the simplest means of generating classes. Since they do not connect terms with one another, they can lend *structure* to a universe only by making the elements co-members in classes. For this reason they have not previously figured in this book; but they are naturally the first topic of a logic that takes classes for granted, as does the "traditional" or "Aristotelian" logic.

In a system where predicates take the place of constituent relations, the formulation of classes by means of these predicates is naturally the first step. A predicative proposition about an element classifies that element, and can do nothing more with it. If the element is generalized, its quantifier delimits the class of which it is a representative member.

A single predicate cannot give rise to more than four classes: A, -A, A × -A or 0, A + -A or 1. Such a system is complete, but trivial. To gain any interest we must have more than one predicate. In dealing with relations of dyadic or higher degree, a beginner cannot hope to use more than one without confusion; but predicates may be multiplied without too much complexity. A great number of simple or compound propositions result from manipulating even two predicates; but many of these are mutually exclusive, so that finally our choice of a very few determines which others can coexist with these.

Whatever our choice among predicative propositions may be, every such proposition defines a class, and its quantifier determines (1) that the class is equal to 1, in which case its complement is equal to 0, or (2) that the class is not equal to 0, i.e. its complement is not equal to 1. The first alternative holds for the universal, the second for the particular quantifier.

Since the only pattern obtained by predication is one of classifications, the notion of *membership in a class* may be substituted by definition for that of *possession of a predicate*. Because every class has a complement, membership in the complementary class takes the place of non-possession of a given predicate. Predicative propositions, then, may be replaced by <-propositions. This in itself would be no gain in economy or psychological ease of expression; but *ε-propositions about general elements may be turned into <-propositions about specific classes*. The latter, in the case of only two classes and their complements, sums, and products, are very simple; they may be diagrammatically represented. Psychologically, it is easier to let predicates define classes, and then to deal with the relations among these classes, than to deal with complex predicative propositions.

But if we are to deal entirely with classes, it is not necessary to start with individuals and predicates and go through elaborate definitions. Every system starts with primitive elements, i.e. undefined elements of the universe, and undefined relations (treating predicates as the "monadic case" of relation). What these are is given by interpretation. So it is perfectly legitimate to *start with a K whose primitive elements, by interpretation, shall be classes, and a primitive* (instead of defined) *relation <.*

Such a system of specific classes has two kinds of proposition: (1) propositions expressing certain "granted" facts, that merely happen to be so and therefore must be inductively known, and (2) propositions stating *necessary* conditions, that belong to the system simply because its elements are classes and its relation is <. The latter do not depend on any K of specific classes; they may be expressed for classes in general. The former, too, may be true for other universes of classes than just the one in hand; they are particular conditions, arbitrarily asserted, but they may none the less be asserted quite generally. Instead of referring to the product of *these* two classes we may refer to the product of *some* two classes. Just as a system of four houses, ten men, or what-not, could be generalized in a previous chapter, so the system of specific classes here given may be generalized, for it is simply an *instance* of what is true of classes in general. Therefore a universe whose elements are classes by interpretation may be written with lower-case letters, just as well as a system of individuals; and we may assume a universe $K(a, b \ldots) <$ containing *any classes of individuals*.

For the sake of typographical ease and visual clarity, dots are used to replace brackets. The greatest group of dots always makes the chief division. In the propositions here symbolized the greatest group divides the form from its quantifiers, because those quantifiers are related to the *form as a whole*. A dot or group of dots without other relation symbol is a sign of *joint assertion* or logical conjunction. Logical relations are separated by dots from the propositions they relate, the number of dots depending on the complexity of the propositions involved.

Practice in logical punctuation should be acquired before attempting any complicated manipulation of propositions, as the use of brackets is difficult and confusing in the long run.

QUESTIONS FOR REVIEW

1. How may a class be generated by use of a dyadic relation?
2. How may a class be generated without the assumption of a fixed term?
3. In what ways are predicates comparable to relations?
4. How many classes may be defined by one predicate?
5. What connections between terms may be established by predicates in place of constituent relations?
6. What is the importance of predicates?
7. What is the advantage of substituting ϵ-propositions for predicative propositions in a context of individuals and predicates?
8. How may the analysis of a predicative system be radically simplified?
9. What are "primitive concepts"? What determines our choice of "primitive concepts"?
10. If you wanted to express symbolically: "There is at least one class which has just one member," what symbols would you employ for classes and members respectively?

11. What are the advantages of "logical punctuation" by dots?
12. What determines the number of dots to be used in any given position?

SUGGESTIONS FOR CLASS WORK

1. Express symbolically the formal context assumed in the following propositions, the statement of the propositions themselves, and four negative propositions implied by them:

> Some men have blue eyes.
> Some men have black hair.
> Some men have neither.
> Some men have both.

2. Express the above propositions (1) in terms of ϵ, (2) in terms of $<$.

3. Draw a diagram showing all the classes which may be formed by the two predicates given above. Mark with a cross each class mentioned by the "granted" propositions. Outline heavily the following classes:

> Men with black hair or blue eyes.
> Men having either not black hair or not blue eyes.
> Blue-eyed men without black hair.
> Black-haired men without blue eyes.

Express those classes as sums or products of classes.

4. State with proper symbolism and logical punctuation three propositions that are true for classes in general.

5. Read the following statements:

A. $(a)\ (\exists b)\ (c): c < a\ .\ c < b\ .\ \supset\ .\ c = 0$
B. $(\exists o)\ (a): a < 0\ .\ \supset\ .\ a = 0$
C. $(a, b)\ (\exists p)\ (c):.\ p < a\ .\ p < b:\ c < a\ .\ c < b\ .\ \supset\ .\ c < p$
D. $(a, b, c): a < b\ .\ b < c\ .\ \supset\ .\ a < c$
E. $(a, b, c): c < \text{-}(a + b)\ .\ \supset\ .\ c < (\text{-}a \times \text{-}b)$
F. $(a, b, c):: a < \text{-}(b + c)\ .\ \supset :.\ \sim : a < b\ .\ \vee\ .\ a < c$
G. $(\exists a)\ (b):.\ b < a\ .\ \supset : b = a\ .\ \vee\ .\ b = 0$

6. Punctuate with dots instead of brackets:

A. $(a, b)\ (\exists s)\ (c): [(a < s)\ .\ (b < s)]\ .\ \big\{[(a<c)\ .\ (b<c)]\supset(s<\supset)\big\}$
B. $(a, b, c, d): [(a < \text{-}b)\ .\ (c < b)]\ \supset \big\{[(d < a)\ .\ (d < c)]\ \supset$
$(d = 0)\big\}$

CHAPTER VIII

THE DEDUCTIVE SYSTEM OF CLASSES

1. The Class-System as a Deductive System

Any system whose elements are *classes of individuals*, taken in extension, may be ordered by the relation $<$. Even though no special facts, such as:

$$(\exists a, b): \sim . a \times b < 0$$

be arbitrarily granted, certain general conditions are known about it; we may assume that *there is* the class $a \times b$, if there is a and there is b; that at all events, there is a 0, and at all events there is a 1; and if there is an a there is an a'; and if there is a and b, then there is the class $a + b$. These propositions *describe the nature of classes*. Moreover, without being told that

$$(\exists a, b) . a < b$$

we know that *if* any class a is included in another class b, *then* $-b < -a$; and that *if* a is included in b and b in c, *then* $a < c$; for such propositions *describe the nature of the relation* $<$.

The number of facts about classes and inclusion that may be asserted merely on the basis of their general nature is astounding. But when these facts are all arranged so as to be easily surveyed, a good many of them are seen to be closely interconnected, so that, if only a small selection of them is explicitly stated, the rest must follow implicitly. Indeed, there are no true general statements about $K(a, b \ldots) <_2$ that do not either follow if certain others are asserted, or themselves have further implications; all possible conditions are related to others, i.e. if any condition is "granted" certain others follow or become impossible.

A system of this sort was characterized, in chapter iii,

as *completely deductive*. It has no "mere" facts, that could not be known from anything else and do not entail anything else. The structure of the concepts "class" and "class-inclusion" is architectonic; however we begin to describe them, whatever characteristics we mention, we cannot assert many propositions together without generating, by implication, a whole system of further classes and their relations. In this respect it has the virtues of a mathematical system; its possibilities lend themselves to *calculation*, like those of the number-system. We can work to and fro, from given facts to implied facts, always relating new hypothetical cases to those already known to discover whether the new ones are possible, impossible, or absolutely necessary.

2. POSTULATES AND THEOREMS

Some facts, of course, must be known to begin with; one cannot deduce propositions where there is nothing to deduce them from. Also—and this should be remembered—*a proposition cannot be deduced from anything but another proposition*. Implication is a relation which holds *only among propositions*. We may say that certain facts "follow from" the nature of classes; but only *propositions about that nature can imply propositions asserting those facts*. So our first knowledge of the system—our knowledge of the nature of classes and the nature of $<$—must be expressed in propositions before we can make deductions from it. These first propositions are not themselves deducible, because there are no propositions before them, from which they could be deduced. They have to be frankly *assumed*, or *postulated*. If the system is completely deductive, then every such "postulate," or assumed proposition, must have consequences, i.e. must imply some further proposition or propositions, either quite by itself, or in conjunction with others. An economical selection of such first assumptions, from which all other propositions of the system in question may be deduced, is called a *set of postulates* for that system.

The classic example of a set of postulates for a system is Euclid's formulation of geometry, which begins with a statement of the assumptions that must be granted, such as: that a line may be extended indefinitely in both directions, that three points in a plane shall determine a triangle, etc. Besides these postulates, we are asked to note a number of facts which he calls "axioms," facts so simple that we *recognize* rather than assume them—such as, that equals added to equals yield equals. These facts are supposed to bear the stamp of *self-evidence*. The truth of an axiom is vouched for by the fact that we admit it intuitively, that it could not be doubted by any sane person; thus, the fact that a whole is greater than any of its proper parts is considered by Euclid to be self-evident, to recommend itself to the untutored mind without argument, and consequently to be *known by intuition*. It may, therefore, be accepted without further proof, i.e. as an *axiom* whereon his system comes to rest.

But the self-evidence of any proposition turns out, on closer scrutiny, to be a very questionable affair. The power to doubt familiar propositions is relative to one's logical imagination and to the force of verbal and mental habits; a carpenter cannot doubt that a whole is always greater than any of its proper parts, but a mathematician can; a little girl would find it self-evident that $365 - 1 = 364$, whereas Humpty Dumpty preferred to see it done on paper. What is intuitively known by one person is a subject for demonstration to another, and what is intuitively accepted by *all* people may turn out to be false. The history of science is full of examples; for instance, that people at the antipode would be suspended from the earth head-down and would fall into space, was undoubtedly self-evident to an age that had not learned to associate "falling" with "motion toward a greater body"; and our own children still find the inverted position of China axiomatic. Also it seems self-evident to every right-minded child that he cannot subtract 13 from

10; yet he will presently learn that this proposition is false.

Euclid himself does not draw the distinction between axioms and postulates very sharply; for instance, the assumption that parallel lines are the only lines which can lie in the same plane and never meet, is sometimes classed as a postulate, sometimes as an axiom; undoubtedly the great geometer applied the standard of self-evidence to postulates, too, though perhaps within the vague and wide boundaries of a "safe" assumption rather than the strict limits of immediate truth

For our part, we know how deceptive intuition may be, and how insecure its guarantees; so, whether or not we consider a proposition self-evident, we shall regard it as an assumption, a postulate, if it is accepted without proof. *All our "granted" propositions are to be regarded as postulates, with no claim to psychological necessity.* This not only obviates the danger that our system may suffer in a very vague and doubtful virtue, but also gives us far more leeway in the choice of postulates, for we are no longer limited to propositions that are simple, obvious, and generally entertained. If we chance upon a fairly complex and even surprising proposition, from which very many simple ones would follow, we are perfectly justified in taking the former as a postulate and deriving the others from it.

All we ask of a postulate is, (1) that it shall belong to the system, i.e. be expressible entirely in the language of the system; (2) that it shall imply further propositions of the system; (3) that it shall not *contradict* any other accepted postulate, or any proposition implied by such another postulate; and (4) that it shall not itself be implied by other accepted postulates, jointly or singly taken.

The first of these characteristics is known as *coherence*. Every proposition in the system must cohere, in conceptual structure, with the rest. The second is *contributiveness*. If a postulate has no implications, it contributes nothing beyond the explicit fact which it states. This is, of course, perfectly permissible, but a system which contains such assumptions is not entirely deductive, and where no deduction is intended we do not class propositions as "postulates," to be distinguished from "theorems." The word "postulate" is ordinarily applied to *premises for deduction*. Contributiveness, therefore, is an important criterion of a good postulate; in fact, if we have two propositions one of which is to be taken for granted, the greater contributiveness of one as against the other may be the deciding factor in a choice between them.

The third requirement is the most important; that is *consistency*. Two propositions which contradict each other, i.e. which cannot both be true, can never be admitted to the same system. Anything that is inconsistent is logically impossible. Incoherence is a grave fault, but often we can ignore the elements which are *meaningless* and still trace systematic connections under a mass of irrelevant concepts; non-contributiveness, or barrenness, is a serious blemish and spoils the deductive character of a system, but does not ruin its validity; but inconsistency is a fatal condition. Where this fault is tolerated there is simply no logic at all.

The fourth criterion is termed *independence*. If a proposition is deducible from one of the postulates already given, then it is a theorem, a necessary fact, not another assumption. The fact that we "assume" rather than "prove" it to ourselves is a purely psychological circumstance which has no bearing on the logical status of a proposition; if it *might* be proved it is a theorem, and to regard it as a postulate is simply an error. Fortunately this error is not serious, since deductions made from a theorem are exactly as good as those made from a postulate; if we regard a theorem as a postulate, and think ourselves to have one more arbitrary assumption than in fact we have, then we merely do not know how nice our system is.

What a theorem is needs little elucidation; any proposition, that is implied by another proposition or conjunction of propositions "granted" or previously proved within the system, is a theorem. Theorems may be positive or negative; that is, we may prove something to be *necessarily so*, or *not possibly so*, i.e. *necessarily not so*. The same theorem may follow from more than one possible selection of premises, as a more detailed study of the class-system will presently show. But *contradictory theorems can never follow from consistent postulates*. No matter how widely developed the system, how far removed a theorem may be from the original assumptions, they and they only are its ultimate premises; if two theorems in a system are incompatible, and there has been no error in the process of deduction, then the postulates, no matter how obvious and simple they may appear, are inconsistent; for two propositions which are consistent can never have contradictory implications. Theorems, or deducible propositions, therefore, are the touchstone of any set of postulates; if the postulates are not contributive, no theorems will result; if the postulates are not independent, then some theorem will be identical with a postulate that was not used to prove it; and if the postulates, though they do not appear to be incompatible yet contain some hidden inconsistency, then at some point we shall have flatly contradictory implications.

A postulate must contain *something* that cannot be proved in the system. At its best it contains *nothing that can* be proved, but that is not necessary in order to make the proposition a postulate. A theorem, on the other hand, must contain *nothing that cannot be proved*. It is not enough that it should contain *something implied*; it must be entirely implied by some proposition or propositions other than itself,* and contain *no assumption not made in the postulates*.

---

* Every proposition implies itself; a postulate, therefore, is properly defined as a proposition which is not implied by any proposition (or conjunction of propositions) except itself. This technicality is not important at the present point, but will recur later.

3. Truth and Validity

In discussing the requirements for logical postulates and theorems, nothing whatever has been said about the *truth* of the propositions assumed or demonstrated. An implied proposition is true if the premises are true; if the premises are false, the implied proposition may or may not be true. For instance, "Brutus killed Caesar" ⊃ "Caesar is dead." Since the premise is true, the implied proposition (sometimes called the "consequent") must also be true. But "Cassius killed Caesar" ⊃ "Caesar is dead," too; the fact that "Cassius killed Caesar" is false does not alter the implication. Yet, if we know the premise in this case to be false, this does not tell us that the consequent is false; the consequence is simply unaffected. It happens in this case to be true. So we cannot say that the theorems have just the same truth-value as the postulates; we may say only that they are true if the postulates are true, i.e. that they are genuinely implied.

For the truth of postulates there is no logical guarantee. There is no formal, i.e. structural, difference between a proposition that expresses an actual state of affairs in the world and one that expresses merely a *conceivable* state; no formal distinction between factual and fictional premises. So, if we are concerned about the truth of a whole system, of the postulates and all that follows from them, we must look to *something else than logic* for this knowledge. That is probably why Euclid justified his choice of premises by their "self-evidence." His avowed principles of deduction made no allowance for *arbitrary* propositions; the deductive process was supposed to assure the truth of theorems; yet this truth seemed poorly attested if there was no surety behind the postulates from which the theorems were descended.

If self-evidence is no guarantee, what criterion have we for the truth of any logical system?

None whatever. Logic does not go bond for any *original fact*. All it stands for is the conceptual possibility of a system, the actual deducibility of its theorems from its premises, the consistency of all its propositions. All it guarantees is that, *if* the premises be granted—whether on sense-evidence, self-evidence, or divine authority—*then* the system follows thus and so. This is not factual certainty, or truth; it is logical certainty, or *validity*. We may start with premises that have no foundation in fact at all, and elaborate a perfectly coherent, consistent, deductive system. Logically, that system is exactly as good as one whose premises are true; for in logic we require only that our assertions shall be *valid*, not that they convey truths about the world. For instance, the two propositions:

> Napoleon discovered America
> Napoleon died before A.D. 1500

jointly imply "America was discovered before A.D. 1500," and the deduction of the third proposition from the two premises is perfectly valid, as there is nothing inconsistent about them, and *if* they are true *then* the consequent cannot be false. The fact that they are both false does not affect their relation to each other or to the consequent, which happens, quite by chance, to be true. Had the second premise been: "Napoleon died before A.D. 1492" the consequent would also have been false; but its logical relations would have been exactly the same as above. On the other hand, suppose I had postulated:

> Columbus discovered America
> Columbus died after 1490

and concluded:

therefore   America was discovered after 1490,

my premises would both be true, the proposition I sought to

deduce would also be true, yet the logical argument would not be sound. The word "therefore" expresses the only untrue assertion I have made; the conclusion is *logically false*, or *invalid*.

So it is evident that a system built upon false propositions may be exactly as valid as one based on facts; that true propositions may fail to imply anything new at all; that false propositions may imply true conclusions, as in our first instance. The only case that is impossible is, that true premises should genuinely imply a false proposition. If we have true premises and valid logical relations, then we have true conclusions. But the *truth* of premises cannot be established by logic; whereas *validity* is its whole concern.

4. POSTULATES FOR THE SYSTEM OF CLASSES,
$$K(a, b \ldots) <_2$$

After all these preambles about the nature of a deductive system, the best means for its description, the limits of demonstrability, and the character of "granted" propositions, let us turn to an actual example, to witness the systematic construction of a logical edifice. The system of classes in the relation $<$, which by this time is generally familiar, is an ideal instance for our purposes. Not only is it completely deductive, but it may be derived by easy reasoning from a fairly small number of postulates; most of its propositions are capable of graphic representation, which brings them home to common sense by that convincing agent, the eye; and there are alternative ways of proof for almost every proposition, so that even a beginner's logical inventiveness is frequently rewarded. Moreover, the relations that obtain among classes may be initially expressed in many ways, so we are not bound to just one possible set of primitive concepts or just one list of primitive propositions (postulates). The readiest formulation from the point of view I have so far developed is in terms of general elements and a dyadic relation, as follows:*

$$K(a, b, c \ldots) <_2 \qquad K = \text{int "classes of individuals"}$$
$$< \, = \text{int "is included in"}$$

Postulates:

1. $(a) . a < a$

"Every element is included in itself."

2. $(a, b, c): a < b . b < c . \supset . a < c$

"If any element is included in another and that other in a third, then the first is included in the third."

3. $(\exists 1) (a) . a < 1$

"There is at least one element 1 such that any element, a, is included in 1."

4. $(\exists 0) (a) . 0 < a$

"There is at least one element 0 such that, whatever element we call a, 0 is included in it." (0 is an "empty class," zero.)

5. $(a) (\exists \text{-}a) (b, c): . \, b < a . b < \text{-}a . \supset . b < 0:$
$$a < c . \text{-}a < c . \supset . 1 < c$$

"For any a, there is at least one $\text{-}a$ and such that any b which is included both in a and $\text{-}a$ must be included in 0, and any c which includes both a and $\text{-}a$ also includes 1." (This means that a and $\text{-}a$ have no common part, and between them constitute the universe-class; $\text{-}a$ is, then, the *complement* of a.)

6. $(a, b) (\exists p_{a, b}): . \, p < a . p < b : (c): c < a . c < b . \supset . c < p$

---

* The following set of postulates is taken, with slight modifications, from E. V. HUNTINGTON's "Sets of Independent Postulates for the Algebra of Logic," *Trans. Amer. Math. Soc.*, vol. v (1904), pp. 288–309. Huntington gives as a postulate what I have treated as definition (i) and does not use strictly symbolic expressions. The set here given is his second set.

"For any a and any b, there is at least one element p (the subscript indicates that p has reference to the given a and b), such that p is included both in a and in b, and any other common part of a and b (i.e. any c included in a and in b) must be included in p." The element p, therefore, is the *greatest common part* of a and b.

7. $(a, b) \, (\exists s_{a, b}): . \, a < s \, . \, b < s : (c): a < c \, . \, b < c \, . \supset . \, s < c$

"For any a and b there is at least one element s such that a and b are both included in s, and any element c which includes both a and b also includes s." The element s for the given a and b is, then, *the smallest element which includes them both*.

8. $(a, b, c): \, c < a \, . \, c < b \, . \supset . \, c < 0 : \supset . \, a < -b$

"For any a, b, and c, if c's being included both in a and b implies that c is zero (i.e. if a and b can have no element in common but zero), then a is included in not-b."

To these postulates may be added, for convenience, three important *definitions*:

(i) $(a, b): a = b \, . \, \equiv \mathrm{df} \, . \, a < b \, . \, b < a$

"$a = b$" shall mean the same thing as "a and b are mutually inclusive."

(ii) $(a, b): a \times b = \mathrm{df} \, . \, p_{a, b}$ cf. postulate 6

"$a \times b$" shall represent the element p defined for a and b in postulate 6.

(iii) $(a, b): a + b \, . = \mathrm{df} \, . \, s_{a, b}$ cf. postulate 7

"$a + b$" shall represent the element s defined for a and b in postulate 7.

Here we have a systematic codification of the general features of classes noted in chapter vi, and the consequences of assuming a relation $<$ with the characteristics there described. Every class includes itself; every class includes the sub-classes of its sub-classes; every class is included in the universe class, and includes the empty class. Every class has a complement; the class and its complement are mutually exclusive, and exhaust the universe class between them. Any two classes have a sum and a product (if they are mutually exclusive, the product is 0). Any two mutually exclusive classes are included in each other's complements. By definition, mutual inclusion is called "equality"; the sum of two elements, a and b, is written "$a + b$," and the product "$a \times b$." With these notions and these fundamental facts we can construct the whole system of classes by a process of logical deduction.

5. RELATIONS AND OPERATIONS

The system of classes presented in this form looks very much like the simple deductive systems cited in earlier chapters, except for one characteristic: namely, that every element here given may generate just one further element, its complement, and any two elements generate a third, their sum, and a fourth, their product. Postulates which *describe ways of finding further elements* are an innovation, and merit some discussion.

Whenever a relation, such as $<$, is used among certain "given" elements to define a certain further element, this use is called an *operation* upon the given elements. Thus, if we introduce a general proposition with the quantifiers: $(a) (\exists -a)$, "for every a there is at least one $-a$, such that . . ." this proposition, which defines the nature of $-a$, is said *to describe the operation*, "$-$," *upon the element* a, whereby the complement, $-a$, is generated. The new element might, of course, bear any name we like; we might perfectly well say,

$$(a) (\exists x) (b, c) : b < a . b < x . \supset . b < 0$$
$$a < c . x < c . \supset . 1 < c$$

and hereafter operate with a and x as complementary terms; but in practice it would be extremely difficult to bear in mind that a and x were complementary, and perhaps d and g, m and y, etc., etc. The symbolism would be correct but in nowise *helpful*. But one of the chief purposes of symbols is to help one think, to make known relations evident, and by visual reminders save one the trouble of sheer remembered distinctions. Therefore a term which is established by an operation involving other terms is properly expressed by a *symbol of operation on those given terms*. We are told that any given term a has a complement; this is most naturally expressed as $-a$, the little sign "-" standing for the rather complicated use of $<$ by which the new term is related to the old. Similarly, the term $p_{a, b}$ established for any a and b is better expressed not by an arbitrary new letter, but by a sign of operation on a and b, such as $a \times b$. Note that this is a single term; the sign $\times$ expresses the whole complicated use of $<$ whereby a and b determine the new element called their product. Being a single term, this new element, $a \times b$, has a complement, $-(a \times b)$; and takes part in the establishment of further terms, such as $(a \times b) \times c$, $(a \times b) + c$, $(a \times b) + -a$, etc. And these new expressions again are single elements, "the class of what is both a and b and also c," "the class of what is either both a and b, or is c," "the class of what is either both a and b, or is not-a." Each of them represents one class, and each of them can enter into further operations. So the process of generating new terms from a given minimum ought to be endless.

The only thing that curtails the power of those postulates which define operations is the fact that a good many of the elements which may be generated from a given set of original terms turn out to be identical. For instance, we know that

$$(a): a + -a = 1$$
$$a \times -a = 0$$

This means that all sums of complementary terms are identical (since they all $= 1$) and all such products are identical (since they all $= 0$). Furthermore we shall find equations such as:

$$(a, b) : (a \times b) + b = b$$
$$(a, b, c) : (a + b) \times c = (a \times c) + (b \times c)$$
$$(a, b) : {-a} + {-b} = {-}(a \times b)$$

and many others, showing that although a set of given terms can be compounded with each other and with their sums and products and complements *ad infinitum*, we soon reach the point where no *new* classes are established, but only more and more elaborate expressions for the *same* classes. For example,

$$(a, b) : (a \times b) + (a \times {-b}) = a$$

This is not a *new* class, but merely a complex (and sometimes very important) description of the class a.

It is not hard to guess that most of the theorems in the deductive system $K(a, b \ldots) <_2$ will be concerned with the determination of sums and products, and their identity or non-identity with each other and with the original elements. This is, indeed, the case; it requires only four or five steps to show that $a + b = b$ means the same thing as $a < b$, so that hereafter this sort of equation may always be written in place of an inclusion, and we deal entirely with our *defined notions*, equations of sums and products, instead of the original constituent relation $<$. In practice, equations are much easier to handle than inclusions; this justifies our shifting, as soon as possible, from one usage to the other.

6. OPERATIONS AS "PRIMITIVE NOTIONS"

Here is another instance of a formal context which is not really suitable for description of the matter in hand, but requires, first of all, a long preamble of definitions; a formal context which makes it possible to define the notions that

are required, but which does not yield a convenient vocabulary directly and naturally. The same moral that was
drawn in the previous case (chap. vii, § 3) is pertinent here:
if we are going to deal entirely, or even very largely, with
operations, why begin with inclusions? Why not choose
our formal context so as to obviate the need of all those
elaborate definitions that lead from $<$ to $+$ and $\times$ and $=$?

An operation is a relation to a given term, or to given
terms, whereby a further term is defined. Such a relation
is, of course, more difficult to grasp than (say) "$<$," "fm,"
or "bt." *But the psychological difficulty of imagining it has
nothing whatever to do with its status in logic.* "Primitive
notions" need not be *obvious* notions, any more than
"primitive propositions" need to be axiomatic, or self-
evident, propositions. Whether they are psychologically
simple or complex, familiar or remote, easy or difficult,
makes no difference to their "primitive" or "derived"
character in a logical context; a relation expressed by $=$
and a sign of operation—that is, the establishment of a new
element from old—is just as respectable a notion as $<$, and
may just as legitimately be taken as "primitive," or undefined. If we regard it as one of the original constituents of
elementary propositions, then it is *logically simple*, though
it may be *psychologically complex*. So, finding that to start
with $K(a, b \ldots) <_2$ leads us at once into a need of complicated definitions whereby we pass from $<$ to the
operations $+$ and $\times$, we may as well assume these, rather
than $<$, at the outset, and so adopt a more suitable formal
context, a universe of discourse, K, whose elements are
classes in general, and two *constituent operations*, or "rules
of combination," $+$ and $\times$, and the relation $=$, which
serves here as a constituent relation (i.e. figures in elementary propositions), though usually in an auxiliary way,
in conjunction with $+$ or $\times$; so that we may write

$$K(a, b \ldots) +, \times, =_2$$
or
$$K(a, b \ldots) (+ =)_3, (\times =)_3$$

or, as is most commonly done, regard $=$ as *understood*,* and write merely: $K(a, b \ldots) +, \times$.

Note that when we combine the two-termed, or *binary*, operations $+$ and $\times$ with $=_2$, the resultant relations, $(+ =)$ and $(\times =)$, are *triadic*. That is because the determination of a third element, say s, or p, by two given elements is, of course, a relationship among *three* terms, a, b, and s, or a, b, and p. Likewise, the definition of the complement of a term a, i.e. the definition of $-a$ by a, is a relation between a and $-a$, and is therefore dyadic. So it is a general rule, where just one new term is defined, that *a unary operation expresses a dyadic relation, a binary operation expresses a triadic relation*, etc. But it is far easier to think of simple operations and the auxiliary "$=$" than of high-degreed relations, so the former practice, first borrowed from mathematics, has become indispensable in logic.

7. Postulates for the System $K(a, b \ldots) +, \times, =$†

With the new notions of *constituent operations* we have an entirely new set of postulates, or "granted" propositions, from which the system of classes may be deduced. We now start from the following assumptions:

$K(a, b . \;.) +, \times, =$

$K =$ int "classes"
$+ =$ int "class-disjunction"
$\times =$ int "class-conjunction"
$= =$ int "is identical with"

---

* There is a good argument for this practice, namely that *identity* and its opposite, *distinctness*, are "prelogical" notions, like "element" and "relation"; that $=$ is a "logical constant" and not an arbitrarily assumed "constituent relation." The problem of "logical constants" belongs to a later chapter. My position is that $=$ figures here as the relating constituent in elementary propositions, and is therefore to be mentioned in the formal context, to avoid confusion and doubt.

† See HUNTINGTON, *op. cit.* This is Huntington's first set.

Postulates:

I. $(a, b) (\exists c) . c = a + b$

"For any two terms, a and b, there is a third term, c, which is the sum $a + b$."

II. $(a, b) (\exists c) . c = a \times b$

"For any a and b there is a third term, c, which is the product $a \times b$" (Note that c has different meanings in these two propositions. In either case, "there is a third term," but the two cases have no relation to each other.)

III. $(\exists 0) (a) . a + 0 = a$

"There is at least one element 0 such that, for any a, $a + 0$ is the same as a."

IV. $(\exists 1) (a) . a \times 1 = a$

"There is at least one element 1 such that, for any a, $a \times 1$ (i.e. the common part of a and 1) is the same as a."

V. $(a, b) . a + b = b + a$

"For any a and b, $a + b$ is the same as $b + a$.

VI. $(a, b) . a \times b = b \times a$

"For any a and b, $a \times b$ is the same as $b \times a$."

VII. $(a, b, c) . a + (b \times c) = (a + b) \times (a + c)$

"For any a, b, and c, the sum of a with the product of b and c is the same as the product of the sums $(a + b)$ and $(a + c)$.

VIII. $(a, b, c) . a \times (b + c) = (a \times b) + (a \times c)$

"For any a, b, and c, the product of a with the sum of b and c is the same as the sum of the two products $a \times b$ and $a \times c$."

These two propositions are much easier to grasp symbolically than verbally; we have come to the point where symbols are easier to manipulate than words.

IX. $(a)\ (\exists\ \text{-}a):\ a + \text{-}a = 1\ .\ a \times \text{-}a = 0$

"For every a there is at least one element $\text{-}a$ such that the sum of a and $\text{-}a$ is the universe class, and their product is the null class."

To these may be added a postulate which is not strictly necessary to make the system workable, but serves the purpose of excluding the trivial case of a K with only one member, so that $1 = 0$ and $(a)\ .\ a = 1$, $a = \text{-}a$, etc. Such a system is perfectly legitimate with the nine postulates; but it is silly, so that we should always make the reservation: "provided there is more than one element." To save ourselves this tedious proviso, we add one more assumption:

X. $(\exists a,\ b):\ a \neq b$

"There are at least two elements which are not identical."

From these ten postulates we may deduce all the relations among classes of individuals, taken in extension, without the need of the elaborate definitions required in the context $K(a,\ b\ .\ .\ .) <_2$. These are, therefore, the postulates we shall henceforth use; with the rules of combination $+$ and $\times$, and the *laws of their manipulation* laid down in the postulates, a complete technique has been developed for finding the relations of any given class to any other given class or classes. The system of classes thus lends itself to *computation*, i.e. to the finding of new terms from old ones and the exact calculation of their relations to 1, the whole, and 0, the limit.

8. The "Calculus" of Classes

Such a system, having definite rules of computation whereby its elements may be *uniquely defined*, i.e. known to exist and unambiguously described, is a *calculus*, in the most general sense of that word. Most people have heard only of "*the* calculus," a slip-shod expression applied to the infinitesimal calculus of mathematics, invented by Leibniz and Newton. That calculus is undoubtedly the most impressive and important ever constructed, and we may forgive its admirers for trying to pre-empt the word "calculus" as its proper name; yet this word is too useful to be lost from the more general science of logic. A calculus is, in fact, any system wherein we may calculate. Ordinary arithmetic, the system of natural numbers with its constituent operations $+$, $\times$, $\div$, and $-$, is a calculus; the famous "hedonistic calculus" of Jeremy Bentham was so named in the fond and sanguine belief that this philosophy furnished a system wherein the relative magnitudes of pleasures could be exactly calculated. But as it involved no *operations* upon the elements called "pleasures," it failed to be a calculus.

The "Calculus of Classes" is a calculus in the strict sense, and has the pleasant distinction of being the simplest known example, and the easiest to manipulate. It is the lowest sort of mathematical system, somewhat resembling ordinary algebra, but unencumbered by coefficients or exponents—a veritable dream of an algebra, a calculus that is a "lower" mathematics than arithmetic! Yet, for all its simplicity, it is of vast importance and interest to all branches of logical thinking, as later chapters will show; and like every very precise discipline, it requires systematic exposition and practice for its correct manipulation. The next chapter, therefore, will deal entirely with the consequences of the second set of postulates here given, the postulates for $K(a, b, c \ldots) +, \times, =$, as they exhibit the general character, the possibilities and limits, of the Calculus of Classes.

SUMMARY

Certain facts about the universe of classes ordered by the relation $<$ may be known from the very nature of classes and of $<$. Without knowing any arbitrary facts, i.e. any conditions that might just as conceivably be otherwise, we can assert certain propositions that are necessarily true for classes. They simply *describe classes* and *describe* $<$.

There are many such propositions, but the greater number of them may be deduced when a certain small selection is given. Every proposition about classes in general either serves to imply some other or others, or itself follows from others. There are no matters of "mere" fact. The system is wholly *deductive*.

Propositions can be deduced only from other propositions. So a deductive system must start with a number of propositions that are not deduced, but are taken for granted. If we choose these wisely for the number and importance of their implications, we may do with very few such initial assumptions. Such "original" propositions are called *postulates*.

The classic example of a deductive system resting ultimately on a group of postulates is Euclid's geometry. Some of these assumptions are treated as beyond reasonable doubt, others as intuitively known or *self-evident*. The latter are classed as "axioms." The line between these two sorts is not sharp, for Euclid believed even his postulates, those propositions which were granted by everybody though perhaps not quite intuitive, to be guaranteed by common sense.

But common sense is variable and sometimes false. What is self-evident to one person may not be so to another. Therefore it is best to treat all postulates as arbitrarily granted, without claiming their psychological necessity or immediacy. This allows us to assume postulates which are far too complicated to be self-evident.

A postulate must belong to the system, have consequences in the system, must not contradict any other postulate or consequence of postulates, either in itself or by its implications, and must not itself follow from any other postulate or postulates in the system. These requirements are known, respectively, as (1) *coherence*, (2) *contributiveness*, (3) *consistency*, and (4) *independence*.

A theorem is anything that follows from the original assumptions by implication. Contradictory theorems cannot follow from consistent postulates. A theorem must contain absolutely nothing that is not implied by the postulates, either directly or by means of intervening theorems.

There is no guarantee within logic for the truth of "primitive propositions," or postulates. If we have reason to believe them as facts of nature or conscience or common sense, this reason must be sought outside the logical system which they generate. For that system they are simply arbitrary, and always to be regarded *as if* true. Consequently we are not really interested in the *truth* of theorems which follow from them, but in the *validity* thereof. The logical connection between postulates and theorems, not the condition that one or the other or both happen to be factual, is the concern of the logician.

The importance of valid deduction, and its connection with truth, lies in the fact that *if* the premises are true *then* the conclusion is true. A true theorem invalidly deduced has no guarantee. A false premise does not affect the truth-value of its consequences at all. But a true premise and a valid deduction always yield a true theorem. The truth of the premise, however, does not figure in logic, which is concerned wholly with the *validity* of its implications.

Since the system $K(a, b \ldots) <_2$ is a deductive system, we may state its arbitrary "original" propositions as a *set of postulates*. In its general characteristics the system differs from any we have so far encountered chiefly by the fact that certain of its relationships serve to define further elements whenever an element or a pair of elements is given. A relationship which unambiguously defines a new term is called an *operation* on the old term or terms. The new term is expressed by naming the elements from which it is derived and symbolizing the operation upon them, as: $-a$, $(a + b)$, $(a \times b)$.

By means of well-chosen postulates for the system $K(a, b \ldots) <_2$, we may define the important operations of *negation* (determining a complement), *class-disjunction*, and *class-conjunction*; also the relation $=$, which turns out to be far more useful than the original constituent relation $<$. Practically all our theorems deal with sums and products and are most readily expressed as equations. Before we come, then, to any interesting deductions, we must go through a process of definition in order to gain the vocabulary wherein such deductions may conveniently be expressed.

This is another case of starting with a primitive notion that is psychologically simple but logically rather ill-adapted to the purpose in hand. Operations express complex relations which are psychologically hard to treat as "primitive," but which are logically very economical and may be taken as perfectly respectable undefined concepts, or primitive notions. It is easier, and therefore commendable, to start with classes in general, two *constituent binary operations* $+$ and $\times$, and an (auxiliary) relation $=$, than to define all these notions by means of $<$. The new formal context requires a new set of postulates. This set, which is the most convenient to work with, howbeit not in all other respects the best, will henceforth be taken as the basis for the development of the calculus of classes.

The "calculus of classes" is a genuine calculus, being a deductive system which allows of computation, i.e. of unambiguous definition of certain elements by means of others and by rules of manipulation. It is the simplest mathematical system of any importance; and its importance makes it worth the detailed study which follows.

QUESTIONS FOR REVIEW

1. What is a postulate? What requirements must it fulfil? What is a theorem?
2. What criterion is there in logic for the truth of a postulate?
3. What is the logical value of self-evidence?
4. What is meant by "validity"? Do valid deductions always yield true statements? Can valid deductions be made from a false premise?
5. What connection, if any, exists between validity and truth-value?
6. What characteristic distinguishes the system $K(a, b \ldots) <_2$ from other deductive systems so far discussed?
7. Turning back to § 4, which postulates seem to you to give the system this characteristic?
8. What is meant by an "operation" in logic? What sort of thing results from an operation?
9. Can operations ever be "primitive notions" in a system? Can they wholly replace constituent relations?
10. What is the advantage of using $K(a, b \ldots) +, \times, =$?
11. What is a calculus? Is the "calculus of classes" a good designation or a misnomer?

SUGGESTIONS FOR CLASS WORK

1. Express symbolically, using $<$:

   > Every class includes itself.
   > The null class is included in every class.
   > The universe class includes every class.

2. Give the formal definition of $=$ in terms of $<$.
3. Express in two ways:

   > All fools are wise, all wise men fools.

4. Express with $+, \times, =$ (remember that *specific* classes are expressed by Roman capitals, *general* classes by l.c. letters):

   > Any class and its complement together make up the universe class.
   > A class and its complement have no members in common.
   > Mules are the descendants of horses and donkeys.
   > Everything is either natural or artificial.
   > Nothing that is artificial is natural.

5. Using the formula mentioned in the text,

"$(a, b): a < b . \equiv . a + b = b$," express with $+$:

$$a < b . b < c . \supset . a < c$$
$$0 < a . 0 < \text{-}a$$
$$a < 1 . \text{-}a < 1$$
$$1 < a . \supset . a = 1$$

6. Draw a diagram to show that $a < b . \equiv . a + b = b$.

CHAPTER IX

THE ALGEBRA OF LOGIC

1. The Meaning of "Algebra," and its Relevance to the Class-Calculus

If we assumed a Universe of Discourse whose elements were certain specific classes, A, B, C, etc., including a universe class 1, a null class 0, and for each given class a negative — -A, -B, -C, etc.—and for every two classes a sum and a product, we should have a perfectly good calculus, the operations and relations of which were expressed as *facts about specific elements*. Yet we might know that *if* the sum of A and B were not equal to B, *then* the product of A and -B could not be *0*; and we might calculate the sum of A × -B and B to be the element A + B. That is, instead of a general theory of classes we might simply have learned the existence and properties of each class; and might be capable of calculating certain relations of one class to another.

This is, in fact, the way people learn arithmetic. They learn counting by rote, addition of single digits by rote, multiplication by "tables" which they say by rote in the most unpleasant hours of childhood. Yet the number system, which is ultimately almost memorized by constant trafficking with innumerable "examples," is a calculus, and arithmetic is calculation. Its *general laws* are never expressed, though of course they are at the back of everyone's mind; we know that *any* two numbers have a sum, a product, a difference, a quotient; that *any* number subtracted from itself equals 0; and so forth. Yet these general facts cannot be stated in numbers, because numbers are, as it were, *specific elements* of the universe of arithmetic.

As soon as the mathematicians contrived a way of stating the fact that for *any* two numbers there is some third number which is their sum, another which is their product, another which is their difference, and finally a number which is their quotient, they were enabled to give the whole calculus of arithmetic *algebraic* expression. *A symbolic language for the generalized expression of operations on a set of elements is an algebra.* The form

$$a + b = c$$

puzzling to anyone who tries to read it as a statement (since an expression with real variables, which have no definite meanings, is neither true nor false), becomes a general rule of arithmetic as soon as its elements are properly quantified:

$$(a, b) \, (\exists c)^*. \; a + b = c$$

Similarly,
$$(a, b) \, (\exists c) \, . \; a \times b = c$$
$$(a, b) \, (\exists c) \, . \; a - b = c$$
$$(a, b) \, (\exists c) \, . \; a \div b = c$$

From such beginnings the *algebra of numbers* is derived; it is a generalization of arithmetic, a systematic statement of what is true for *any* numbers or for *some* numbers. It states in general terms the laws of operation, the structure of the number series, the existence of the peculiar elements *1* and *0* (*1* being "the element whereby any number, *a*, may be multiplied without being altered," and *0* "the element which may be added to any *a* without altering that *a*"), and allows us to calculate, from these conditions, the relations of various constructs to each other [such as: "$(a, b) : (a + b) \times (a + b) = (a \times a) + (2 \times a \times b) + (b \times b)$"].†

---

* Note that the *a*, *b*, and *c* of any one proposition have nothing to do with the *a*, *b*, and *c* of any other.

† Any one who is interested in the logical derivation of mathematics will probably be able to read, at this point, the excellent rendering of PEANO's system (from his *Formulaire de Mathématiques* (Turin, 1895–1908) in Young's *Lectures on the Fundamental Concepts of Algebra and Geometry* (New York, 1911), or Bertrand Russell's *Introduction to Mathematical Philosophy* (London, 1919) (a little more advanced logic).

The generalized deductive system of classes does exactly the same thing. Its operations are a little different, its peculiar elements *1* and *0* are differently defined, wherefore it has very different propositions; so that its K cannot be a universe of numbers, just as the universe of arithmetic cannot mean, by interpretation, "classes." But the generalized class-calculus is none the less an algebra, howbeit not a numerical algebra; it is known as the *Algebra of Logic*, and sometimes, in honour of George Boole its founder, as *Boolean Algebra*. According to its laws, we are able to work with "examples," to establish equations and solve problems of logic by the methods of genuine mathematics. The laws which govern these procedures are the "primitive propositions" which constitute our initial set of postulates.

2. FURTHER DISCUSSION OF THE POSTULATES

The ten postulates for $K(a, b \ldots) +, \times, =,$ given in the previous chapter, had best be reiterated here, so that in deducing theorems we may have the premises compactly and conveniently before us. We start, then, with the following concepts and general propositions:

$$K(a, b, c \ldots) +, \times, =$$

K =int "classes of individuals"
$+$ =int "class-disjunction"
$\times$ =int "class-conjunction"
$=$ =int "is identical with"

IA	$(a, b) \, (\exists c) \, . \, a + b = c$
IB	$(a, b) \, (\exists c) \, . \, a \times b = c$
IIA	$(\exists 0) \, (a) \, . \, a + 0 = a$
IIB	$(\exists 1) \, (a) \, . \, a \times 1 = a$
IIIA	$(a, b) \, . \, a + b = b + a$
IIIB	$(a, b) \, . \, a \times b = b \times a$
IVA	$(a, b, c) \, . \, a + (b \times c) = (a + b) \times (a + c)$
IVB	$(a, b, c) \, . \, a \times (b + c) = (a \times b) + (a \times c)$
V	$(a) \, (\exists -a) : a + -a = 1 \, . \, a \times -a = 0$
VI	$(\exists a, b) \, . \, a \neq b$

Altogether, we have here ten postulates, or primitive propositions, unproved and unchallengeable assumptions about the system. Now, if these postulates are grouped according to their general characteristics, they will be found to fall into three general categories, according to the types of their respective contributions to the system. They may be characterized as:

(1) Those which allow us to derive new terms from old, i.e. which permit the use of the operators; (2) those which assert categorically the existence of certain elements; (3) those which permit certain ways of manipulating terms, i.e. which state the general conditions on which the relation $=$ depends. The first group comprises I_A, I_B, and V; the second II_A, II_B, and VI; the third, III_A, III_B, IV_A, and IV_B. Now it will immediately be noticed that the different kinds of postulate are distinguished by the type and order of their quantifiers. A universal quantifier followed by the particular, e.g. $(a) (\exists b)$, expresses the determination of a certain element by whatever elements have been given, that is to say, it expresses the *universal* fact that from any given term or terms at least one other may be derived in a way which the following formula conveys. A particular quantifier, which may or may not be followed by a universal one, $(\exists a) (b)$, makes a categorical assertion that "there is at least one such-and-such," or "there are at least two such-and-such," having certain relations to "any element" in the system, or to each other if there be more than one, which relations are given by the formula that follows. A completely universal proposition, i.e. one introduced by (a) or (a, b), or any number of universals without any $(\exists -)$, expresses a condition which governs the whole system; such a condition is an *algebraic rule* of the system. So it may be said that the postulates grant *the existence of certain elements, rules for deriving new elements, and rules for manipulating whatever elements there are.* In a system based on *operators*, like $+$ and $\times$, the second kind of postulate will naturally

be the first to engage our attention. IA and IB must be granted before we can proceed to the definitions of 0 and 1, of two elements such that $a \neq b$, the rules for relating derived elements, or the establishment of the *defined operation* "not."

3. Principles of Proof: Substitution, Application, and Inference

Before we undertake the systematic deduction of theorems, a few words might be said about the principles of logical reasoning. The method whereby all other propositions of the system are derived from its postulates rests on a few very general *canons of logical procedure*, which are universally known, though seldom explicitly stated.

The first of these is the *principle of substitution*. It is assumed that, whenever two terms are *identical*, i.e. are names for the same element, either one may be used in place of the other. That is, if $a = b$, then $a \times c$ may be written $b \times c$, or $c + b$ may be written $c + a$ Similarly, if two propositions are *equivalent*, one may be asserted in place of the other; thus, if $a < b \, . \equiv . \, a + b = b$, then wherever $a < b$ occurs we may write $a + b = b$ instead, and *vice versa*.

The second canon might be called the *principle of application*. This is the assumption that a statement about *any* element applies to *each* element; that is to say, if it is granted that

$$(a, b) \, . \, a + b = b + a$$

and if we know there is a certain x and there is a certain y, then it is true of this x and this y that $x + y = y + x$.

The third rule of reasoning is the *principle of inference*, the only one which is not usually taken unconsciously for granted, but has received extensive recognition in the literature. On this principle, if a proposition may be asserted (i.e. is "granted" or otherwise "known as true"), and this proposition implies another proposition, then the latter may also be asserted. Thus, if we know that $(\exists\, a, b)\,.\, a = \text{-}b$ and also that $(a, b) : a = \text{-}b\,.\,\supset\,.\,b = \text{-}a$, then we may assert $b = \text{-}a$ henceforth as an independent proposition, not merely as a part of "$(a,\ b): a = \text{-}b\,.\,\supset\,.\,b = \text{-}a$." This is the process of passing from premises to their conclusion, which may be called deductive reasoning proper, as against the principles of substitution and application, which are in a sense auxiliary devices, however important they may be to the very possibility of deduction.

These . general rules of argument, together with the postulated rules of manipulation for the calculus in question, and the conventions governing the use of symbolism (such as letting a repeated symbol in one total assertion mean the same thing whenever it occurs, or letting the greater number of dots always extend over the lesser number, etc.) which have been expounded in earlier chapters, must suffice for all further developments of the algebra of logic, which are now to be exhibited in the form of *deduced propositions or theorems*.

4. ELEMENTARY THEOREMS

In developing the calculus of classes, one might begin with the proof of almost any proposition that happens to follow directly from the postulates. But in logic, as in mathematics, there are certain unwritten laws—one might fairly say logical "ideals"—which limit our caprices in this matter, though they do not prescribe any hard and fast order wherein the derived propositions must be marshalled: these tacit principles are logical economy, and what the mathematicians call "elegance," plan and symmetry in exposition. We want to exhibit as soon as possible all the *general laws of the algebra*, the fundamental facts which are most frequently used in processes of proof, and leave for later derivation the details of the system, to which one rarely appeals for further deductions. That is to say, we want to explicate first of all the *rules of manipulation* which are characteristic of this system.

Two of these rules are given as postulates; each one is expressed by two primitive propositions. IIIA and IIIB state what is called the *commutative law*, one for the operator $+$, the other for $\times$. This law grants one the right to *commute the elements* in a sum or in a product whenever it is convenient to do so, i.e. to write either $a + b$ or $b + a$, either $b \times a$ or $a \times b$. Postulates IVA and IVB together express the so-called *distributive law*, one for an element *added to a product*, the other for an element *multiplied with a sum*. IVA states that an element a which is added to a product, $(b \times c)$, may be "distributed" to each member of the product, but not in the usual sense of "distributed," which is to be broken up and divided among the members; the whole of a is added to each member of the product. It is "distributed" rather in the way a cold may be distributed, by one sufferer, to a whole roomful of people, each person receiving the whole cold in all its glory. IVB asserts this law for the multiplication of an element with a sum; each member of the sum may be separately multiplied by that element, so that it is "distributed" over the members of the sum without being itself split up. Thus $a \times (b + c)$ may be written $(a \times b) + (a \times c)$.

Such laws supply us with forms that may be substituted for one another. The possibility of making deductions from given facts depends so often on the *form* in which these facts are given, that a large supply of interchangeable forms is the first requirement for an interesting deductive system. The establishment of more such forms is therefore our first ambition in developing the algebra, and the theorems we are most anxious to prove are such as yield more laws of manipulation.

Most of our proofs, however, involve the elements *1* and *0*, and require that there should be *just one* element such as *1* and *just one* such as *0*. The postulates tell us there is *at least* one class *1* and *at least* one class *0*; but not that there is *at most* one of each. Before we can treat *1* and *0* as unique it behooves us, then, to demonstrate their uniqueness. Let us begin with a proof of the proposition:

Theorem 1a

The element *0* in IIA is unique.

This proposition arrests attention because, unlike all previous propositions of the system, it is stated in words, not symbols. Huntington, who made this and the corresponding *1*-proposition his first two theorems, stated them verbally, and all subsequent writers, to my knowledge, have followed the practice. The symbolic statement is a bit complicated, and without quantifiers (most writers dispense with them, regarding generalization as "understood"), it is impossible.* To avoid the use of a rather complex formula in the very first theorem, I follow the fashion of rendering this proposition in words.

Proof:

Assume an element 0_2 having the properties of *0*, so that we have 0_1 and 0_2.

Then $\qquad\qquad (a) \,.\, a + 0_2 = a$

By the principle of application, what is true of *a* is true of 0_1,

so $\qquad\qquad 0_1 + 0_2 = 0_1$

Likewise, what holds for *a* in IIA holds for 0_2, so

$$0_2 + 0_1 = 0_2$$

But $\qquad\qquad 0_2 + 0_1 = 0_1 + 0_2 \qquad\qquad$ by IIIA

But *0* $\qquad 0_2 + 0_1 = 0_2 \quad$ and $\quad 0_1 + 0_2 = 0_1$

---

* Symbolically the statement that there is at least one *0* which if added to any other term, *a*, leaves it unaffected, and that any *b* having the same property is identical with *0*, is:

$$(\exists 0) :: (a),\, a + 0 = a : .\, (\exists b)(c) \,.\, c + b = b : \supset : b = 0$$

So, by the principle of substitution, 0_2 may be written for $0_2 + 0_1$ and 0_1 for $0_1 + 0_2$ and we have

$$0_2 = 0_1 \qquad \text{Q.E.D.}$$

Any element, therefore, which has the property ascribed to 0 in IIA is identical with 0; which is to say, 0 is unique.

Theorem 1b

The element 1 in IIB is unique.

The proof of this theorem is exactly analogous to that of Theorem 1a, applying IIB in place of IIA and IIIB in place of IIIA.

The uniqueness of 0 and 1 being thus guaranteed, we are able to demonstrate another important equation, a characteristic of the system known as the *Law of Tautology*:

Theorem 2b*

$$(a) \cdot a \times a = a$$

Proof: $a = a \times 1$ by IIB

$1 = a + \text{-}a$ by V

hence $a = a \times (a + \text{-}a)$

$a \times (a + \text{-}a) = (a \times a) + (a \times \text{-}a)$

         by IVB, the "distributive law" for products

$a \times \text{-}a = 0$ V

hence $a = a \times (a + \text{-}a) = (a \times a) + (a \times \text{-}a)$

$$= (a \times a) + 0 = a \times a$$

or: $a = a \times a$ Q.E.D.

Theorem 2a

$$(a) \cdot a + a = a$$

The proof of this theorem is analogous to that of 2b, and

*Theorems dealing with sums will bear the suffix "a," those dealing with products, "b"; sometimes "a" will be proved and the analogous "b" left to the reader, and sometimes *vice versa*, so as to give equal insight into the treatment of sums and products respectively.

may easily be carried out, using IIA in place of IIB and IVA in place of IVB.

These propositions are called laws of "tautology" because they show that it makes no difference how many times a term is mentioned in a sum or a product; a product is not changed by being multiplied by something that is already a factor of it, nor a sum by having one of its summands added to it any number of times. Naturally, the common part of a and a is the whole of a and nothing more; the class of dogs that are also dogs is simply the class of dogs; and what is either a or is a must likewise be just exactly the class a; what is either a cat or a cat is a cat. The tautology is obvious.

It is owing to these two propositions that the algebra of logic has no exponents and no coefficients. If $a \times a = a$, we need not bother about an a^2, since $a^2 = a$; if $a + a = a$, we can never arrive at $2a$; hence the peculiar simplicity of the class-calculus.

Before we proceed to the next "laws" of the algebra, it is necessary to prove that if 1 is added to anything, the sum is 1, and if anything is multiplied by 0 the product is 0. The next two theorems, therefore, describe the behaviour of these two unique elements more fully than the minimum description that defines them in the postulates.

Theorem 3a

$$(a) \cdot a + 1 = 1$$

Proof: $\quad a + 1 = (a + 1 \times 1)$

by IIB, since $(a + 1)$ is a simple term, and may take the place of a in the formula

$$(a + 1) \times 1 = 1 \times (a + 1) \qquad\qquad \text{IIIB}$$
$$1 = a + \text{-}a \qquad\qquad\qquad\qquad \text{V}$$

hence $\quad 1 \times (a + 1) = (a + \text{-}a) \times (a + 1)$ Substitution

$$(a + \text{-}a) \times (a + 1) = a + (\text{-}a \times 1)$$

by IVA (the second form in the equation here stands first)

hence $1 \times (a + 1) = a + (\text{-}a \times 1)$

Substituting back, 1 for $(a + \text{-}a)$

but $1 \times (a + 1) = a + 1$ IIB

and $\text{-}a \times 1 = \text{-}a$ IIB

hence $a + 1 = a + \text{-}a$ Substitution V

or $a + 1 = 1$

Q.E.D.

Theorem 3b

$$(a) \;.\; a \times 0 = 0$$

The proof is analogous to that of 3a, using IIA instead of IIB, IIIA instead of IIIB, IVB instead of IVA.

There are certain points of procedure to be noted in the proof of theorem 3a. In the first place, the sum $a + 1$, which is to be proved equal to 1, is treated as a *single term*, so that a truth about "any term, a" may be applied to it. It is easy to forget that a sum or a product has the same characteristics as a single letter. In the second place, it was sometimes wise to write 1, sometimes its equivalent $a + \text{-}a$. The guiding principle here is to use, whenever possible, a form which makes the resultant expression exemplify some familiar formula. Thus, to write $a + \text{-}a$ instead of 1 makes the expression $1 \times (a + 1)$ a product of two sums, $(a + \text{-}a) \times (a + 1)$, and in this we recognize the *right-hand* member of the equation in postulate IVA. Since "$=$" holds between its terms in either order, we may assert: $(a + \text{-}a) \times (a + 1) = a + (\text{-}a \times 1)$.

All the steps in this proof are very simple; yet to survey the possibilities and make a practical choice of forms requires a certain ingenuity. There is no thumb-rule to indicate the next move in a calculation. The rules of logic merely *permit* some moves and *forbid* others, but never *dictate* a line of argument. One might say that to understand logic is a science, resting purely on reason; but to *use* logic, to select postulates or demonstrate theorems, is an art, and requires imagination.

The next proposition is again a "law" of the system, applying to all its elements:

Theorem 4b

$$(a, b) \, . \, a \times (a + b) = a$$

Proof:

$$a \times (a + b) = (a + 0) \times (a + b) \qquad \text{IIA}$$

$$(a + 0) \times (a + b) = a + (0 \times b) \qquad \text{IVA}$$

$$= a + (b \times 0) \qquad \text{IIIB}$$

$$= a + 0 \qquad \text{3b}$$

$$= a \qquad \text{IIA}$$

Q.E.D.

Theorem 4a

$$(a, b) \, . \, a + (a \times b) = a$$

The proof is analogous to that of theorem 4b, using the postulates or theorems which express for the other operator the laws used above.

These two propositions state the so-called *laws of absorption*, whereby a term, *a*, "absorbs" any sum of itself and another term when multiplied with this sum, and any product of itself and another term when it is added to this product. For, by interpretation, "$a \times (a + b)$" means "the common part of *a* and $(a + b)$," and this is, of course, just *a*. The class of books that are also either books or chairs is the class of books. Also, "$a + (a \times b)$" means "the class of either *a* or $a \times b$," and that again is just *a*; the class of people who are either soldiers or German soldiers is the class of soldiers.

Theorem 5a

$$(a, b) . (a + b) \times (a + \text{-}b) = a$$

Proof: $(a + b) \times (a + \text{-}b) = a + (b \times \text{-}b)$ IVA

$a + (b \times \text{-}b) = a + 0 = a$ Q.E.D.

Theorem 5b

$$(a, b) . (a \times b) + (a \times \text{-}b) = a$$

The proof is similar to that of 5a, using IVB for IVA.

The law expressed in these theorems is called the *law of expansion*, because it allows us to "expand" a term, a, to any length by introducing complementary pairs of other terms into its description. Thus, $a = [(a \times b) + (a \times \text{-}b)] + [(a \times c) + (a \times \text{-}c)] + [(a \times d) + (a \times \text{-}d)] \ldots$ since each bracketed expression equals a, and the total, $a + a + a + \ldots$, by the law of tautology, is also identical with a.

The value of this formula is that it allows us to use a single term as a sum of products or a product of sums, in making calculations. A term may be "expanded" until it matches some other expression with which it is to be compared in mânipulation, so that we can often produce a convenient symmetry of forms, which allows all sorts of mathematical tricks and transformations.

At this point, the operation -, or "negation," requires some further elucidation. The postulates state that for every given element, a, there is at least one element $\text{-}a$ which has no part in common with a, but together with a makes up the universe class. Is there, however, *only* one such element? Theorem 6 proves this point, showing that any element b having the postulated relations of $\text{-}a$ to a is identical with a, i.e. that there is just one complement for every a.

Theorem 6

$$(a, b, c) : a = -c \quad b = -c . \supset . a = b$$

Proof: $\quad a = a \times 1$ IIB

$\quad\quad = a \times (c + b)$ V

$\quad\quad = (a \times c) + (a \times b)$ IVB

$\quad\quad = (c \times a) + (b \times a)$ IIIB

$\quad\quad = 0 + (b \times a)$ V

$\quad\quad = (c \times b) + (b \times a)$ V

$\quad\quad = (b \times c) + (b \times a)$ IIIB

$\quad\quad = b \times (c + a)$ IVB

$\quad\quad = b \times 1$ V

$\quad\quad = b$ IIB

Q.E.D.

This proves that for every *a*, -*a* is *uniquely determined* by the operation -on *a*. Every term has just one complement. From this it is easy to prove

Theorem 7

$$(a, b) : b = -a . \supset . a = -b$$

Proof: $\quad b = -a . \supset . a + b = 1 . a \times b = 0$ V

then $\quad\quad\quad b + a = 1 . b \times a = 0$

              IIIA, B, commutative law

therefore *a* fulfils the condition for -*b*, and by theorem 6 this makes it identical with -*b*

hence $\quad\quad a = -b$ Q.E.D.

This is known as the *law of contraposition*, from which follows, as a corollary, the *law of double negation*,

Theorem 8

$$(a) . a = -(-a)$$

The proof is obvious; a term and its complement are *each other's* complements, i.e. every element is the complement of its complement.

One further pair of theorems may here be adduced, before

we discuss the "law of duality," although that law is employed in proving these two propositions, so that the proofs cannot be given here. These theorems are properly numbered 11a and 11b. As they are long and complicated they may as well be relegated to a later section.* The theorems in question assert the *laws of association*.

Theorem 11a

$$(a, b, c) \cdot (a + b) + c = a + (b + c)$$

Theorem 11b

$$(a, b, c) \cdot (a \times b) \times c = a \times (b \times c)$$

Here it is stated that it makes no difference in what order summands are added to each other, or in what order factors are combined into a product. In practice, it allows us to dispense with parentheses where all the operators are alike; that is to say, if

$$a + (b + c) = (a + b) + c$$
and $\quad a \times (b \times c) = (a \times b) \times c$

the parentheses lose their significance, and the expressions may as well be written

$$a + b + c \text{ and } a \times b \times c$$

Only where we wish to treat part of such an expression as a single term we employ parentheses to set it off.

At this point, a simple notational device, borrowed from ordinary algebra, may be introduced: the product of two elements, $a \times b$, is often written without a $\times$, simply as ab. This is a familiar usage which allows us to dispense with a good many parentheses where sums and products are mixed. Thus, to abbreviate

$$(a \times b) + (-a \times b) + c + (a \times d)$$

by simply omitting parentheses would be confusing, since

* They may be found in Appendix B.

$a \times b + \text{-}a \times b + c + a \times d$ might as well be construed to mean $a \times (b + \text{-}a) \times (b + c) + (a \times d)$; but $ab + \text{-}ab + c + ad$ is unmistakable.

5. THE DUALITY OF $+$ AND $\times$

Anyone who has followed the exposition to this point has undoubtedly noticed a peculiar symmetry in the postulates and theorems, namely that for every proposition about sums there is an analogous one about products. If there is an entity which, when multiplied with any term, leaves that term unaffected, then there is also one which may be added to any term without altering it; if there is a term which is unchanged by anything that is added to it, then there is one that does not change by being multiplied with anything else. Moreover, any law of the algebra that holds for addition holds for multiplication; if products are "associative," so are sums, if sums are "commutative," so are products, etc. The reason for this duality is that *any class which may be formed with the operator $+$ may also be expressed in terms of $\times$ and negation*, and *any class that may be formed with $\times$ could also be expressed with $+$ and negation*. The exact relation between sums and products appears in the following theorems:

Theorem 10a

$$-(a + b) = \text{-}a \times \text{-}b$$

The theorem asserts that $\text{-}a \times \text{-}b$ is $-(a + b)$, i.e. is the complement of $a + b$; if we can show that $(a + b) + \text{-}a\,\text{-}b = 1$ and $(a + b) \times \text{-}a\,\text{-}b = 0$, then the theorem is proved. But there are several steps, or lemmas, in this demonstration. First of all we must prove that, with any term b, whatever:

$$-a + (a + b) = 1$$

and

$$-a \times ab = 0$$

Call this lemma 1.

Proof: $-a + (a + b) = 1 \times [-a + (a + b)]$ IIB
          $1 = -a + a$ V

hence $1 \times [-a + (a + c)] = (-a + a) \times [-a + (a + b)]$
                                   $= -a + [a \times (a + b)]$ IVA

but $a \times (a + b) = a$ 4b

then $-a + [a \times (a + b)] = -a + a$
                                  $= 1$ V

Similarly $-a \times ab$ may be shown to equal 0; the proof need not be explicitly rehearsed here, but may be designated as lemma 2.

Now we can prove

Lemma 3, $(a + b) + -a -b = 1$

Proof: $(a + b) + -a -b = [(a + b) + -a]$
                               $[(a + b) + -b]$ IVA

but $(a + b) + -a = -a + (a + b)$ IIIA

and $-a + (a + b) = 1$ lemma 1

         $(a + b) + -b = -b + (b + a) = 1$
                                        IIIA and lemma 1

then $(a + b) + -a -b = 1 \times 1 = 1$

Finally we have

Lemma 4, $(a + b) \times -a -b = 0$

Proof: $(a + b) \times -a -b = -a -b \times (a + b)$ IIIB

            $-a -b \times (a + b) = (-a -b) a + (-a -b) b$ IVB

                                 $= a (-a -b) + b (-a -b)$ IIIB

$\left.\begin{array}{l} a \times (-a -b) = 0 \\ b \times (-a -b) = 0 \end{array}\right\}$ lemma 2

$0 + 0 = 0$

Since $(a + b) + \text{-}a \text{-}b = 1$

and $(a + b) \times \text{-}a \text{-}b = 0$

$$\text{-}a \text{-}b = \text{-}(a + b) \qquad \text{Q.E.D}$$

The rather elaborate proof of theorem 10a is given because of the great importance of the proposition in question. Analogously, we might demonstrate

Theorem 10b

$$(a, b) \, . \, \text{-}(a \times b) = \text{-}a + \text{-}b$$

But this is left to the brave and ambitious reader.

The significance of theorems 10a and 10b is that by their means we may write any product in the form of a sum, and any sum as a product. For, if $\text{-}a + \text{-}b$ is the complement of ab, then ab may be written as the complement of $\text{-}a + \text{-}b$, i.e. $ab = \text{-}(\text{-}a + \text{-}b)$. Now, if every sum may be turned into a product and *vice versa*, it is not hard to see why the laws for sums should be exactly like the laws for products; since $a + b$ is a term, $\text{-}(a + b)$ is also a term, and what holds for $a + b$ holds also for $\text{-}(a + b)$; but $\text{-}(a + b) = \text{-}a \times \text{-}b$; *for every $a + b$ there is a $c \times d$ which is its complement*, namely the product of the terms $\text{-}a$ and $\text{-}b$.

This characteristic of the algebra of logic is called *the duality of $+$ and $\times$*, and the two theorems which express the relation between sums and products state the so-called *law of duality*. Throughout the entire system, whatever rule applies to one operator, applies also to the other (where 0 occurs with one operator, 1 will occur with the other, and *vice versa*). That is why the postulates involving $+$ and $\times$ come in pairs, numbered IA, IB, IIA, IIB, etc., or—like V— make a compound statement whose clauses constitute just such a pair; and why the theorems dealing with operations follow two by two, like Noah's animals.

The duality of $+$ and $\times$ has some astonishing consequences. If every sum is expressible as a product, then certainly everything we have said about sums could have been said about those same entities expressed as products; and if we said everything there is to say about products, this must include all there is about sums expressed as products; so it must contain by implication anything that could be said about sums. Why, then, assume *both* sums and products as "primitive notions"? Sums are just another way of writing products. If we assume as "primitive" the meaning of $\times$, and admit

$$(a, b) \, (\exists c) \, . \, a \times b = c$$

then we may regard $a + b$ as merely another way of saying $-(-a \, -b)$; everything that is true of $a + b$ is true of $-(-a \, -b)$, and *vice versa*. So, *if we take $\times$ and $-$ as "primitive,"* $+$ may be defined as follows:

$$(a, b) : a + b \, . \, =\text{df} \, . \, -(-a \, -b)$$

This has, indeed, been done; postulates for the algebra of logic have been given entirely in terms of $\times$. Of course they are a little different from the $\times$-postulates here given. The characterization of *1* and of $-a$ in our set, for instance, would be impossible without $+$, so a different description is necessary if we use $\times$ alone. The distributive law cannot be expressed to any purpose, i.e. as a recognizable "law," at all, in terms of one operator, so it is useless as a postulate, but must wait upon the introduction of the *defined notion* $+$, and follow as a theorem; the postulates, consequently, must be chosen in such a way that this important law can be deduced from them. But all these are perfectly straightforward, soluble problems. Professor Lewis, in *A Survey of Symbolic Logic*, has given a perfectly adequate, simple, and workable set of postulates for Boolean algebra, with a formal context $K(a, b \ldots) \times$ (the relation "$=$" is tacitly assumed, as usual), nine primitive propositions, and three definitions.

Exactly the same thing may be done for the other operator,

+. We may take *logical disjunction* as a primitive notion, and, with the help of the postulated (i.e. described, not *defined*) operation -, define the notion of *logical conjunction*, thus:

$$(a,\ b) : a \times b\ . = \mathrm{df}\ .\ -(-a + -b)$$

The whole algebra may be determined by a handful of "primitive propositions" in terms of + alone; the definition of "$a \times b$" figures in such a system as a mere convenience, since it could always be replaced by $-(-a + -b)$, but the convenience of this abbreviation is so great that the essential form, the simplicity and symmetry of the whole system would be practically undiscoverable without it. Imagine the "distributive law" in terms of $\times$ alone:

$$(a,\ b,\ c)\ .\ a \times -(-b \times -c) = -[-(a \times b) \times -(a \times c)]$$

This sort of proposition is too clumsy to be useful. Therefore, if we begin with +, the notion of $\times$ is introduced as soon as possible by definition. Professor Huntington has given a set of postulates for the algebra of logic in terms of + alone ("=" being understood).*

I have used the formal context $K(a,\ b\ .\ .\ .) +,\ \times,\ =$, because (1) it does not give preference to either operator, and therefore does not create the false impression that either one is, in its own right, more "essential" than the other; (2) it shows in the clearest form the duality of + and $\times$; and (3) it furnishes the greatest variety of forms to be used in the process of deducing theorems, so that it is the easiest version of the calculus for a novice to handle. But now that we see how either operator may actually be defined in terms of the other, we must admit that the primitive notions here adopted do not constitute the smallest selection that may be made to serve, and the algebra thereby falls short of the ideal of conceptual economy.

* HUNTINGTON, *op. cit.*, the third set.

6. The Definition of $<$, and Inclusion-Theorems

So far, we have operated entirely with primitive notions, since our formal context is a very generous one. There has been no need, as yet, of concepts established by definition. But now it is convenient to introduce a new *relation*, which must, of course, be duly defined in terms of previous notions: this relation may be called *inclusion*, symbolized by $<$, and determined thus:

$$(a, b) : a < b . \equiv \mathrm{df} . a + b = b$$

" 'a is included in b' is always to mean the same thing as: the sum of a and b is b itself."

The duality of $+$ and $\times$ is so thoroughgoing that even where a mere definition is given in terms of $+$, its equivalent for $\times$ may be found. We might as well have defined $<$ through an equation containing a product:

$$(a, b) : a < b . \equiv \mathrm{df} . ab = a$$

" 'a is included in b' is always to mean the same thing as: the product of a and b is a itself."

The new symbol, $<$, is to be officially defined as $a + b = b$. But often it is very convenient that a proposition about products may be substituted for $a + b = b$, i.e. that this expression is equivalent to $ab = a$; so it is advisable to establish this equivalence.

Logical equivalence is mutual implication. So the theorem must be demonstrated in two lemmas, one to prove that $a + b = b . \supset . ab = a$, the other that $ab = a . \supset . a + b = b$.

Theorem 12

$$(a, b) : a + b = b . \equiv . ab = a$$

Proof:

Lemma 1 $a + b = b . \supset . ab = a$

Dem. $a + b = b . \supset . ab = a (a + b)$
$$= a$$ 4b

Lemma 2 $(a, b) : ab = a . \supset . a + b = b$

Dem. $ab = a . \supset . a + b = ab + b$

$$= b + ba$$ 4a

$$= b$$

Therefore, $a + b = b . \equiv . ab = a$ Q.E.D.

This gives us the right to substitute $ab = a$ for $a < b$ or $a + b = b$ whenever it suits our purposes to do so.

Although definitions are, in a sense, quite arbitrary, and are to be taken as mere shorthand for complicated terms or propositions, they are of course employed to describe some *state of affairs* which is important wherever we use our algebra. Just as 2^2 is shorthand for 2×2, we none the less call it the "square" of 2 because it expresses the formula for a *geometrical square* whose side-measure is 2. Similarly, the proposition $a < b$ is shorthand for $a + b = b$; but $<$ is read "inclusion" because $a + b = b$ holds, always and only, for cases where a is totally included in b. The diagram makes this doubly clear.

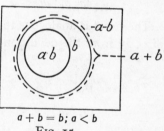

$a + b = b; a < b$
Fig. 15.

Whenever what is either a or b is b, a is included in b; whenever this is the case, what is both a and b, is a, or, $a < b$; or, $ab = a$.

With the defined notion of $<$, we can prove several interesting theorems for cases of total inclusion of one class in another. Remember that, since $a < b$ *in this system* means $a + b = b$, and this has been proved equivalent to $ab = a$, a proposition about $<$ always permits a correlative pair of propositions, one in terms of $+$, one of $\times$; so even where the explicit pairing of theorems is abandoned, it remains implicitly understood.

Theorem 13 $(a) . a < a$

Proof: $a < a . \equiv df . a + a = a$

                $a + a = a$ 2a

Therefore, $a < a$ Q.E.D.

Theorem 14a

        $(a, b) . a < a + b$

   Proof: $a < a + b . = df . a + (a + b) = a + b$

This is equivalent to $a (a + b) = a$ 12

but $a (a + b) = a$ 4b

hence $a < a + b$ Q.E.D.

Theorem 14b

        $(a, b) . ab < a$

The proof is analogous to that of theorem 14a, and follows directly from the definition of $<$.

Theorem 15a

        $(a, b, c) : a < c . b < c . \supset . a + b < c$

Proof: $a + c = c . b + c = c . \supset . c + c = (a + c) + (b + c)$

              $c + c = c$ 2b

              $(a + c) + (b + c) = a + b + c + c = a + b + c$

              $a + b + c = c . \equiv df . a + b < c$ Q.E.D.

Theorem 15b

        $(a, b, c) : c < a . c < b . \supset . c < ab$

The proof is analogous to that of 15a, using the equivalent of the definition of $<$.

Theorem 16

$$(a, b, c) : a < b \quad b < c . \supset . a < c$$

	$a = ab$	hyp. and def.
	$b = bc$	hyp. and def.
hence	$a = a(bc)$	
but	$a(bc) = (ab)c$	11b
	$(ab)c < c$	14b
hence	$a < c$	Q.E.D.

Theorem 17a

$$(a) . a < 1$$

Proof:	$a = a \times 1$	IIB
Therefore,	$a < 1$	Q.E.D.

Theorem 17b

$$(a) . 0 < a$$

The proof is analogous to theorem 17a.

Theorem 18b

$$(a, b) : a < b . a < -b . \supset . a = 0$$

Proof:	$a = ab . a = a -b$	df. and hyp.
	$a -b = (ab) -b = 0$	
Therefore,	$a = 0$	Q.E.D.

Theorem 18a

$$(a, b) : a < b . -a < b . \supset . b = 1$$

The proof is analogous, using the equivalent of the definition of $<$.

Theorem 19

$$(a, b) :. (c) : c < a . c < b . \supset . c < 0 : \supset . a < -b$$

Proof:	$c < a . c < b . \supset . c < ab$	15b
	$(c) . c < ab . \supset . c = 0 : \supset : ab < ab . \supset . ab = 0$	
		application
but	$ab < ab$	13
	$ab = 0 . \supset . \text{-}(ab) = 1$	
	$-a + -b = 1$	10b
	$a < -a + -b$	
	$\equiv\text{df} . a = a (-a + -b)$	
	$\quad = a \times -a + a \times -b$	IVB
	$\quad = a \times -b$	
but	$a = a \times -b . \equiv\text{df} . a < -b$	Q.E.D.

Theorem 20

$$(a, b) : a < b . \equiv . a -b = 0$$

It must be remembered that the sign of equivalence, $\equiv$, denotes mutual implication between the two expressions it connects; so the proofs of 20 and 21 require two steps apiece, or—short and simple though they be—two lemmas each, for their demonstration.

Proof of 20:

Lemma 1	$a < b . \supset . a -b = 0$	
Dem.	$a < b . \equiv . ab = a$	def. and 12
then	$a -b = (ab) -b$	
	$\quad = 0$	
Lemma 2	$a -b = 0 . \supset . a < b$	
Dem.	$a = ab + a -b$	
then	$a -b = 0 . \supset . a = ab + 0 = ab$	
	$a = ab . \equiv . ab = a . \equiv . a + b = b$	12
	$a + b = b . \equiv . a < b$	def.
hence	$a < b . \equiv . a -b = 0$	Q.E.D.

Theorem 21

$$(a, b) : a < b . \equiv . -a + b = 1$$

Proof:

Lemma 1 $a < b . \supset . -a + b = 1$

Dem. $a < b . \equiv . a + b = b$ def.

then $-a + b = -a + (a + b)$
$$= (-a + a) + b$$
$$= 1 + b$$
$$= 1$$

Lemma 2 $-a + b = 1 . \supset . a < b$

Dem. $-a + b = 1 . \supset . a < -a + b$ 17a
$$. \supset . a = a (-a + b)$$ IIB
$$= a -a + ab$$ IVB
$$= 0 + ab$$ V
$$= ab$$ IIA
$$a = ab . \equiv . a + b = b$$ 12
$$. \equiv . a < b$$ def.

Therefore, $a < b . \equiv . -a + b = 1$ Q.E.D.

Many of these theorems are so simple that their proof is almost a matter of stating definitions. But they have a significance, none the less, for the general understanding of Boolean algebra, as the next section will show.

7. COMPARISON WITH POSTULATES FOR $K(a, b \ldots) <_2$

If now one turns back to chapter viii, § 4, one is struck immediately by the close resemblance of the postulates there given, in the context $K(a, b \ldots) <_2$, to some of the theorems just proved in the present system. The first postulate with $<$ is theorem 13 above. Theorem 14a expresses the first half of the condition laid down for s in postulate 7, 15a adds the second part, so that all of $(K, <)$-postulate 7 that remains unproved in our system is the *existence* of the element s—and that, of course, was taken care of in our postulate IA. Likewise, theorems 14b and 15b correspond to the conditions assumed in $(K, <)$-postulate 6, and the existence of p is given in our postulate IB. Theorem 16 in the present system corresponds to postulate 2 of the other; theorem 17a to postulate 3, 17b to postulate 4 (the *existence* of *1* and *0* being previously established for us), 18a and b express the two conditions for -*a* in postulate 5, where again the force of the particular quantifier is lost because -*a* is already accepted, and finally 19 derives, from the premises with + and ×, the $(K, <)$-postulate 8 (20 and 21 need not concern us here; their significance will be shown in chapter xi). *Everything that is assumed in the context $K(a, b \ldots) <_2$ may be proved in the context $K(a, b \ldots)$* +, ×, =.

It may be remembered, moreover, that in the first formulation of the class system, i.e. the $(K, <)$-system, +, ×, and = were *defined concepts*. In that system, *every postulate of the present system would follow as a theorem from the postulates* 1–8. Anyone who doubts this statement may be referred to Professor Huntington's paper* from which the two postulate-sets here adduced have been taken (howbeit with some modifications), where the proofs are indicated and can easily be completed.

The moral of this long tale is, that *it is possible to make more than one selection among all the propositions of Boolean algebra, such that the chosen set of propositions shall imply all the rest.* The two different sets of "primitive" propositions are two *implicit descriptions* of the whole system; they are two different descriptions of one and the same thing. Just as a man who has the blue prints of a house and a scale of proportions can construe for himself its measurements, and the man who has only the measurements can select a scale and make a blueprint from them, so a person with either postulate-set can deduce the other. We can translate from one system to the other. The only dictionary we need for this translation is *a definition of the symbols we have not*

* HUNTINGTON, *op. cit.*

assumed, in terms of those which we have. But however we start—with $<$, with $+$, with $\times$, or with $+$ and $\times$—we can select a set of postulates from which all the "laws" of the algebra can be deduced; in any of these terms we can define all the others; and consequently, from any set of propositions that implicitly holds all the "laws" given above, we can deduce any other set of propositions that does the same thing.

8. FUNDAMENTAL TRAITS OF BOOLEAN ALGEBRA

At this point it might be well to sum up the characteristic laws of the class-calculus, which must be accounted for in any system that claims to be Boolean algebra. No matter what set of propositions we take as "primitive," they must suffice to describe these typical relations among classes of individuals taken in extension:

1. The existence of a complement for every term.

2. The existence of a sum for any two terms.

3. The existence of a product for any two terms.

These are the *operational assumptions* of the algebra.

4. The existence of a universe class.

5. The existence of a null class.

6. The existence of more than one term (not essential, but usually assumed).

These are the purely *existential assumptions* of the algebra.

7. The laws of tautology:

$$a + a = a \qquad a \times a = a$$

8. The laws of commutation:

$$a + b = b + a \qquad a \times b = b \times a$$

9. The laws of association:

$$(a + b) + c = a + (b + c) \quad (a \times b) \times c = a \times (b \times c)$$

10. The laws of distribution:

$$a + (b \times c) = (a + b) \times (a + c)$$
$$a \times (b + c) = (a \times b) + (a \times c)$$

(Note that the first of these differs from ordinary algebra, whereas the second does not.)

11. The laws of absorption:

$$a + ab = a \qquad a \times (a + b) = a$$

These are the *laws of combination*.

12. The laws of the universe class:

$$a \times 1 = a \qquad a + 1 = 1$$

13. The laws of the null class:

$$a + 0 = a \qquad a \times 0 = 0$$

These are the *laws of the unique elements*.

14. The laws of complementation:

$$a + \text{-}a = 1 \qquad a \times \text{-}a = 0$$

15. The law of contraposition:

$$a = \text{-}b \, . \, \supset . \, b = \text{-}a$$

16. The law of double negation:

$$a = \text{-}(\text{-}a)$$

17. The laws of expansion:

$$ab + a\,\text{-}b = a$$
$$(a + b) \times (a + \text{-}b) = a$$

18. The laws of duality:

$$\text{-}(a + b) = \text{-}a \times \text{-}b$$
$$\text{-}(a \times b) = \text{-}a + \text{-}b$$

These are the *laws of negation*.

This algebra, which in its fundamental traits is extremely simple (owing chiefly to the laws of tautology and of double-negation), lends itself to considerable further development, to algebraic devices for eliminating "unknowns," to a peculiar theory of "logical functions," a treatment resembling integration; but all these technicalities rest entirely on the laws of the system which have just been enumerated. In the calculus of classes we have an ideal instance of systematization of far-reaching deductions from relatively few and simple assumptions. Boolean algebra combines the lucid consecutiveness of geometry with the obviousness of ordinary logic, and gives the rigour of mathematics to materials of common sense. Its significance for symbolic logic, however, lies not so much in its systematization of classes, as in its exhibition of *relatedness per se*, in its character as a structure rather than in the material of which it has been constructed. The facts to bear in mind, the traits that have made it a nucleus for logical theory are, that this system is describable in several ways; that what is "assumed," "unproved," "axiomatic," and what is "definable" or "describable," is a purely relative matter, so that no operation, relation or proposition is more "essential" than any other in any absolute way; and finally, that it tells us nothing whatever about classes except their *formal relations to each other*. We may have divergent ideas as to what particular classes of things we are talking about, what individuals are their members, or even just what a "class" is, in a full, philosophical sense. All the algebra describes is, *what sort of relations hold among classes*. This purely formal character of the calculus is the real source of its importance for logic; but that is the burden of the following chapter.

SUMMARY

A calculus is any system wherein we may calculate from some given properties of our elements to others not explicitly stated. Such a calculus may deal with specific elements, as arithmetic, the calculus of numbers, deals always with specific numbers. As soon as a calculus is expressed in symbols meaning *general* terms and their relations *in general*, it is an *algebra*. Therefore the calculus of classes, which is given through general (quantified) propositions, is a genuine algebra.

There are different ways of expressing the algebra; the propositions here selected as "primitive" are ten postulates in the formal context $K(a, b \ldots) +, \times, =$. These postulates fall into three groups: (1) those asserting the existence of certain elements, (2) those permitting the derivation of further elements from existing ones, and (3) those expressing the rules of combination of elements. Any set of postulates adequate to the description of the class-calculus must contain these three kinds of proposition. The first kind is quantified $(\exists -)$, or $(\exists -) (x)$, the second $(x) (\exists -)$, or $(x, y) (\exists -)$, the third has only universal quantifiers.

The principles of proof employed in deducing theorems are (1) substitution—replacing an element by another which is known to equal it, or a proposition by another which is known to be its equivalent. (2) Application—the assertion that a condition which holds for *any* element or elements holds for a *certain case*. (3) Inference—the independent assertion of a new proposition which is *implied* by previously asserted ones. This is "deduction" in its narrowest sense.

The rules of symbolic usage expounded in former chapters, the postulates, and these three principles of proof should be sufficient to develop a deductive system of class-relations.

The theorems express the laws of the calculus which are not already stated as postulates. These laws are already summarized in § 8. By means of them, one and the same element may be *transformed* so as to exhibit new aspects, i.e. it may be expressed now by a single letter, now as a sum, a product, a sum of products, etc., etc. The more forms it may take the easier it is to establish its relations to all the rest of the system. For instance, if it is to be related to a certain sum we may express it as a sum itself, and then calculate from a general relation among sums. Sometimes it is advantageous to write a, sometimes $a \times 1$, $a + 0$, $a(b + -b)$, $a + b -b$, $a + ab$, $a(a + b)$, aa, $a + a$, or $-(-a)$. To know which one of all these equivalent forms is most suited to our demonstration requires a certain imagination and a good deal of practice.

The duality of $+$ and $\times$ is a peculiarity of Boolean algebra. The so-called laws of duality,

$$(a, b) . -(a + b) = -a -b$$
$$(a, b) . -(ab) = -a + -b$$

allow us to express any product as a sum, any sum as a product; for if $-(a + b) = -a \; -b$, then $a + b = -(-a -b)$. Consequently $a + b$ and $-(-a -b)$ mean the same thing; and if the notions of conjunction and negation are given, the operation $+$ may be *defined* in terms of them. Likewise, if we start with disjunction and negation, we may define conjunction. Hence a set of postulates could have been expressed with only one binary operator. The set we have chosen is not the most economical, but has the great advantage of being easy to handle, exhibiting the important features of duality, and giving the equal and correlative operations $+$ and $\times$ equal emphasis.

In the context $K(a, b \ldots) +, \times, =$, the notion of *inclusion*, $<$, may be defined as a special case of conjunction or a special case of disjunction—the two cases being, of course, always equivalent. Thus,

$$(a, b) : a < b . \equiv df . a + b = b$$
or $$(a, b) : a < b . \equiv df . a \times b = a$$

Since it may be shown that $a + b = b$ and $a \times b = a$ are equivalent (mutually implied), either definition may be used at any time. With the defined relation $<$ we may state a long list of inclusion-theorems which follow easily from the rest of the $(K +, \times, =)$-system; and *these theorems correspond to the postulates given in chapter* viii *in terms of*

$K(a, b \ldots) <_2$. The propositions which are "primitive" in one formulation are "derived," i.e. figure as theorems, in another. And this is only an example of a far more general fact, that any set of propositions adequate to convey implicitly all the "laws" of Boolean algebra, i.e. any selection of such propositions which may be taken as "primitive," is *deducible* from any other such set, so that there is no one selection of "primitive" propositions which must *always* be assumed, which is "prior" to the rest of the system in any absolute sense, either philosophically or psychologically. *What is a postulate and what a theorem is always a relative matter.* But any selection which shall constitute a set of "primitive propositions" must contain by implication the eighteen laws listed in § 8.

All that the calculus can tell us about classes is, what relations in extension they bear to each other. It does not convey the metaphysical nature, the reality or ideality, of classes, nor tell us how to construct a class out of concrete objects, but merely shows the *pattern* of class-relationships which we may call disjunction and conjunction, or total and partial inclusions, or overlapping, or anything that *fits the formal conditions*. In this formalism lies its value for the greater science of logic.

QUESTIONS FOR REVIEW

1. What is meant by an "algebra"?
2. What are the three general types of proposition that are required in a postulate-set? What indicates the type to which a given proposition belongs?
3. What are the principles of logical proof?
4. What is the use of having several equivalent expressions for the same term or the same proposition?
5. What is the importance of the "duality" in Boolean algebra?
6. Which "laws" of the algebra are stated in the postulates used in this chapter?
7. What do you think is the source of greatest difference between numerical algebra and Boolean?

8. Which law of duality holds for both algebras, and which for Boolean alone?

9. Is $<$ a relation or an operation?

10. Which do you think is the most fundamental notion: $<$, $+$, or $\times$?

SUGGESTIONS FOR CLASS WORK

1. Express the analogous proposition for the other operator:

   (A) $a + 0 = a$
   (B) $a + 1 = 1$
   (C) $a \times -a = 0$

2. Write in as many forms as you can: $a < b$.

3. Give as many equivalents as possible for 1.

4. By shading the required portions in the following diagrams, illustrate the equations asserted beneath:

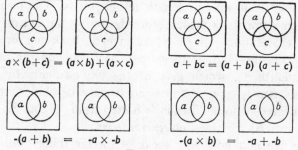

$$a \times (b+c) = (a \times b) + (a \times c) \qquad a + bc = (a + b)(a + c)$$

$$-(a + b) = -a \times -b \qquad -(a \times b) = -a + -b$$

FIG. 16.

5. Express in terms of $+$ and then in terms of $\times$:

$$(a, b, c, d) : a < b \,.\, c < d \,.\, \supset \,.\, ac < bd$$

   Illustrate by a diagram.

6. Find an example for the following forms:

$$a + b \,\text{-}c$$
$$-a + b$$
$$abc + d$$

7. Illustrate by an example the following equation:

$$-(a + b) = -a \times -b$$

8. Using the indications in the text, prove theorems 1b, 2a, 3b, 4a, and 5a.

CHAPTER X

ABSTRACTION AND INTERPRETATION

1. DIFFERENT DEGREES OF FORMALIZATION

Logic—so this book announces in its very beginning—is the study of forms; and forms are derived from common experience, reality, life, or whatever we choose to call it, by *abstraction*. The science of logic is a steady progression from the concrete to the abstract, from contents with certain forms to those forms without their contents, from instances to kinds, from examples to concepts.

The first step in the process is the replacement of concrete individual elements by *formalized* elements of variable meaning, dealt with at length in chapter iv. The meaning of such elements is presently fixed, not by the old method of interpretation—which would give us back our original specific terms—but in an entirely new way, by the use of the quantifiers, which give us the old elements by new terms, namely *general terms*. So it may be said that the first degree of formalization is a step from *specific elements* to quantified variables, or *general terms*.

We can now no longer speak of specific things, but only of any or some things of a certain kind. That is to say, meanings are no longer given by direct interpretation of A, B, C, etc., but only by interpretation of K and the constituent relation. The interpretation of K determines the *kind* of thing we are talking about in the general terms a, b, c, etc. The separate elements are formalized, and interpretation given only to the system. If none of the K elements are named specifically, then we have a *general system*.

But a general term, a general statement, or a whole system treated in general, is not necessarily *abstract*. For instance, "Someone must have lost something" is a perfectly general proposition, but there is nothing abstract about it. "There is one house that is North of any other house" is also general, but entirely concrete. The elements in these statements are formalized, i.e. they are not individually interpreted, or *specified*. But the total collection of elements, K, and the constituent relation are interpreted; consequently the elements, though mentionable only in general, have *content*, or concrete meaning. "A certain house" is not an abstraction. It is just as concrete as "Mt. Vernon," "Sunnyside," or "The Elms." The first degree of formalization, i.e. formalization of the individual elements in a system, leads to *generalization*.

A familiar example is the context $K(a, b \ldots)$ nt_2, where $K =$int "houses" and "nt" $=$int "to the North of." Without being acquainted with the houses themselves, or even knowing just how many there are, we may make such general statements as:

$$(a) . \sim (a \text{ nt } a)$$
$$(a, b) : a \text{ nt } b . \supset . \sim (b \text{ nt } a)$$
$$(a, b, c) : a \text{ nt } b . b \text{ nt } c . \supset . a \text{ nt } c$$

Yet nothing we have stated is *abstract*; a house, no matter how little we say about it or how generally we say it, is still something perfectly concrete.

Suppose, however, that we now omit the interpretation of K. What becomes of (say) the statement

$$(a) . \sim (a \text{ nt } a)?$$

Does it still refer to the universe of certain houses, or even of all houses in the world?—No. Does it make any sense at all? Well, certainly it may be read: "For any element of any sort, it is always false that this element is to North of itself." And this, undoubtedly, is true. *So long as the constituent relation has an interpretation, the expression has meaning*; (a) and $(\exists a)$ may be read "anything" and "something," and the quantified formula with an interpreted relation (or predicate, or operation) is a proposition.

This proposition, of course, belongs to a wider universe of discourse than the *K* interpreted to mean "houses." The scope of an uninterpreted *K* is what might be called the "realm of significance" for the relation which is involved. Obviously, "Nothing is to North of itself" applies only to physical things on the earth's surface; we cannot even ask, except in very modern poetry, whether 3 is to the North of wisdom, or perfection to North of purple, or whether science is to North of itself. Such terms do not belong to the universe of discourse which is "understood" in the use of the relation "nt," i.e. to the *greatest possible universe for this relation.**

A system which covers the greatest possible universe for its relation, i.e. which has an uninterpreted *K*, is certainly more *general* than one whose reference is restricted to houses. But even so, it has no dealing with abstractions. "Houses and hills" is no more abstract than "houses"; "houses, hills, boxes, bridges, and horses" is still a collection of perfectly concrete objects. The universe is widened, immensely widened, when we pass from an arbitrarily interpreted *K* to the greatest possible universe for "nt," from "any house" to "anything" and from "there is at least one house, such that ——" to "There is something, such that ——"; but the character of the system is not changed. So it may be said that *by formalizing the individual elements of K, we obtain general statements about specified concrete things. By formalizing* (i.e. leaving uninterpreted) *K, we obtain general statements about unspecified concrete things.*

The two different degrees of formalization have given us corresponding degrees of generalization.

Now, suppose we introduce a new system, a *K*, uninterpreted, of elements *a, b*, etc., and a constituent

---

* The fact that every relation is significant only within a certain greatest possible universe was noted by De Morgan, and is the origin of his "universe of discourse." Whether a "universe" may be arbitrarily chosen or is always delimited by the relation was a bone of contention among logicians for many years.

relation #, which means "higher in pitch." The elements of K are, of course, automatically limited to things which might be said to be "higher in pitch" or "not higher in pitch" than others, i.e. to *sounds* of one sort or another. In this context, certain common-sense assertions are possible without any arbitrary assumptions, and we may begin with:

$$K(a, b, \ldots) \#_2$$

$\# =$int "higher in pitch"

$(a) . \sim (a \# a)$

$(a, b) : a \# b . \supset . \sim (b \# a)$

$(a, b, c) : a \# b . b \# c . \supset . a \# c$

These three propositions look astoundingly like the three of our previous system:

$(a) . \sim (a \text{ nt } a)$

$(a, b) : a \text{ nt } b . \supset . \sim (b \text{ nt } a)$

$(a, b, c) : a \text{ nt } b . b \text{ nt } a . \supset . a \text{ nt } c$

In fact, the only visible difference is in the symbol that represents the constituent relation. If we took the second group of propositions and substituted # for every occurrence of "nt," the result would be three true assertions, namely the very three that constitute the first group. The two relations operate among different sorts of elements, but *operate in exactly the same way*; they hold and fail under exactly similar formal conditions.

There is nothing sacred about a symbol; "nt" does not mean, intrinsically, eternally, and by some deep law, "to the North of"; it means this only by interpretation. Neither does "#" necessarily mean "higher in pitch than"; this meaning has to be arbitrarily given to it. Suppose, now, that I adopt a new notation, and write the following three expressions:

$(a) . \sim (a R a)$

$(a, b) : a R b . \supset . \sim (b R a)$

$(a, b, c) : a R b . b R c . \supset . a R c$

The symbol R (for "relation") may be taken to mean either "nt" or "‡." Whichever relation is substituted for R, the three expressions become true propositions. Moreover, *any expression with an ambiguous R, which becomes a true proposition when ‡ is substituted, will become true for "nt" as well, and vice versa*. A system of true propositions with ‡ has *the same form* as one with "nt."

This is true of a number of other relations as well. For instance, if R in the above expressions be interpreted as "older than," "ancestor of," or "under," exactly the same constructs will hold that hold for "nt" or for "‡." So it appears that to leave the constituent relation uninterpreted is not to reduce the whole system to chaos and nonsense, but to *make the entire context ambiguous*. The expressions have no fixed meaning, but are capable of various meanings; R may represent any relation that fits the arrangement of elements in which it appears, i.e. any relation for which propositions of the prescribed forms would be true.

These prescribed forms, however, automatically set limits to the variety of relations which R may mean. For instance, R could not mean "next to," because $(a, b) : a\,R\,b\,.\,\supset\,\sim (b\,R\,a)$ would then be false, and $(a, b, c) : a\,R\,b\,.\,b\,R\,c\,.\,\supset\,.\,a\,R\,c$ would hold only if $a = c$, or if $a, b,$ and c always formed a triangle. "Next to" is not the type of relation that universally fits the given arrangement of elements; "before," "greater than," and many other common relations are of the required type, and all such relations are *values for the variable R*.

It appears, then, that R is a real variable, and consequently the expressions in which it figures are *propositional forms*. When R is interpreted, they become concrete general propositions, for the interpretation of R determines what sort of element a, b, c, etc., may be. But suppose that, instead of giving R some arbitrary meaning, we say simply that there are certain relations—or, according to the best logical usage, there is at least one relation, R—having the postulated properties. This turns our propositional forms into one completely generalized proposition about the relation R:

$$(\exists R) :: (a) . \sim (a\,R\,a) :. (b, c) : b\,R\,c . \supset . \sim (c\,R\,b) :. \\ (d, e, f) : d\,R\,e . e\,R\,f . \supset . d\,R\,f$$

"There is at least one R, such that for any term a, $a\,R\,a$ is false; and for any two terms, b and c, $b\,R\,c$ implies that $c\,R\,b$ is false; and for any three terms, d, e, f, if $d\,R\,e$ and $e\,R\,f$, then $d\,R\,f$ is true."

Now, since R is named only as a certain relation, or maybe various and sundry relations, there is no interpretation of any constituent in the proposition that could give us a clue to the nature of a, b, etc. These are given merely as "elements," not things of any specified sort, physical, mental, sensory, conceptual, or what-not. They are left entirely empty of meaning, apart from their logical function of being "terms" to the relation. The resultant elementary propositions, which enter into the description of R, are not general concrete propositions, for there is no concrete K; they are purely and genuinely formal, that is to say, *abstract*.

By formalizing the elements of a system we obtain general concrete propositions; *by formalizing the constituent relations (or predicates, or operations), we obtain abstract propositions.* An abstract statement is a *completely generalized propositional form.* No constituent in it is interpreted; everything is quantified, and all that the proposition is about is the functioning of the relation or relations among the elements. That is to say, all it conveys is the rule of combination for its constituents. Such a proposition presents an empty form, and asserts merely that there is a relation which yields this form. So, when we generalize the constituent relation(s) as well as the elements of any system, we properly *abstract the form from the content*; and this is the essential business of logic.

2. PROPERTIES OF RELATIONS

The completely general, or abstract, proposition given above was said to assert that there is at least one relation, R, *having certain properties*; and the form of the proposition to be expressive of those properties. Relations which have all their logical properties in common are of the same type, and are possible values for the same variable R.

The logical properties of a relation are simply the conditions of its functioning, i.e. the arrangements of elements that may or may not be made by means of it. These may, of course, be very simple, or they may be elaborate; and they may be familiar by dint of many known instances, or quite rare and novel. The more complicated ones, as well as those which are rarely exemplified, are more readily exhibited by symbolic structures than named or described by words; but the commonest and most important modes of functioning, or properties of relations, have been given convenient names, and are worth noting.

The most fundamental characteristic of a relation is its *degree*. This is the property of always forming dyads, triads, tetrads, etc., which has been sufficiently discussed, in previous chapters, to serve our purposes. All other properties of relations presuppose that of degree; and, for reasons which cannot be shown here, all those traits which have received distinctive names belong to relations of dyadic degree.

Let us assume, then, that we are dealing with an unspecified (i.e. uninterpreted) relation, R_2, so that any elementary proposition we might assert must be of the form $a\,R\,b$. Some relations can yield true propositions of this form when the two terms, a and b, are identical, that is, for the special case of $a\,R\,a$. In fact, for some relations— for instance, $=$ -or $<$ -propositions of the form $a\,R\,a$ are always true; for it is true the $(a)\,.\,a = a$, and $(a)\,.\,a < a$. Such relations are called *reflexive*. Those for which $a\,R\,a$ is always false are *irreflexive*; thus "brother of," "higher in pitch," "North of," are all irreflexive, since

$$(a) \, . \sim (a \text{ br } a)$$
$$(a) \, . \sim (a \text{ \# } a)$$
$$(a) \, . \sim (a \text{ nt } a)$$

If, however, a relation *possibly but not necessarily* combines a term with itself, it is called *non-reflexive*. Such relations are: "likes," "hurts," "defends," etc., for we may have either

$$(\exists a) \, . \ a \text{ likes } a$$
or
$$(\exists a) \, . \sim (a \text{ likes } a)$$

and likewise a creature may hurt itself, though not every creature necessarily does so; and it may or may not defend itself. A non-reflexive relation *allows* of the case $a \, R \, a$ but does not *require* it.

Another important property is known as *symmetry*. A relation which combines its terms regardless of their order, i.e. for which $a \, R \, b$ always implies $b \, R \, a$, is said to be symmetrical. The relation $=$ is symmetrical; for if $a = b$, then $b = a$ in any case. "Married to," "resembles," "parallel with" are symmetrical. If, on the other hand, $a \, R \, b$ *precludes* $b \, R \, a$, then R is called *asymmetrical*; examples are: "greater than," "descendant of," and the familiar \# and nt of previous sections. For it is true that

$$(a, b) \, . \ a \text{ nt } b \, . \supset . \sim (b \text{ nt } a)$$
and
$$(a, b) \, . \ a \text{ \# } b \, . \supset . \sim (b \text{ \# } a)$$

The only remaining alternative, that of a relation which *may, but need not* combine two terms in both orders, is called *non-symmetrical*. Examples are: "likes," "fears," "implies."

Finally, there is a somewhat complicated, but very common characteristic which deserves a name, and has been called *transitivity*. As the word implies, transitivity is the property of being *transferable* from one pair of terms to another; a transitive relation is one which, if it holds between two terms *a* and *b*, and between *b* and a third term *c*, holds also between *a* and *c*. Symbolically, it fufils the condition:

$$(a, b, c) : a R b . b R c . \supset . a R c$$

A transitive relation is such that if it relates two terms to a mean, it relates the extremes to each other. The significance of this trait lies in the fact that it allows us to pass, by the agency of a mean term, to more and more terms each of which is thus related to *every one* of the foregoing elements. This creates a chain of related terms; in ordering a whole universe of elements, such a relation, which transfers itself from couple to couple when new terms are added one at a time, is of inestimable value. This is the type of relation by virtue of which we reason from two premises, united by a mean or "middle term," to a conclusion:

All Chinamen are men
All men are mortals

Therefore, all Chinamen are mortals

The conclusion is justified by the fact that the verb "to be," which here has the force of $<$ (since "Chinamen," "men," and "mortals" are taken as classes), is transitive:

$$(a, b, c) : a < b . b < c . \supset . a < c$$

A relation which never holds between *a* and *c* when *a R b* and *b R c* are granted is *intransitive*; thus, "son of" is intransitive, for if *a* is the son of *b* and *b* is the son of *c*, *a* cannot be the son of *c*. Where the relation of *a* to *c* is possible but not implied, *R* is *non-transitive*.

There are, of course, many other properties of relations; for instance, the property of holding between one term and just two others, if holding between that one and any other. "Child of" exhibits such a condition, where $(a, b) \cdot a$ ch b implies there is at least one and at most one c, unequal to a or b, such that a ch c. But this property is not important enough to rank a name of its own. It is more readily described by a formal proposition, such as:

$$(\exists R) \, (a, b) :: a \, R \, b \cdot \supset \cdot (\exists c) :. \, c \neq a \cdot c \neq b \cdot a \, R \, c \cdot (d) :$$
$$a \, R \, d \cdot \supset \cdot d = b \lor d = c$$

To honour every peculiar condition, every possible type of relation, with an English adjective would be too cumbersome, but it should always be remembered that the named characteristics are by no means the only ones which a relation may possess.

3. POSTULATES AS FORMAL DEFINITIONS OF RELATIONS

If we assume a universe, K, of unspecified elements, and an unspecified R—for convenience, let us say R_2—and then, without interpretation, set up a number of abstract propositions to be taken as "primitive," these primitive propositions, or postulates, will be absolutely all we know about either K or R. What they tell us, is how R operates among the elements of K, i.e. under what conditions it combines any or some such elements with some or any others. Now, what K may represent depends upon the meaning of R*; and the possible meanings of R are restricted to such relations as behave like R; and the behaviour of R is laid down in the postulates. These postulates, then, constitute a *formal definition of R*. They tell us what are the properties of a certain *type* of relation; the symbol R, uninterpreted, stands for this type rather than for any nameable relation,

---

* The converse is also true, i.e. any interpretation of K sets limits to the possible meanings of R. But the progressive generalization from K to R is so much easier, psychologically, than *vice versa* that I have chosen this approach. Only when *both* K and R are generalized we have an *abstract form*.

but may be interpreted to mean any concrete relation of the given type. So long as we abide by purely logical, i.e. purely general, concepts such as "element," "relation," "proposition," and the so-called "logical relations" among propositions, we shall find ourselves dealing always with *types* of constituent relations, and hence with types, or forms, of systems, rather than with systems themselves; with patterns rather than with concrete things. The description of such a pattern, the set of abstract postulates, is a *formula for systems of a certain sort*.

All we know about the constituent relation is what the postulates say. These formulae or abstract primitive propositions, then, must describe its *properties*; whether the properties of a relation happen to have names, or not, they are all expressible in symbolic form, and for our purposes this is by far the most powerful, convenient, and accurate means of expression.

There are certain relations whose properties all together constitute patterns which lend themselves to particularly many and important interpretations. Take, for instance, the nature of R in the following formalized system, or abstract description:

$$K(a, b \ldots) R_2$$

1. $(a, b) \, . \sim (a \, R \, a)$
2. $(a, b, c) : a \, R \, b \, . \, b \, R \, c \, . \supset . \, a \, R \, c$

These formulae express two of the three conditions which could be asserted by common sense for the systems dealt with above. The third, namely

$$(a, b) \, . \, a \, R \, b \, . \supset . \sim (b \, R \, a)$$

may be deduced from them. Since these propositions about an uninterpreted $K \, R$ are supposedly postulates, it is no longer fitting to assume conditions which may be deduced, and the statement that R is *asymmetrical* must here be treated as a theorem, proved as follows:

Assume $\qquad$ $(\exists a, b) . a R b . b R a$

then $\qquad$ $a R b . b R a . \supset . a R a$ $\qquad$ 2

but $\qquad$ $\sim (a R a)$ $\qquad$ 1

$\qquad\qquad$ $\sim (a R a) . \supset . \sim (a R b . b R a)$

therefore, $\qquad$ $a R b . \supset . \sim (b R a)$ $\qquad$ Q.E.D.

A third postulate is to be added, however:

$$3. \; (a, b) : a \ne b . \supset . a R b \lor b R a$$

This asserts that the relation R, which never combines two terms in *both* orders, always combines them in at least one order. Such a relation, holding among any two terms of the universe in one order or the other, is said to be *connected*.*

Relations having the properties here stipulated, i.e. irreflexiveness, transitivity, connexity, and (by implication) asymmetry, are so important to mathematics, science, and even common reasoning, that they bear a name: they are called *serial relations*. There are a great many serial relations; that is to say, there are many possible interpretations for the $K R$ above. Whenever R is interpreted, K assumes a definite character. Let R, for instance, mean "to left of"; then K must represent elements ranged in a straight line from right to left—places, things, points, or what-not, but they must be *spatial elements* and they must lie in a straight line. Or, let R mean "greater than"; K will then represent *magnitudes*, or things ranged in order of magnitude.

Any system ordered by a serial relation, that is, any interpretation of the abstract system $K R$ above, is a *series*. The system of natural numbers, the succession of days, of months, of years, the points on a line, the progeny of a person in one unbroken line of descent, all constitute *series*. Every one of these systems is ordered by a relation having the properties of the abstract $K R$ cited above. R may

---

* I find it difficult to regard connexity as a property of relations, since a relation may be connected in one universe and not in another. Despite the fact that the postulate of connexity has only universal quantifiers, it seems to me to express a property of K, not R. But here I follow common usage in ascribing the property to R.

mean "greater than," and K mean "numbers"; then $K R$ is a *number-series*. Or $R =$ int "follows" and $K =$ int "days"; then $K R$ is a *span of time*. Or $R =$ int "to left of" and $K =$ int "points"; then $K R$ is a *straight line*; or R may mean "descendant of," and K, "persons"; then $K R$ is a *lineage*, or line of progeny. Note that in the systems K nt and $K \sharp$, the former is not a series, because two places or things may lie in the same latitude; but $K \sharp$ is a series, since two tones (apart from their tone-quality, merely as *notes*) of the same pitch are identical.

There are many kinds of series—finite and infinite, series with a beginning but no end (e.g. "future time"), or with an end but no beginning (e.g. "the past"). In some there is always a next neighbour to each term (as, the next natural number), in others there is no definite "next" (as in the continuous flow of a river). All these different types of series are determined by special postulates, such as:

$$(\exists a) \ (b) : \ \sim (a \ R \ b) \ . \ \supset \ . \ a = b$$

which asserts that any b which is different from a certain a must follow a, i.e. a is the *first term* of the series. But whatever further conditions we may impose, every series requires a *serial relation*, and this requirement is fulfilled by any R that is irreflexive, transitive, and connected.

Of course there are many other types of relation, and consequently many other abstract patterns, that might be named; I have adduced the serial type, and the form called a "series" in the most general sense, because of the great importance and relative simplicity of this sort of structure. The import of this whole discussion is, that *a whole system may be taken as an abstract form*, a relational pattern rather than a complex of concrete things, an empty design described by postulates and their consequences (theorems) which are entirely abstract, i.e. uninterpreted general propositions.

4. BOOLEAN ALGEBRA: THE CALCULUS OF CLASSES AS A FORMULA

Every actual relation may be viewed as just one instance of a certain type. If it is highly complicated, then perhaps there is no other nameable relation of exactly the same form; if it is simple, like "nt," then we are likely to find various other concepts, such as "greater than" or "after," to follow the same lines. But whether common or rare, obvious or abstruse, every relation allows us to abstract its pure form, i.e. to restrict our interest to that formal definition which is symbolically expressed by the postulates, and ignore the particular interpretation; to write R instead of "nt," or "is the nearest male relative of," or "is equidistant from," or what-not.

What has here been said of relations holds equally, of course, for operations, since the latter are really abbreviated expressions for such relations as define a new element from old. Operations are modes of combination; and "to be combined to form an element" is a relationship among elements. Just as simpler relations have their general properties, so do operations; and two different operations having the same properties are both instances of one and the same form, which may be called a "formalized" operation, written "op" ("O" would cause confusion with zero). Thus, instead of

$$(a, b) \cdot a + b = b + a$$

we might have the completely general uninterpreted proposition,

$$(\exists op)\ (a, b) : a\ op\ b = b\ op\ a$$

This being the case, it should be possible to view even so elaborate a system as the class-calculus in the light of an exemplification for some general pattern. And this may, indeed, be done. We may start with

$$K(a, b \ldots)R_2$$

instead of

$$K(a, b \ldots) <_2$$

and let the postulates describe the conditions under which R is to hold or not to hold among the elements of K, exactly as the behaviour of $<$ was described; or we may adopt symbols for "a certain operation" which will function like $+$ and "a certain other operation" which acts like $\times$, and these new symbols will represent, not class-disjunction and class-conjunction respectively, but *any* operation having the same formal properties as $+$, and *any* operation having the formal properties of $\times$. Suppose we adopt the notations $\oplus$ and $\otimes$ to represent these two generalized operations.*

The elements combined by $\oplus$ and $\otimes$ (or related by an R which acts like $<$ and may therefore be designated by $\leqslant$), are not necessarily classes; they are entirely unspecified. They are merely terms, without interpretation, without any character, except such formal traits as the postulates bestow on them. Instead of a calculus of classes, we have now an empty relational form with certain rules of manipulation by which one element may be substituted for another or one formula derived from another.

The system presented in the foregoing chapter was there described as an "algebra," sometimes called the "Boole-Schroeder Algebra of Classes." The form is, essentially, due to Boole, though it was perfected by Schroeder; therefore it is fitting as well as convenient to call *all systems that have the same form as the class calculus* "Boolean systems,"† and the abstracted pattern itself, "abstract Boolean algebra." It is the latter that is expressed

---

* These symbols were used by Huntington, who adopted them from Leibniz. Cf. HUNTINGTON, op. cit., p. 292.

† Some writers speak in the plural of "Boolean algebras," since (1) each concrete system expressed in *general terms* is an "algebra" (cf. chap. ix, § 1), and (2) even among abstract systems, different numbers of K-elements, if specifically given, really generate different algebras (as the "two-valued algebra," § 6, below). See SHEFFER, H. M., "Five Postulates for Boolean Algebras," *Trans. Amer. Math. Soc.*, vol. 14 (1913).

in our new symbolism, by the following abstract propositions:

$$K(a, b \ldots) \oplus, \otimes, =*$$

Iᴀ $(a, b) (\exists c) . a \oplus b = c$

Iʙ $(a, b) (\exists c) . a \otimes b = c$

IIᴀ $(\exists 0) (a) . a \oplus 0 = a$

IIʙ $(\exists 1) (a) . a \otimes 1 = a$

IIIᴀ $(a, b) . a \oplus b = b \oplus a$

IIIʙ $(a, b) . a \otimes b = b \otimes a$

IVᴀ $(a, b, c) . a \oplus (b \otimes c) = (a \oplus b) \otimes (a \oplus c)$

IVʙ $(a, b, c) . a \otimes (b \oplus c) = (a \otimes b) \oplus (a \otimes c)$

V $(a) (\exists -a) : a \oplus -a = 1 . a \otimes -a = a$

VI $(\exists a, b) . a \neq b$

Obviously, the theorems deducible in this system will be exactly analogous to those of the class-calculus, being actually the form, abstractly considered, of those propositions themselves. The system $K \oplus, \otimes, =$ is Boolean algebra *in abstracto*, the formula of which the class-calculus is an interpretation.

5. Other Interpretations of the Boolean Formula

Once we regard the algebra as an empty form, a shell of a system, it may be possible to find meanings other than "class," "disjunction of classes," and "conjunction of classes" for the symbols a, b, etc., $\oplus$, and $\otimes$. Of course, any new meanings the symbolism is made to convey must be such that the *entire form* will bear interpretation; the defined symbol $\ominus$ must automatically assume a meaning, 0 and 1 must be identifiable, there must be sense in the dichotomy between a and $-a$. It may be that another system having all the formal traits of the class-calculus

---

* Note that = has not been modified because its meaning is "constant," i.e. is the same whether it refers to the extension of classes or to anything else; it is not dependent on interpretation. That is why most writers take = for granted and do not list it among constituent or "variable" relations.

will not be interesting in itself, so that no one would have noticed its existence were it not for the exemplification of a notable form; but the triviality of an interpretation need not trouble us. It is satisfaction enough to find any alternative meaning for abstract propositions of such complexity as a Boolean algebra.

We might regard the elements of the algebra as *areas in a plane space*. Their shape does not matter. Let *a*, *b*, etc., be *any* areas in one plane. Let $\oplus$ between two terms mean their sum, so that $a \oplus b$ is the area composed of *a* and *b* added together; let $\otimes$ mean "overlapping," so that $a \otimes b$ is the superimposed portion of *a* and *b*. Regard *1* as the greatest area, i.e. the whole extent of the plane, and *0* as "nowhere." With this new formal context, every proposition of the abstract algebra becomes, by interpretation, a true, general, concrete proposition. Since our signs are no longer purely formal, they should no longer be $\oplus$ and $\otimes$; by rights we should employ new symbols for spatial addition and overlapping, but for typographical reasons I shall employ $+$ and $\times$, with the explicit understanding that these have *new, though equally concrete meanings* as in the class-calculus.

The ten propositions of the algebra now take the following meaning:

Iᴀ. "For any two areas, *a* and *b*, there is an area *c* which is their joint extent, $a + b$."

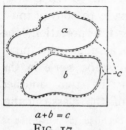

$a+b = c$

Fɪɢ. 17.

In the diagram (Fig. 17), the whole plane is represented as a square; any two areas illustrate Iᴀ. Note that in the example given, *a* and *b* do not overlap. But the postulate provides that they are to be regarded, none the less, as one area, *c*.

Iʙ. "For any two areas, *a* and *b*, there is a third area, *d*, which is the overlapping part of *a* and *b*, $a \times b$."

I have called this area *d* because in using the same

diagram, the a and b of IA become identified with the a and b of IB, so that $a + b$ and $a \times b$ must go by different letters. The product of a and b is, in this illustration, "nowhere," but is none the less existent in the system. The next postulate explains its status:

IIA. "There is at least one area, 0, 'nowhere,' such that, for any a, the joint extent of a and 'nowhere' is the extent of a."

"Nowhere" cannot be drawn; like the "empty-class," it is a purely intellectual construction, but of such pragmatic value that common sense as well as logic assumes it.

IIB. "There is at least one area 1, 'everywhere,' such that for any a, the overlapping part of a and 'everywhere' is the extent of a."

"Everywhere" is, of course, the entire square.

IIIA. "For any two areas, a and b, the extent of a and b together is the extent of b and a together."

IIIB. "For any two areas a and b, the overlapping part of a and b is the overlapping part of b and a."

IVA. "For any three areas, a, b, and c, the joint extent of a and $b \times c$ is the overlapping part of $a + b$ and $a + c$.

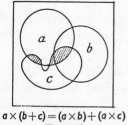

$$a \times (b+c) = (a \times b) + (a \times c)$$
Fig. 18.

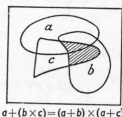

$$a + (b \times c) = (a+b) \times (a+c)$$
Fig. 19.

For convenience, the areas in Figs. 18 and 19 have been drawn so that no sum or product mentioned in IVA and IVB shall be 0.

IVB. "For any a, b, and c, the overlapping of a with $b + c$ is the total extent of $a \times b$ and $a \times c$."

The disconnected portion $a \times c$ in Fig. 19 is a reminder that $b + c$ may enter into a at different points, i.e. that even a product need not be a *continuous* area.

V. "For any a, there is an area $-a$, everywhere-but-a, such that the joint extent of a and everywhere-but-a is the whole space, 1, and the overlap of a and $-a$ is nowhere, 0."

VI. "The plane is divided into at least two distinguishable areas, a and b."

What becomes of the defined relation $\ominus$? A very natural concept, that of *spatial inclusion*, $<$. For, $a < b$ means

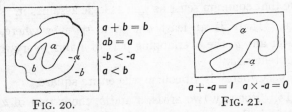

$$a + b = b$$
$$ab = a$$
$$-b < -a$$
$$a < b$$

FIG. 20.

$$a + \text{-}a = 1 \quad a \times \text{-}a = 0$$

FIG. 21.

by definition $a + b = b$, or $ab = a$; in the accompanying diagram, these two conditions are fulfilled, and the area a must obviously lie within b; furthermore, $-b < -a$, and all other abstract propositions of the algebra involving become true concrete propositions when $<$ is read as space-inclusion, or "lying within."

All formal conditions, then, are satisfied by the new interpretation; the relational system of areas within a plane is a Boolean algebra.

We could, of course, have drawn all our areas as circles, since their shapes are irrelevant. Had this been done, the result would have been the very diagrams, known as "Euler's circles," which were used to illustrate the relations of classes in the class-calculus. This peculiar fact points to a highly important connection between any two systems of the same logical form; *they may always be each other's diagrams.* To a person who cannot see a plane space before his mind's eye—a blind person, perhaps—the collection of objects filling a space, i.e. *a class of objects*, might serve as an illustration of a given area in a plane. To most people of normal visual imagination, the area is easier to conceive than the extension of a class, so the second interpretation of Boolean algebra is the more "visible," "conceivable," or as the Germans aptly express it, the more *"anschaulich."* Therefore it is used as a diagram for the first. The relation of a map or diagram to the object (or state of affairs) it illustrates is always that the former is *easier to visualize,* literally *to imagine,* than the latter, and that *it has the same logical form.* No matter how different its content, its appearance, may be—no matter in what "projection" a map is drawn, or how elaborate is the "key" to a graph or a diagram—*the physical symbol exemplifies the same logical form that is exemplified by its object.* The relation between them is *analogy.* That is why not only Euler's circles, but any interpretation of abstract Boolean algebra into visible, tangible, or otherwise easy and familiar terms could serve as a symbolic picture of class-relationships.

The interpretation for areas in a plane has one disadvantage, namely that "nowhere" is taken as an element included in all other elements. A far more plausible spatial interpretation has been given by Chapman and Henle,* who restrict their spatial areas to a circle, its possible sectors, and its centre. But just to vary interpretations as much as may be, I prefer to view it as a pie and its possible cuts: *1* is the whole pie; *0* is the centre; *a, b, c,* etc., if they are distinct from *1* or *0,* are cuts of the pie. The cuts, of course, are hypothetical, that is to say they are merely planned, not made, so they may be re-planned as often as we like. One possible cutting may overlap another, as in the diagram (Fig. 22) overlaps *a;*

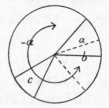

FIG. 22.

the disputed part is $a \times b$. Also, someone may by favouritism receive two cuts, say $a + c$. What is left of the pie

* *Fundamentals of Logic,* New York, 1933, p. 215.

after one cutting, say *a*, is *-a*. Every element includes the centre, *0*, and is included in the whole, *1*; every cut plus the rest of the pie, i.e. every $a + -a$, makes up *1*; any two completely disjoined cuts have only *0* in common, and are completely contained in each other's negatives; thus, $ac = 0 . \supset . a < -c . c < -a$. No matter how complicated we make our equations, they still fit this household example, and we are faced with the astonishing fact that the mathematics of pie-cutting is a Boolean algebra.

6. THE TWO-VALUED ALGEBRA

In all the interpretations here given, we have assumed that there are several elements distinct both from *0* and from *1*. But as a matter of fact, the postulates provide for a minimum of only two distinct elements (post. VI), and if there were just two, these would have to be *0* and *1*, since the further conditions of the system would otherwise not be satisfied. Suppose that we assume that there are really only two elements in *K*. Then "any *a*" could have reference to nothing but *1* or *0*; "any *a* and any (same or other) *b*" would refer to *1* and *0*, *1* and *1*, *0* and *1*, or *0* and *0*; and so forth. Postulate IIA would mean:

$$(\exists 0) . 1 + 0 = 1 . 0 + 0 = 0$$

and IIB, $\quad (\exists 1) . 1 \times 0 = 0 . 1 \times 1 = 1$

Likewise, $\quad (a) (\exists -a) . a + -a = 1 . a \times -a = 0$

becomes, by application (see chap. ix, § 3):

$$(\exists -1) . 1 + -1 = 1 . 1 \times -1 = 0$$
$$(\exists -0) . 0 + -0 = 1 . 0 \times -0 = 0$$

Since *0* fulfils the conditions of *-1* and *1* the conditions of *-0*, this form is valid in the system.

If there are only two elements in *K*, then "any *a*" or "some *a*" has *only two possible values*. Note that "value" here refers to *terms in the system, which may be substituted for a*, by the principle of application; not to *possible inter-*

pretations of a (or any other K-elements). A general term has "value" in two senses: (1) being general, it may be *exemplified by*, or *applied to*, an arbitrary term in the system, as (a, b). "$a + b = b + a$" is exemplified by the *special case* where $b = a$, so that from it we may derive $a + a = a + a$; or by the unique terms 1 and 0, i.e. $1 + 0 = 0 + 1$; which represents another exemplification. These special instances are "values" for the formula $(a, b) . a + b = b + a$. (2) if the system is abstract, then the terms have *interpretational values, so $(a, b) . a + b = b + a$* may mean: "For any two classes, a and b . . .," or "For any two regions, a and b . . . , etc." Now, the former kind —let me call them "exemplary values"—are determined by the formal character of the system. If K is infinite, then (a) has an infinite number of values; if K has a finite but unrestricted number of elements, (a) has a finite but unrestricted number of values; if K has a definite number of elements, say 6, then $(a) : a = a_1 . \text{V} . a = a_2 . \text{V} . a = a_3 . \text{V} . a = a_4 . \text{V} . a = a_5 . \text{V} . a = a_6$. This is a formal condition *which holds whatever the interpretational values of "a" may be.* Interpretation is always something that is given to the symbolic structure after that structure is complete, and can therefore never be rendered as part of the structure itself. But the exemplary values of a general term may be indicated symbolically, as in the disjunctive proposition above.

Now, if we are to have only two K-elements, 0 and 1, this fact is easily expressed by the formula:

$$(a) : a = 1 . \text{V} . a = 0$$

Such a statement, is, of course, a new and special condition to be added to the given conditions of the algebra, since the existing postulates provide for a *minimum* of two elements, but this proposition asserts that two is the *maximum* number. So, if we accept it, we must regard it as a further postulate; let us call it postulate VII.

The structure which results from the addition of postulate VII, being a Boolean algebra wherein every general term has just two exemplary values, is known as the *two-valued algebra*. Its propositions are, of course, extremely boresome and redundant; since every term is 0 or 1, such complicated terms as, for instance, $a + b + c - b + cd + - ab$, must all mean either 1 or 0, since $a = 1 . \lor . a = 0$, $b = 1 . \lor . b = 0$, etc. Such a system seems, in itself, just silly and trivial. But strangely enough, it lends itself to a highly interesting *interpretation*, of which the algebra without postulate VII is incapable. The two-valued character of this form expresses what is known as "the principle of all-or-none," or "the law of excluded middle," which students of Aristotelean logic have met among the famous "laws of thought"; and to these laws, by virtue of postulate VII, we may now apply the familiar mould of Boolean algebra.

SUMMARY

Logic, the science of forms, proceeds by steps from totally concrete notions to such as are totally formal. These successive steps give rise to as many *degrees of formalization*. The first step is the formalization of the separate elements of a concrete (i.e. interpreted) universe of discourse. This produces general propositions about a concrete and arbitrarily limited K. It is a partial generalization of a system, $K R$. The next step is to leave K uninterpreted, regarding it merely as the range of significance of the relation R; its meaning is then completely determined by R, and its quantified elements stand for "anything" and "something" that is said to enter into the relation R. This step, the formalization of K, represents the *greatest generalization* of the system $K R$.

The third step is the formalization of R. As soon as R is no longer interpreted to mean some specific relation, the system becomes an empty form, a pattern, a system *in abstracto*, and all its quantified propositions become abstract propositions. Instead of: $(a, b) \,.\, a < b \,.\, b < a \,.\, \equiv \,.\, a = -b$, we should now write:

$$(\exists R)\,(a, b) : a\,R\,b \,.\, b\,R\,a \,.\, \equiv \,.\, a = b$$

If the quantification $(\exists R)$ is omitted, but R is not interpreted, the proposition becomes a propositional form. An abstract system is usually presented in this way, as a system of propositional forms wherein the only unquantified constituent is the uninterpreted relation.

Relations have certain properties by which they may be described. All relations having exactly the same properties are of the same kind, and are interpretational values for the same R. Some of these properties are so important and common that they bear names, notably: *reflexiveness*, and its correlatives *irreflexiveness* and *non-reflexiveness*; *symmetry*, and the derived notions of *asymmetry* and *non-symmetry*; *transitivity*, and its derivatives *intransitivity* and *non-transitivity*. The third case is always present when neither of the others is definitely established.

The logical properties of a relation, i.e. its ways of functioning among its terms, determine what type of relation it is; and some types are so important that they have received names. Thus a relation which is irreflexive, connected, and transitive is said to be *serial*.

Any two systems ordered by relations of exactly the same type follow the same pattern, and are interpretational values for the same abstract system. Some such patterns have been named, because of their importance; any system made by a serial relation is a *series*, and varieties in the functioning of serial relations have given us various types of series.

Postulates are formal definitions of relations, for they describe how the relations function among the terms of a universe. In an abstract system, this is absolutely all that the postulates tell us. The result is an empty form, or pattern of relationships.

Such a pattern may be very complicated. If we replace
the relations or operations (abbreviated complex relations)
of the Boolean class-calculus by uninterpreted, unfamiliar
symbols, the resulting structure is an abstract system
expressing the form of the calculus, but not referring to
classes or their relations.

An empty formula is capable of various interpretations.
Any relation having the stipulated properties may be
denoted by its relation-variables (or operation-variables);
in this case, by the formalized concepts $\oplus$, $\otimes$, and the
defined $\ominus$. The meaning of K follows automatically from
that of the relational constituents. Thus, $\oplus$ may mean
"addition," $\otimes$ "overlapping," $\ominus$ "being completely surrounded by" or "contained in"; then a, b, etc., stand for
areas in a plane, 1 for the total area, 0 for "nowhere"; or
a, b stand for things occupying areas, and (by special
limitation) 1 is the sum of these things and 0 some point
of convergence of all the elements; as in the case of the
properly cut, indefinitely divisible pie, its total area, and its
centre.

Usually a system having the form of a Boolean algebra is
supposed to have an indefinite number of elements; but all
that the postulates really call for is a minimum of two
elements. If we limit the system arbitrarily to two elements
then they must be 1 and 0, since these are provided for.
Then every general term in the system has only two possible
exemplary values, 0 and 1.

In the existing postulates there is no proposition by
means of which such a limitation to just two elements
could be deduced. If we want this limitation, it must be
added as a new postulate:

VII $(a) \cdot a = 1 \cdot \vee \cdot a = 0$

A Boolean algebra incorporating this postulate is called a
two-valued algebra.

On the face of it, the great redundancy and simplicity

of a two-valued Boolean algebra makes it appear silly; but, though it cannot be interpreted for so trivial a matter as cuts of pie, it has a most important possible content, namely the laws of deductive reasoning, the structure of logic itself. To this end it is worth considering in detail.

QUESTIONS FOR REVIEW

1. What are the successive degrees of formalization of a system?
2. What is the difference between generalization and abstraction?
3. What is meant by the "realm of significance" of a relation?
4. What is meant by the properties of a relation? What properties can you name? How can one express properties that have no English names?
5. If a system is given *in abstracto*, with uninterpreted signs of relations or operations, how do we know what those signs may mean?
6. What determines a type, or sort, of relation?
7. What are the characteristics of a serial relation?
8. Why do we speak of "Boolean algebras" in the plural case? What have several such algebras in common? What distinguishes them from each other? What is abstract Boolean algebra?
9. Why can Euler's circles serve to symbolize the class-calculus?
10. What is the two-valued algebra? How does it differ from other Boolean algebras?
11. Do you think classes and their relations would be a good interpretation of the two-valued algebra?

SUGGESTIONS FOR CLASS-WORK

1. Express symbolically that R_2 is symmetrical, reflexive, and transitive. Find an interpretation for this R.
2. Express symbolically that a certain relation, $\rightarrow_2$, is serial; that the series it produces has a first term; that it has a last term.
3. Find an interpretation for $\rightarrow_2$.
4. Name a reflexive, an irreflexive, and a non-reflexive relation; a symmetrical, an asymmetrical, and a non-symmetrical one; a transitive, an intransitive, and a non-transitive relation; a connected relation.
5. Express symbolically the characteristic postulate of the two-valued algebra.

CHAPTER XI

THE CALCULUS OF PROPOSITIONS

1. PROPERTIES OF LOGICAL RELATIONS AND OPERATIONS

So far, we have considered the formal properties of constituent relations and operations, such as nt, #, <, +, ×, etc., and taken the existence and the behaviour of *logical* relations, ∨, . , and ⊃, for granted. Such relations hold, not among individuals, like nt, nor among classes, like +, × and <, but always among *propositions*; that is to say, *the terms of these relations are propositions*, and consequently *any propositions to which these relations and their terms give rise, are propositions about propositions.*

Of course, logical relations have formal properties, as all relations do. Consider, for instance, how the relation of *implication functions*. This relation, symbolized by ⊃, holds between two propositions whenever, *if* the first is true, *then* the second is true also. For instance, *if* Napoleon was born in February, *then* his birthday is in Winter, or:

"Napoleon was born in February" . ⊃ . "Napoleon's birthday is in Winter."

Now, if a proposition is true, then of course it is true; *if* Napoleon was born in Winter, *then* it is true that he was born in Winter; every proposition, therefore, implies itself, so that ⊃ is *reflexive*. Also, an implication, like the above, may be irreversible; "Napoleon's birthday is in Winter" does *not* imply "Napoleon was born in February"; or it may be reversible, as in

$$(a, b) . a + b = b . ⊃ . a < b$$
and $$(a, b) . a < b . ⊃ . a + b = b$$

Therefore ⊃ is neither symmetrical nor asymmetrical, but *non-symmetrical*. Moreover, if $a + b = b . ⊃ . a < b$, and $a < b . ⊃ . ab = a$, then we are ready to grant that

$a + b = b . \supset . ab = a$; so $\supset$ is found to be transitive. All these are familiar properties of relations. The only remaining difference between $\supset$ and various other reflexive, non-symmetrical, transitive relations is that $\supset$ is not a constituent in elementary propositions, but a link *between* such propositions. It is hard to see its form because of the complexity of its terms. But suppose we call a given proposition P, and another, which is implied by P, Q; then we may write:

$$P . \supset . Q$$

and either $$Q . \supset . P$$

or $$\sim (Q . \supset . P)$$

which shows symbolically that $\supset$ is non-symmetrical.

Also, $$P . \supset . P$$

and $$Q . \supset . Q$$

and if R is any third proposition

$$R . \supset . R$$

for $\supset$ is reflexive. Finally, if

$$P . \supset . Q \text{ and } Q . \supset . R, \text{ then } P . \supset . R$$

which is the principle of transitivity.

Often enough, when there are three propositions, P, Q, and R, it takes two of them together to imply the third; as for instance, if A, B, and C are three classes, it is true that

$$A < B . B < C . \supset . A < C$$

Here, if P =int "A < B," Q =int "B < C," and R =int "A < C," we have

$$P . Q . \supset . R$$

But $\supset$ is a dyadic relation, and can have only two terms; P . Q, therefore, must be a single term, just as $a + b$ or $a \times b$ is a single term in the proposition: $a \times b < a + b$.

The dot between P and Q *combines these two propositions into one proposition*, which implies R. Such a relationship, by which a new *compound term* is established, is an operation. So the "and" between two propositions, which combines them into one compound proposition, P . Q, is a *logical operation*.

Sometimes a proposition implies that either one or the other of a certain *pair* of propositions must be true: for instance, if P =int "A B = 1," Q =int "A = 1," and R =int "B = 1," then it is true that

$$P . \supset : Q . V . R$$
for $\qquad A B = 1 . \supset : A = I . V . B = 1$

Here the implied proposition is *that either* A = 1 *or* B = 1; this is, again, a compound proposition, i.e. a compound term for the logical relation $\supset$, made by means of the *logical operation* V.

The properties of operations within a system are laid down in those postulates which express equations (or inequations) among compound expressions, for any terms of the system; the properties of $\oplus$ and $\otimes$ in Boolean algebras are described by such postulates as:

$$(a, b) . a \oplus b = b \oplus a$$

which asserts that $\oplus$ is commutative, and is called the *commutative law*; or by the *associative law*,

$$(a, b, c) . a \oplus (b \oplus c) = (a \oplus b) \oplus c$$

or the *distributive law*,

$$(a, b, c) . a \oplus (b \otimes c) = (a \oplus b) \otimes (a \oplus c)$$

and others. If we were to express symbolically the obvious fact that "P and Q" is the same thing as "Q and P," i.e.:

$$P . Q = Q . P$$

and then assert this equation for *any* two propositions, we should be laying down the commutative law for the logical operation " " This operation is, in fact, commutative, associative, distributive, and absorptive; and so is the other logical operation "V". A few examples, which the reader can surely find for himself, will demonstrate these attributes convincingly.

2. PROPOSITIONAL INTERPRETATION OF BOOLEAN ALGEBRA

It is· a striking fact that the properties just enumerated for . and V, "logical conjunction" and "logical disjunction," are exactly those which the Boolean algebra of classes postulates for × and +, "class-conjunction" and "class-disjunction." If × and . , + and V have the same logical properties, then they must be *alternative meanings* for ⊗ and ⊕ respectively; that is, it must be just as legitimate to say:

$$\otimes = \text{int "logical conjunction"}$$
$$\oplus = \text{int "logical disjunction"}$$

as it would be to say:

$$\otimes = \text{int "class-conjunction"}$$
$$\oplus = \text{int "class-disjunction"}$$

But what, in the former case, becomes of *K*? *The elements of K must be propositions, if ⊗ and ⊕ become logical operations.* Let us assume that they are simple propositions, such as "A nt B," "Napoleon was born in February," etc. But since we do not care *what* propositions they are, let us generalize P, Q, and R, and write this newly interpreted system,

$$K(p, q, r \ldots) . , V$$

with the following postulates:

$$\text{IA} \quad (p, q)\, (\exists r)\,.\, p \vee q = r$$
$$\text{IB} \quad (p, q)\, (\exists r)\,.\, p \,.\, q = r$$
$$\text{IIA*} \quad (\exists 0)\, (p)\,.\, p \vee 0 = p$$
$$\text{IIB\dagger} \quad (\exists 1)\, (p)\,.\, p \,.\, 1 = p$$
$$\text{IIIA} \quad (p, q)\,.\, p \vee q = q \vee p$$
$$\text{IIIB} \quad (p, q)\,.\, p \,.\, q = q \,.\, p$$
$$\text{IVA} \quad (p, q, r)\,.\, p \vee (q \,.\, r) = (p \vee q) \,.\, (p \vee r)$$
$$\text{IVB} \quad (p, q, r)\,.\, p \,.\, (q \vee r) = (p \,.\, q) \vee (p \,.\, r)$$
$$\text{V\ddagger} \quad (p)\, (\exists \text{-}p) :.\, p \vee \text{-}p = 1 : p \,.\, \text{-}p = 0$$
$$\text{VI} \quad (\exists p, q)\,.\, p \neq q$$
$$\text{VII\S} \quad (p)\,.\, p = 1 \,.\, \vee .\, p = 0$$

Note that this *Boolean system of propositions* is a *two-valued algebra*, including the limiting postulate VII. The reason for this will be immediately apparent when 0 and 1 are given their interpretation for the propositional calculus.

Let $1 =$ int "truth," and $0 =$ int "falsity"; so that "$p = 1$" is to be read "p is true," and "$p = 0$," "p is false." Then the seventh postulate becomes, "for any proposition p, either p is true, or p is false." This is certainly true for any proposition. But how about the other postulates wherein 1 and 0 figure? Take IIA,

$$(\exists 0)\, (p)\,.\, p \vee 0 = p$$

Here the 0 means "some proposition which is false" (i.e. known to equal 0), for example: "England is larger than Asia." The other element, p, is "any proposition," true or false. Suppose it is true; then $p = 1$. Let it be: "The ocean is salty." $p \vee 0$, then, becomes: "Either the ocean is salty, or England is larger than Asia"; one *or* the other is to be taken as a fact. And since the ocean really is salty, "$p \vee 0$" is true, that is, $p \vee 0 = 1$. But $p = 1$; therefore $p \vee 0 = p$.

---

* The "unique elements" are interpreted below.   † *Idem*
‡ The unary operation is interpreted below.
§ Same as 1 and 2 above.

Now assume that $p = 0$; for instance, let $p =$ int "Berlin is in France." The $p \lor 0$ becomes: "Either Berlin is in France, or England is larger than Asia." But since neither is the case, we cannot say one or the other is a fact; the whole disjunction is false, i.e. $p \lor 0 = 0$. Since $p = 0$, $p \lor 0 = p$. What the postulate asserts is that the truth or falsity of a disjunction, where one member is known to be false, depends entirely on the other member. And this holds for any disjunction of two propositions.

IIB, $(\exists)1 \; (p) \cdot p \cdot 1 = p$, is analogous. A logical conjunction is a *joint assertion* of two propositions. If one is known to be true, so that it may be denoted by 1, then the truth or falsity of the conjunction depends entirely on the other. Let the true member, 1, $=$ int "The ocean is salty." Now take p so that $p = 0$, e.g. "England is larger than Asia." Then $p \cdot 1$, "The ocean is salty *and* England is larger than Asia," is false; so $p \cdot 1 = 0$ if $p = 0$, and consequently $p \cdot 1 = p$. But take p to be true, as: "Asia is larger than England." The conjunction $p \cdot 1$ will be "The sea is salty, and Asia is larger than England," which is true; so if $p = 1$, then $p \cdot 1 = 1$, or $p \cdot 1 = p$.

The only remaining postulate into which the unique elements enter is V; and this involves also the unary operation -, which has not yet been interpreted. If p is a proposition, then it is not satisfactory to let $-p$ mean "everything else that is assertible," for this is a vague term. But one proposition that is entirely determined by p, and conforms to all the requirements in V, is *the denial of p*. For instance, if p means "The ocean is salty," than $-p$ means "The ocean is not salty." But this is the same as "It is false that the ocean is salty," $\sim$ "The ocean is salty." The proper interpretation of "-" is "$\sim$"; so, if we write $\lor$ for $+$ and $\cdot$ for $\times$, we must write $\sim p$ for $-a$. Obviously, either p or $\sim p$ must be true, if p makes any sense, i.e. if p is a real proposition; so we have, by common sense, $p \lor \sim p = 1$. And equally clearly, not both can be true; $p \cdot \sim p = 0$.

Here are all the primitive ideas of abstract Boolean algebra interpreted so as to yield a *calculus of true or false propositions and their relationships*. It is by virtue of their truth or falsity that *all* propositions may be related to each other; and, since there are only two alternatives—either truth or falsity, either *0* or *1*—for any proposition, the "propositional interpretation" is feasible only if we grant the limiting postulate for a "two-valued algebra," postulate VII, which restricts us to the narrowest conditions for a Boolean system.

Before we may safely assume that this abstract system may be interpreted, *in toto*, as a calculus of propositions and their relations, one more requirement must be fulfilled; there must be a significant interpretation for the relation $\ominus$, whether this be defined (as when we begin with $K \oplus$, $\otimes$, $=$) or whether it be assumed (as when we start with K, $\ominus$). The interpretation must give sense to all formal expressions in which $\ominus$ may figure in the abstract algebra; for instance, $(a, b) : a \oplus b = b . \equiv . a \ominus b$ or $(a, b) : a \otimes b = a . \equiv . a \ominus b$. What logical relation answers to these demands?

Suppose we let $\ominus$ mean, by interpretation, "$\supset$". To say that a proposition p implies another, q, is to say that if p is true, then q is true; or, in the form of a disjunction, either p is *not* true, or q must be true, i.e. either p is false or q is true. Notice that "p is false" may be expressed either by $p = 0$ or by $\sim p = 1$, since $p = 1$ and $\sim p = 1$ would imply $p . \sim p = 1$, which is impossible by V; so $p = 1$ is equivalent to $\sim p = 0$, and $p = 0$ to $\sim p = 1$. To say $p \supset q$, then, means that if p is true, q is true; that is, if q is false, p is false; or, *either* p is false *or* q is true. Let us take the last condition as its equivalent, since it can be expressed in terms of V:

$$\sim p \vee q . = . 1$$

"Either not -p or q" is true.

Now, consider the equivalence laid down by definition in the algebra:

$$a + b = b . \equiv \mathrm{df} . a < b$$

and translate it into the language of the propositional calculus:

$$p \vee q = q . \equiv \mathrm{df} . p \supset q$$

If $p \supset q$ *means* "p is false or q is true," i.e. $\sim p \vee q = 1$, then $\sim p \vee q = 1$ must be equivalent to the formal definition of $\supset$ in the algebra, $p \vee q = q$; otherwise the "meaning" of $\supset$, that is, the concept we denote by it, is not an acceptable value for $\bigcirc$, which is defined by the latter propositional form. Fortunately, however, we know that

$$(p, q) : p \vee q = q . \equiv . \sim p \vee q = 1$$

for this is an exact translation of the proposition

$$(a, b) . a + b = b . \equiv . \text{-}a + b = 1$$
or $\quad (a, b) . a < b . \equiv . \text{-}a + b = 1$

proved as theorem 21 of the class-algebra in chapter ix.

All further properties of $\supset$ which are set forth in theorems, such as:

$$(p, q) : p \supset q . \supset . \sim q \supset \sim p$$
$$(p, q, r) : . p \supset q . q \supset r : \supset : p \supset r$$

are all obviously fitting; any examples from ordinary discourse will show them to be entirely respectable.

The interpretation of the calculus for propositions and logical relations is, then, completely possible; it remains, now, to consider the effects of this circumstance upon logic itself, i.e. upon our knowledge of relations, systems, deductions, and the whole structure of reason.

3. The Propositional Calculus as an Algebra of Truth-Values

In an earlier chapter, it was said that every proposition must possess one of two *truth-values*: truth, or falsity.

These two concepts are here denoted by 1 and 0, respectively; and, by postulate VII, every proposition is to be *equated* either to 1 or to 0. If p and q are two true propositions, then $p = 1$ and $q = 1$; from which it follows that, in our calculus, $p = q$. If every element is equal either to 1 or to 0, then there can be only two elements, and all the letters $p, q, \sim p, \sim q$, etc., are just so many different *names* for 1 and 0.*

Now, if p means, say, "Russia is big," and q means "Mark Twain wrote *Tom Sawyer*," then $p = 1$ and $q = 1$. But it certainly sounds strange to say that $p = q$. These two propositions seem as different as they can be; *the only point in which they agree is their truth-value*. This, however, is just the point at issue. If they have the same truth-value, then their negatives have the same truth-value, i.e. if p is true and q is true, then $\sim p$ is false and $\sim q$ is false; then, if r be any third proposition, $pr = r$ (i.e., $pr = 1$ if $r = 1$ and $pr = 0$ if $r = 0$) and $qr = r$, and $\sim p \vee r = r$ and $\sim q \vee r = r$; in short, in any expression involving p, we could substitute q without changing the result. If we know that p and q are both true, then it does not matter which one we use to represent "truth"; their conceptual content— that is, what they assert, what they are about—plays no rôle whatever in this system. Two elements in a system which may always take each other's places, such as the elements "$2 + 2$" and "2×2" in arithmetic, are said to be equal, though conceptually they are not identical ("$2 + 2$" is a sum and "2×2" a product, quite different concepts); and in the propositional calculus, *all true propositions are equal*, and *all false propositions are equal*.

The fact is that this calculus does not deal with the meanings, and relations among meanings, of propositions;

---

* This notion, that all true propositions were *names* for "the truth" and all false propositions *names* for "the false," was introduced, and maintained for many years, by GOTTLOB FREGE, a German mathematician who was one of the founders of symbolic logic, and especially of "logistics" (see next chapter).

it is a *calculus of truth-values* and their relations, *a system of truths and falsehoods.* *

Now, if the elements of the system are *truth-values*, of which there are just two, and these are represented by *1* and *0*, how is it that we have also an indefinite number of symbols such as $p, q, \sim p, \sim q$, which are supposed to represent diverse *propositions*?

This usage rests upon the fact that *only propositions can be true or false*. A proposition always represents a truth-value, but we may not know which; therefore, if we write p, we know that this means either *1* or *0*, but are not committed to one or the other. Whatever, then, is true for both elements, *0* and *1*, may be asserted of p. For instance, each of the two elements has a negative; the disjunct of the two negatives is *1* and their conjunct is *0*; or,

$$(p) \: (\exists \sim p) \: . \: p \vee \sim p = 1 \: . \: p \sim p = 0$$
Also $\quad 0 \vee 1 = 1, 1 \vee 1 = 1; 0 \: . \: 0 = 0, 1 \: . \: 0 = 0;$
or $\quad\;\, (p) \: . \: p \vee 1 = 1$
$$(p) \: . \: p \: . \: 0 = 0$$

Propositions about p and $\sim p$, then, are propositions about truth-values in general, even though there are only two such values; and the quantification (p, q) may be read either: "for any two propositions, p and q," or: "for any truth-value p, and any *same or other* truth-value q." The latter reading keeps one reminded of the fact that *truths and falsehoods as such*, and not *what* is true or false, are the subject-matter of the calculus; but the former reading also has its virtues; for it emphasizes the fact that the *application* of a truth-value system is always to the realm of propositions, so that it incorporates a *criterion of proper reasoning*. Any conclusion of an argument, if it runs counter to a theorem of the calculus, is wrong. A true conclusion must be consistent with its premises by all the laws that govern the relations of truths to each other, i.e. the logical relations, which are subject-matter, or constituent relations, of the system.

* See Appendix C.

4. THE NOTION OF "MATERIAL IMPLICATION"

The fact that truth-values, not meanings, are the elements of the system is reflected in the definition, given above, of the implication-relation:

$$(p, q) : p \supset q \: . \: \equiv\mathrm{df} \: . \: \sim p \vee q = 1$$

"For any p and q, 'p implies q' means 'either not-p or q' is true"; i.e., "p implies q" means "either p is false or q is true." This is entirely a relation among truth-values, for we have no idea what propositions p and q may be. It is, indeed, a relation which always holds when one proposition, p, implies another, q. Let p, for instance, mean "The fourth of May is a Monday," and q "The fifth of May is a Tuesday." This is a case of "p implies q"; and q must certainly be true *unless p is false*. That is to say, either p is false, or q is true. If p is true, then q cannot be false.

Now, although this relation of truth-values, $\sim p \vee q = 1$, always holds if $p \supset q$, our ordinary view of implication demands a further relation between the two propositions, namely a relation of *meaning*. For instance, if p retains its assigned meaning, but q means "Napoleon was Emperor of France," then the relationship "p is false or q is true" may hold for p and q, but it would not ordinarily be thought that p implies q. The two propositions have no relation of *intension*, i.e. of meaning, so that we could *infer* the truth of q from the truth of p. Ordinary reasoning deals with meanings as well as truth-values. But the propositional calculus does not. The import, or intension, of its propositions is entirely irrelevant. The relation $\supset$, therefore, in the calculus *mirrors only the relation of truth-values which obtains whenever $p \supset q$*; and that is, $(p = 0) \vee (q = 1)$, or $\sim p \vee q = 1$.

This treatment of "implication" makes it a broader concept than the ordinary one, and has certain consequences that startle and estrange one until the new notation is entirely familiar. If $p \supset q$ means "p is false or q is true," then it holds whenever p and q are both true, since "q is true" is then fulfilled; whenever both are false, since "p is false" is then fulfilled; and whenever p is false and q is true. In fact, *the only case in which $p \supset q$ does not hold is, that p is true and q is false.* If q is true it holds, whether p be true or false; if p is false it holds whether q be true or not. So, if we really mean by $p \supset q$ no more and no less than $\sim p \lor q = 1$ "p is false or q is true," we are forced to admit two famous, or perhaps infamous, propositions, known as the "paradoxes" of symbolic logic:

$$(p, q) : p . \supset . q \supset p$$

"A true proposition is implied by any proposition"

$$(p, q) : \sim p . \supset . p \supset q$$

"A false proposition implies any proposition."

Obviously these peculiarities do not belong to the "ordinary" concept of implication. So, in order to distinguish the relation $\supset$ from the "intensional" relation whereby p entails q, $\supset$ as it figures in the calculus has been called *material implication*. As long as this distinction is recognized, there is really nothing paradoxical in the theorems,

$$(p, q) : p . \supset . q \supset p$$
and
$$(p, q) : \sim p . \supset . p \supset q$$

Only, they should be read: "A true proposition is *materially implied* by any proposition," and "A false proposition *materially implies* any proposition." Thus, "Coal is black" materially implies "Grass is green," because the latter is true; and "Coal is white" materially implies "Christmas is in July," because the former is false. But "Coal is black" does *not* materially imply "Grass is pink," for the former is true and the latter false, so we have not $\sim p \lor q$; we have $p \lor \sim q$—the only case for which $p \supset q$ does not hold.

(Note, however, that in this case $q \supset p$; for $p \vee \sim q = \sim q \vee p$ by IIIA, and $\sim q \vee p . \equiv df . q \supset p$).

Is there any sense in calling this relation "implication" at all? What has it to do with "real" implication? What is its use for purposes of argument, or *inference*?

The character it shares with "real" implication, by virtue of which it merits that noble name, and enters into deductive processes, is this: *that if p is known to be true and $p \supset q$, then we may accept q.* This is exactly the condition for real inference. The "paradoxical" cases arise (1) when p is known to be *false*, in which case its intensional implications are as useless for inference as the "material" ones, and (2) when q is already known to be true, so that inference is unnecessary, and $p \supset q$, even if true, is gratuitous. In both cases the implication is *irrelevant* for purposes of deduction. The only case where inference is in question, is that of a *true* proposition in the relation $\supset$ to some other proposition; and here, material implication guarantees that this other will be true. The ground upon which we admit that the relation $\supset$ holds between the two propositions, is usually an intensional connection between them; this generally regarded as the essence of "real" implication, has nothing to do with the system of truth-values. But *wherever "real" implication exists, we have $p \supset q$; and wherever $p \supset q$ holds and "real implication" does not, inference is irrelevant anyway.* The important proposition for inference is:

$$(p, q) : p . p \supset q . \supset . q$$

"If p is true, and p materially implies q, then q is true." And this is the sense of "real" implication.

5. The "Reflexiveness" of a Propositional Calculus

In all previous systems we have reasoned *about* constituent relations, *by means of* the logical relations. We cannot reason by any other means; for reasoning is nothing else than the employment of logical relations and operations to determine the truth-values of new propositions from old-established ones. As soon as we doubt the validity of, say, the relation $\supset$, we can no longer pass from premises to conclusions. We cannot even offer a reason for doubting this validity, for if implication is invalid, then the best reason in the world can no longer imply anything, so nothing can imply that $\supset$ is valid or that it is invalid. *The laws of logic must be taken for granted before any calculus can be used*; so the question naturally arises, whether a calculus that lays down these very laws does not commit us to reasoning in a circle, and to lifting ourselves up by our boot-straps.

The answer is, that a calculus of logical relations serves only to *exhibit*, but not to *sanction*, the formal properties of logical relations. As Professor Sheffer has put it, "Since we are assuming the validity of logic, our aim should be, not to validate logic, but only to make explicit, at least in part, that which we have assumed to *be* valid."* And when the formal properties of those logical relations are thus made explicit, they are seen to follow the general pattern of a Boolean algebra. For this reason, the algebra, interpreted for propositions, is frankly "reflexive"; it makes logically related statements, about statements in logical relations. It makes assertions about what may or may not be asserted, and exhibits deductively the conditions for valid deduction.

This means, of course, that we have some symbols denoting the relations which we assert to hold among propositions, and others of exactly the same sort expressing the structure of complex propositions that we happen to be talking about. Our *terms* are propositions, and so are the assertions we make about them. Thus, for any given term p, "$p = 1$" is a proposition about p; but p *itself is already a proposition*. Now, if p is true, then of course $p = 1$ is true, since $p = 1$

* Review of *Principia Mathematica*, vol. i (2nd ed.), in *Isis*, vol. viii (1926), pp. 226–31

means "p is true"; and if p is false, then $p = 1$ is false. In fact, p and "$p = 1$" *always have the same truth-value*, which means in this system that $(p) : p . = . (p = 1)$. Likewise, if $p = 0$, then $\sim p = 1$; and (by the principle of application) what is true for any p, is true for the special case $\sim p$, so $(p) : p . = . (p = 1)$ means the same as $(\sim p) : \sim p = (\sim p = 1)$, and $\sim p = 1$ is equivalent to $p = 0$; so we have the odd-looking equation

$$p = (p = 1)$$

This form is not valid for any system whose elements are not propositions; for $p = 1$ *is a proposition of the system*, so if $p = (p = 1)$, then p must be a proposition. Thus, if we accept the above equation as a further postulate (since it cannot be deductively derived from the two-valued algebra as an abstract system, but is merely *true* with its "propositional" interpretation), then we have, in what I shall call postulate VIII, a purely formal condition committing the abstract system to just one interpretation.

It is not hard to prove, with the help of VI, VII and VIII, that if $p = (p = 1)$, then $\sim p = (p = 0)$. If p means "p is true," then $\sim p$ means "p is false." Moreover, since every proposition is either true or false (VIII), $\sim (p = 1)$ is the same as $p = 0$, $\sim p = 1$, or simply $\sim p$. So we have, in this algebra, a tremendous variety of equivalent forms:

$$p = (p = 1) = (\sim p = 0) = \sim (\sim p = 1) = \sim (\sim p), \text{etc}$$
$$\sim p = (p = 0) = (\sim p = 1) = \sim (p = 1) = \sim (\sim p = 0), \text{etc}.$$

Now, by postulate I, if p and q are any two elements of the algebra, then $p \lor q$ is an element; so that $p \lor q = 0$ or $p \lor q = 1$. But if $p = (p = 1)$ and $q = (q = 1)$, then $p \lor q = (p = 1) \lor (q = 1)$: meaning "either p is true or q is true." This proposition, which might well be a postulate or a theorem of the algebra, here figures as an *element* in the system. Furthermore, if p is an element, $\sim p$ is an element, and therefore, for any q, $\sim p \lor q$ must be an element. But

$\sim p \lor q . = . (p = 0) \lor (q = 1)$, meaning "$p$ is false or q is true"; and that is the same thing as $p \supset q$. So it follows that $p \supset q$, "p implies q," is not only a statement *about* the elements p and q in the system, but *is itself an element of the system.*

Here the "reflexiveness" of the two-valued "propositional" algebra (i.e. Boolean algebra with postulates VII and VIII) is in its full glory. Every proposition of the system is at once an element in the system, about which further algebraic statements might be made, only to become terms, themselves, in further statements. The algebra of truths and falsehoods is like Chronos devouring his offspring. Everything we can say about truths and falsehoods is itself a truth or falsehood, to be used in producing new true or false propositions of the algebra.

6. The Significance of a Propositional Calculus

This very "reflexiveness," which certainly makes one suspect the validity of the Boolean calculus of propositions, has made it a touchstone of logical theory. Certainly logical relations can be talked about; but does a calculus of propositions and their relations really make sense? Can they be talked about *systematically*, or is any effort to systematize the principles of systematic procedure necessarily self-defeating? It has already been said, above, that to *deduce* laws of logic from anything *by* laws of logic is impossible and absurd. One may question further, whether a universal proposition about propositions is possible; since such a proposition must, of course, be about itself as well as about all other propositions. That is, if we say:

$$(p) . p = (p = 1)$$

this universal p applies to *any* proposition—"Nelson was an admiral" = ("Nelson was an admiral" = 1), and

$$[(p) . p = (p = 1)] = \{[(p) . p = (p = 1)] = 1\}$$

The proposition in this case should itself be an instance of the general truth it asserts. Since this gives every term in the system an infinity of equivalent forms, and every statement is really a term, it may well be asked whether any universal facts about propositions can be categorically stated at all.

These and other difficulties, which lie unsuspected until we begin to express the science of logic itself *in abstracto*, make the propositional calculus the most intriguing of all systems. Do the baffling limitations, which keep running us into absurdities, lie in the particular formulation which the system of propositions inherits from its original model, the calculus of classes? Would a different form of expression do better? Or is logic in itself something beyond symbolic expression, something that cannot be systematically presented?

Here we stand on the threshold of contemporary logical theory. Its centre is the problem of expressing *logical relations* in general. Its historical root is the Boolean calculus, the two-valued algebra of truth and falsehood. By careful analysis of the notions there involved, by gradual modifications in their notation, one paradox after another has been eliminated, and unsuspected powers of the simple calculus discovered.

As a great result of all this labour we have the masterpiece of symbolic logic, the *Principia Mathematica* of ALFRED N. WHITEHEAD and BERTRAND RUSSELL. It begins with a calculus of propositions in logical relations, exhibiting the orthodox Boolean characteristics; it ends with the laws of arithmetic, algebra, and geometry.* Where its logical theories and technical exposition begin, is practically the point for an introductory text-book to end; my closing chapters, therefore, will be concerned with the transition from Boolean algebra to the language and outlook of *Principia Mathematica*, and make no attempt to present the system itself which is there developed. My intention is only to usher the

* The volume dealing with geometry has not yet appeared.

reader into the ante-rooms of logistic, mathematical philosophy, and science.

SUMMARY

Logical relations hold always among propositions, so the propositions they produce contain propositions as terms. Like all relations and operations, V, . , and $\supset$ have formal properties. Logical conjunction and disjunction are commutative, absorptive, associative, and distributive with respect to each other, just like the class-operations $\times$ and $+$; implication is reflexive, non-symmetrical and transitive, like class-inclusion, $<$. Consequently the logical relations, like class-relations, are possible meanings, or values, for the abstract $\otimes$, $\oplus$, and $\otimes$ of Boolean algebra.

If $\otimes$, $\oplus$, and $\otimes$ become by interpretation . , V and $\supset$, then the K-elements must become propositions. So we have $K(p, q, r \ldots)$ V, . , and a set of postulates in these terms corresponding exactly to the two-valued algebra, i.e. Boolean algebra inclusive of postulate VII. The "unique elements," 0 and 1 are interpretable as *"truth"* and *"falsehood"*; and the complement of a term p, $\sim p$, becomes the *denial* of the proposition p. The seventh postulate, $(p) : p = 1$. V . $p = 0$, now reads "Any proposition is either true or false." Also, $p \vee \sim p = 1$ and p . $\sim p = 0$ hold upon this interpretation, for "p is true or p is false" is true for any p, and "p is true and p is false" is false for any p.

The calculus is given in terms of V and . , corresponding to $\oplus$ and $\otimes$; $\supset$, which corresponds to $\otimes$ of the Boolean algebra, is defined by the formula: $p \supset q$. $\equiv$ df . $\sim p \vee q = 1$. This corresponds to ordinary usage in that, if p implies q, then it is always true that *if* p is true, *then* q is true; or, either p is true, or q must be false.

If the calculus is truly two-valued, so that every true proposition $= 1$ and every false proposition $= 0$, then all true propositions are equal to each other, and all false propositions are equal to each other, regardless of their import. Meanings, or "intensions," are irrelevant; only their truth-value counts. Therefore the "propositional" calculus is a calculus of truth-values.

Since $p \supset q . \equiv$df$. \sim p \lor q . = 1$, and $\sim p \lor q = 1$ is merely a relation among truth-values, which holds whenever p is false or q is true, $p \supset q$ may occur when p and q have no intensional relation whatever; $p \supset q$, in fact, holds whenever p is false, and whenever q is true; therefore *a true proposition is implied by any proposition,* and *a false proposition implies any proposition.*

The concept symbolized by $\supset$ is, then, somewhat broader than the ordinary notion, though $p \supset q$ always holds when p "really" or "intensionally" implies q. Bertrand Russell has given the algebraic concept the name of "material implication."

What saves "material implication" from being utterly useless is, that the cases in which it differs from "real" implication are all cases where p is known to be false, so its "real" implications are irrelevant, or q is already known to be true, so it does not need to be inferred. In all cases where p is known to be true, and q is not known, "material implication" serves the purposes of inference.

A calculus of propositions uses the principles of logical relationship to reason about logical relations. It states the laws of reasoning, so its systematic laws are sometimes taken as criteria of valid reasoning. This is an error, for the laws of logic must be accepted before any calculus can be used. It can only *exhibit* the formal properties of those laws which we do, in fact, accept as valid in reasoning.

But since the calculus makes true or false statements about true or false statements, it is necessarily and frankly "reflexive." If p is a true proposition, then $p = 1$; and $p = 1$ is a true proposition. Therefore, $(p = 1) = 1$; and, since $p = 1$, $p = (p = 1)$. This peculiar proposition results from the propositional interpretation, and is not tenable with any other; therefore, $p = (p = 1)$ is a formal proposition which, if taken as a postulate, *guarantees* the pro-positional interpretation. Of course, if $p = (p = 1)$, $\sim p = (p = 0)$. This makes for a tremendous variety of equivalent forms and gives the system a redundant character. Every statement made in the system is again equal to 0 or 1. All its facts, such as: $p \lor q . \supset . q \lor p$, are also elements, for they always equal 1. So it becomes impossible to distinguish elementary from logical propositions; $p = (p = 1)$, $\sim p = \sim (p = 1)$, and $\sim [p = (p = 1)]$. If $p = (p = 1)$, then the denial of p, $\sim p$, may be written $\sim p$; and $\sim p \lor q = 1$ may be written $\sim p \lor q$, or $p \supset q$.

The very difficulties of this calculus are the source of its importance in logical theory; for in order to obviate them, the calculus has been modified until it reached the form now presented in the first part of *Principia Mathematica*, which is the starting-point of the greatest logical work that has yet been done, a foundation of mathematics and science.

QUESTIONS FOR REVIEW

1. What formal properties of "implication" can you name?
2. Why may $\oplus$ and $\otimes$ be interpreted as logical operations?
3. In the "propositional" version of Boolean algebra, what meanings are given to 1 and 0?
4. Could postulate VII be omitted from an algebra of propositions?
5. What formula of the abstract algebra $(K \oplus, \otimes, =)$ corresponds to the definition: $p \supset q . \equiv df . \sim p \lor q = 1$?
6. What is meant by calling the propositional calculus an algebra of truth-values?
7. What is "material implication"? How does it differ from "real" implication? Does it, in your opinion, merit the name of "implication" at all?
8. What is the importance of the proposition, $(p) . p = (p = 1)$?
9. What objections could be made to this proposition? Do you think the objections are valid?
10. Is the "propositional calculus" a guarantee for the validity of deductive reasoning? Does it express the laws of such reasoning?

11. What is meant by calling the calculus of propositions "reflexive"? What problems arise from the "reflexive" character?

SUGGESTIONS FOR CLASS WORK

1. In the two-valued algebra, find five equivalent expressions for p.
2. Let $p =$ "Dickens wrote *Oliver Twist*." Let $q =$ "Nelson was a French general." Express all the material implications that hold among p, q, $\sim f$, and $\sim q$.
3. Give an example of $p \supset q$ where q may be inferred from p; one where q may not be inferred from p.
4. Express $p \supset q$ as a disjunction *and as a conjunction*. (Hint: use the "law of transposition.")
5. Express in the terms of the "propositional" calculus:

$$(a, b, c) : (a \oplus b) \otimes (a \oplus c) = a \oplus (b \otimes c)$$
$$(a, b) : (a \otimes -b) \oplus (-a \otimes b) = 1 . \supset . a \otimes b = 0$$

CHAPTER XII

THE ASSUMPTIONS OF *PRINCIPIA MATHEMATICA*

1. Limitations and Defects of the "Propositional" Algebra

There is a type of logical theory, commonly called "logistic," which applies to the whole body of mathematical reasoning, reveals the precise relations between arithmetic and algebra, algebra and geometry, between cardinal and ordinal notions, and many other basic problems. Obviously such a powerful logic could never have sprung from the syllogistic science of Aristotle; neither could it derive from any system as rigid, simple, and limited as a two-valued algebra, of the form that yields the propositional calculus. This calculus is complete and closed; it has, in its peculiar Boolean form, no possibilities of further expansion and complication of its laws. We may find new interpretations for it, and so discover that many things in the world, which look as unlike as propositions and (say) circles intersecting one another, have an essential trait in common, namely the logical form of their respective inter-relations. But in using Boolean algebra we must talk *either* about propositions, *or* about circles; we cannot make a reasonable statement about *a proposition and a circle*. Likewise we may talk in Boolean terms *either* about propositions *or* about classes, but a class and a proposition cannot be talked about in the same terms. *The only way to pass from class-concepts to truth-value concepts is by a change of interpretation for the whole calculus.*

Such limitations, however, are not defects, any more than the walls of a small chamber are defects because they make it small. The algebra as an abstract system is quite perfect. Yet the propositional calculus is in many ways unsatisfactory; it is a possible formulation of the systematic relations among propositions, but by no means

the happiest one. This is due to two circumstances, namely:
(1) that the system was originally constructed to present
important facts about *classes*, and the formulae which are
interesting in this connection may convey facts of no particular interest when they concern propositions; (2) that this
system, designed as a class-calculus, really fits the structure
of propositions in logical relations, *with exception of the
presence of two unique elements*. There are not two "unique"
propositions. Consequently these elements require a slightly
warped interpretation. They are taken to represent *specific*
truth-values, where the other terms, p, q, etc., represent
ambiguous truth-values, and at the same time are said to
represent propositions which "have" truth-values. For, if
p were only a truth-value, like 1 and 0, then it could not be
identified with "$p = 1$," which is not only a truth-value,
but a proposition possessing truth-value. To make the
Boolean algebra fit the universe of propositions, therefore,
involves a certain vagueness of interpretation, which is a
real defect, and gives rise to spurious algebraic forms.

The history of the propositional calculus is a story of
emendations and alterations designed to correct the weaknesses it inherits from its origin in a class-calculus. The
great result of this process is the system which two eminent
logicians and mathematicians, ALFRED N. WHITEHEAD and
BERTRAND RUSSELL, have given us in a book which will
probably remain the highest classic of symbolic logic, their
Principia Mathematica. When one first encounters this
system, it looks utterly different from the familiar Boolean
algebra; the very language is different, some of the primitive
ideas are new, the general propositions (at least in the
first chapters) have no quantifiers, and it looks very much as
though the authors had simply scrapped the old logic and
made a new one. This, however, is not the case; their system
is essentially a Boolean algebra; and the best way to note
the changes they have made, and yet maintain the connection between the new and the old symbolic logic, is to

follow the reasoning which led to these changes, which is a careful, progressive critique of the ineptitudes and fallacies of the two-valued propositional calculus.

First of all, consider the postulate which restricts the interpretation of the algebra to propositions in logical relations: $(p) \cdot p = (p = 1)$. Clearly, we may state as a *fact* that $p = 1$; this is a possible combination of elements, and is true or false in the system; 1 is an element, p is an element, and $p = 1$ is an elementary proposition. Furthermore, we may state that $p = 1 \cdot \supset \cdot \sim (\sim p = 1)$; this is a logical proposition, an assertion that the logical relation $\supset$ holds between two elementary propositions of the system. So far, so good. But now we encounter the eighth postulate,

$$(p) \cdot p = (p = 1)$$

Here it is said that an *element*, p, is identical with an *elementary proposition* relating that element to another. The entire structure of logical systems, the combination of elements into elementary propositions and of the latter into logical propositions, breaks down upon this equation, for hereafter there is no telling what is an element, and what an elementary proposition; if $(p) \cdot p = (p = 1)$, then of course $(\sim p = 1) = \sim p$; so we may write, instead of $p = 1 \cdot \supset \cdot \sim (\sim p = 1)$,

$$p \cdot \supset \cdot \sim \sim p$$

and as this is *the same thing* as $p = 1 \cdot \supset \cdot \sim (\sim p = 1)$, and $\supset$ is by interpretation a *constituent relation* of the system $(\oslash = \text{int} \supset)$, $p = 1 \cdot \supset \cdot \sim (\sim p = 1)$ must be regarded as *an elementary proposition of the system*. The distinction between elementary and logical propositions fails us when the constituent relations are identical with logical relations (as they are, by interpretation), and the elements with elementary propositions. Moreover, if $p = (p = 1)$, then $[p = (p = 1)] = (p = 1)$, so $p = [p = (p = 1)]$, and $[p = (p = 1)] = \{p = [p = (p = 1)]\}$, etc., etc. There is no end to the increasing complication of forms that are all identical with p, and with 1. Likewise, $\sim q = (\sim q = 1)$, and $(q = 1) = 0$, and $[(q = 1) = 0] = 1$ and so on *ad infinitum*. There results a tremendous redundancy of forms and endless number of "names" for the element 1 and the element 0; for note that $p \supset q$ means $\sim p \vee q = 1$, which is the same as $\sim p \vee q$, and the same as 1; that $\sim(\sim p \vee q = 1)$ means $\sim p \vee q \,. = .\, 0$, or $\sim (\sim p \vee q) = 1$, or $(p \,.\, \sim q)$, etc. Here the *denial of a condition*, expressed by $\sim (\sim p \vee q = 1)$, "It is false that $\sim p \vee q$ is equal to 1," is *identified with an element*, $p \,.\, \sim q$. It becomes impossible to distinguish what we are saying from what we are talking about.

Such a confusion is not logically tenable. Even if we are talking about propositions, there must be a distinction between the subject-matter and the proposition which is "about" it. In a system where the constituent relationships are, *by interpretation*, $\vee$, $.$, and $\supset$, there must simply be two classes of logical relationships—those which *function as constituents* and those which *function as logical mortar for the system*. As Professor Lewis has remarked: "The framework of logical relations in terms of which theorems are stated must be distinguished from the *content* of the system even when that content is logic."*

This distinction is abrogated by postulate VIII, $(p) \,.\, 1 = (p = 1)$; and this postulate is the very one which is supposed to guarantee that the system which fits a universe of propositions and their logical relations fits nothing else in the world, that its form has just this unique interpretation. The reason for that uniqueness is, that the form is a spurious one; for *an element can never be identified with a proposition involving that same element*, without throwing the *formal assertions* of the system into confusion. Where the form is obscure, it is not surprising that there is no other interpretation. Every other set of meanings makes the absurdit

* C. I. Lewis, *Survey of Symbolic Logic*, Berkeley, Cal., 191 p. 225.

of $p = (p = 1)$ apparent; only if p is a proposition, and 1, instead of being also a (same or other) proposition, is an attribute of propositions, namely "truth," can we say that "$p = 1$" means "p is the truth." The meaning of "is" in this case is not supposed to be identity, but equivalence of truth-value. But to say that 1, which is not any single proposition, *has* a truth-value—as we must, to make $p = 1$ mean that p and 1 are equivalent in truth-value—rests upon a slipshod interpretation; and only by some such slip can $p = (p = 1)$ ever be made to look like a possible proposition. The Boolean algebra of classes fits the system of propositions, provided that we make 1 and 0 at once elements and properties of elements, at once propositions and characteristics of propositions. But to do this leads us into grave difficulties of distinguishing our assertions from the things they are about, and the truth of our statements from the truths and falsehoods with which those statements are concerned.

To correct this serious weakness, Whitehead and Russell abandon the special form known as "Boolean algebra," the form of the class-calculus, and adopt a set of basic assumptions suited primarily to the treatment of propositions and their relations. Whether the universe of classes may be described in similar terms need not concern us just now, though it is clear enough that the authors of *Principia Mathematica* saw far ahead, when they made their new systematization of Boolean materials. The new formulation involves some changes in language; each one of these changes is aimed directly to make *explicit* the ideas about propositions which are *tacitly accepted* in the "propositional" calculus of 0 and 1. Moreover, they found that by selecting a different set of "primitive" statements they could deduce much more promptly and simply those formulae which express important facts about logical relations, than by sticking to the postulates which were designed to yield important facts about class-relations. Most of their *postulates*, therefore, correspond to *theorems* of Boolean algebra.

2. ASSERTION AND NEGATION

If p is, by interpretation, a proposition, then p is something that may be *asserted*, just as the postulates and theorems of a system are asserted. This has led to the belief that when we assert a fact such as : $p = 1$, we have therein another *case of p*. The notion of *assertion* is involved in the propositional interpretation given to the K-elements in this calculus, so that, if I write "p," then this is *ipso facto* an assertion of the proposition p. Now, if $p = 1$ means "p is true," and p means that p is asserted, there is indeed no difference between the two. *The concept of assertion is furnished twice, once by the interpretation of p, and once by the explicit symbolic statement*, $p = 1$. The meaning of " $= 1$" is already contained in p. Hence the redundancy of expressions in the propositional calculus.

The same difficulty arises with the interpretation of the negative, $\sim p$, as the *denial* of p, and the use of "$= 0$" to express "is false." Negation is at once an operation upon p, which yields an element $\sim p$, and a fact about p, namely, that $\sim (p = 1)$. Also, if $p = (p = 1)$, then $\sim (p = 1)$ may be written $\sim (p)$; and is exactly the same thing as $\sim p$. The operation of negation is, by interpretation, denial, the logical operation $\sim$.

In this embarrassment of symbolic language, the authors of *Principia Mathematica* have decided to abandon the use of "$= 1$" and "$= 0$," and accept the concept of assertion as a *primitive idea*, necessitated by the fact that they want to talk about propositions. Denial is, then, the assertion of a proposition with the operation of *negation* upon it, and is expressed in only *one* way: if the assertion is p, the denial is $\sim p$; and this is called the *negation of p*. There is no other negation-sign than the logical one of denial.

Now it is not strictly true that every proposition, by merely being mentioned, is asserted or denied, i.e. that p always means $p = 1$. If I say: "Some people believe that four-leaved clovers bring luck," I am not asserting or denying that "four-leaved clovers bring luck," but that this proposition is believed by some people. Let us call p "four-leaved clovers bring luck." What I assert is, "Some people believe p." *When p is used in another proposition, it is not asserted or denied.* It is merely *talked about.* This is a fact which the interpreters of the Boolean calculus overlooked. If I say:

$$p \supset q$$

I am asserting the implication between two propositions, but not the propositions themselves. I may hold that " 'Gold is cheap' implies 'Wheat is dear,' " even at a time when gold does not happen to be cheap, and I know it is not. Here p and q in themselves are not asserted.

What is asserted is always that relation which functions as the *main verb* in a proposition about propositions. Thus, in $(p \supset q) . \supset . (\sim q \supset \sim p)$, it is the implication between the two parentheses that is asserted. The propositions p and q are not asserted in $p \supset q$, nor denied in $\sim q \supset \sim p$; nor are even these implications asserted; only the fact that one of them, $p \supset q$, implies the other, is asserted.

To distinguish between asserted and unasserted propositions, Whitehead and Russell have used a special sign, $\vdash$, called the *assertion-sign;** wherever this sign appears, *the whole expression which follows it* is an asserted proposition. The separate *parts* of the expression are not asserted Thus, if I write:

$$\vdash . p$$

then p is asserted; but in

$$\vdash : p \supset q . \supset . \sim q \supset \sim p$$

p is not asserted; the sign refers to the expression governed by the two dots, for the two dots follow the sign. All the

* This sign was first used, for the purpose in hand, by GOTTLOB FREGE, in his *Grundgesetze der Arithmetik*, Jena, 1893.

elements or constructs separated from each other by less
than two dots are unasserted here.

If a proposition, say p, is to be *denied*, then it is sufficient
to *assert the negative*, i.e.

$$\vdash . \sim p$$

The assertion-sign always stands at the beginning of a total,
independent proposition, and governs its main verb. If the
dots following the sign are immediately followed by $\sim$,
then the total proposition is a denial.

But we can never make, symbolically, *assertions about
assertions*. The assertion-sign is the strongest symbol in the
system. Nothing further can be said about it *in the language
of the system*. So the assumptions we make about its meaning
and behaviour have to be expressed as *informal postulates*,
as also the assumptions which rest upon the *interpretation*
of the universe $K(p, q, r \ldots)$. If this interpretation, or the
import of the sign $\vdash$, play any part in the calculus, then
this is a non-formal part, and the symbolism, which conveys
only forms, cannot render it.

In this new and more precise symbolism, we can distinguish between the *element* p and the *assertion that* p, or
"$p = 1$." Consequently $a \oslash b$, which is an *assertion* in the
algebra, and is defined by the propositional form $a \oplus b = b$,
equivalent to $-a \oplus b = 1$, must be translated into the
language of *Principia Mathematica* as $\vdash . p \supset q$, or (by
definition) $\vdash . \sim p \lor q$, since the sign $\vdash$ means "$= 1$."
In the two-valued algebra, where $-a \oplus b = 1$ meant the
same as $-a \oplus b$, $p \supset q$ could always be written for $a \oslash b$;
but in the more careful ideography of Whitehead and
Russell, $p \supset q$, or $\sim p \lor q$ corresponds to $-a \oplus b$, and
$\vdash p \supset q$, or $\vdash . \sim p \lor q$, corresponds to $-a \oplus b = 1$ or
$a < b$. So the proper translation of a proposition with $\oslash$
is an *asserted* implication. Any unasserted implication
translates the formula $-a \oplus b$.

The "key" by which the system $K(\oplus, \otimes, \oslash)$ is to be translated into the language of a "propositional" system is, then, not quite so simple for *Principia Mathematica* as for the "two-valued algebra" of propositions. It may be stated as follows:

Boolean algebra	*Principia Mathematica*
a, b, c, etc.	p, q, r, etc.
$= 1$	$\vdash$
$\oplus$	$\vee$
$\otimes$	
$-$	$\sim$
hence, $-a \oplus b$	$\sim p \vee q$, or (by definition, see below) $p \supset q$
$-a \oplus b = 1$	$\vdash . \sim p \vee q$, or $\vdash . p \supset q$
or $a < b$	

3. The Calculus of Elementary Propositions of *Principia Mathematica*

One further difficulty to be avoided is the representation of a proposition *about* p by the very same symbol, p. Somehow, p must be restricted so that it cannot be a proposition about itself, else we run into all the confusion of elementary with logical propositions which beset the Boolean calculus. But in a system where the elements are propositions, and relations among elements are logical relations by interpretation, how can we ever maintain "elementary propositions" at all?

Well, a slight shift of meanings is indeed necessary, to draw a line between p and propositions about p, and yet allow the elements of the system to be themselves propositions. Whitehead and Russell have given the following meaning to "elementary proposition": *An elementary proposition is one which takes only individuals (things, persons, etc.) for its terms.* It may be composed of further propositions, but it is *not about propositions*.

An elementary proposition in this sense is not always (as in the sense formerly used) made entirely with constituent relations among elements. It is quite possible to make a conjunctive or disjunctive statement about individuals, as:

> "Smith took Jones's hat and wore it,"

or:

> "Smith took Jones's or Evans's hat."

Both are statements about Smith, Jones's hat, Evans's hat, etc. Yet the first is a conjunct, "Smith took Jones's hat and Smith wore Jones's hat," which is of the form $p \cdot q$; the second is a disjunct, "Smith took Jones's hat or Smith took Evans's hat"; symbolically, $p \vee q$. Yet both are "elementary" by the above definition. On the other hand, "Jones believes that Smith took his hat" is not elementary, for it relates an individual, Jones, *to a proposition*, namely what Jones believes. Such propositions are not acceptable meanings of p.

With this understanding, let us turn to the *calculus of elementary propositions* given in the first chapters of *Principia Mathematica*. It rests upon four primitive concepts, namely: *elementary proposition, assertion, negation,* and one binary operation, *disjunction*. These may be enumerated symbolically:

$$K(p, q, r \ldots) \vdash, \sim, \vee$$

Furthermore, there is one important *definition*:

$$p \supset q . \equiv\mathrm{df.} \sim p \vee q$$

The sign $\supset$ is read "implies"; and the very first postulate is an informal one, for it involves the notion of *truth* (which has no symbolic expression but belongs to the interpretation of p, q, etc.), and its relevance to $\supset$:

∗1.1 Anything implied by a true elementary proposition is true.   Pp.∗

There follow five formal principles:

∗ Pp. denotes, in *Principia Mathematica*, "Primitive proposition."

*1.2 $\qquad \vdash : p \lor p \, . \, \supset . \, p$ Pp.

" 'Either p is true, or p is true' implies 'p is true,' is asserted."

*1.3 $\qquad \vdash : q \, . \, \supset . \, p \lor q$ Pp.

" 'q is true' implies 'either p or q is true,' is asserted."

*1.4 $\qquad \vdash : p \lor q \, . \, \supset . \, q \lor p$ Pp.

" 'Either p or q is true' implies 'either q or p is true,' is asserted."

*1.5 $\qquad \vdash : p \lor (q \lor r) \, . \, \supset . \, q \lor (p \lor r)$ Pp.

" 'Either p is true, or q or r is true' implies 'either q is true, or p or r is true,' is asserted."

*1.6 $\qquad \vdash : . \, q \supset r \, . \, \supset : p \lor q \, . \, \supset . \, p \lor r$ Pp.

" 'q implies r' implies 'p or q implies p or r,' is asserted."

Note that in every case what is asserted is the *whole proposition*, in which the relation is the "implies" which connects the two clauses that have inverted commas. These clauses themselves are not asserted. All that the postulates maintain is that wherever the first clause is true, the second is true also; but no postulate asserts that its first proposition *is* true.

The remaining two assumptions are again concerned with limiting the interpretation of K, and must therefore be given informally:

*1.7 If p is an elementary proposition, $\sim p$ is an elementary proposition. Pp.

*1.71 If p and q are elementary propositions, $p \lor q$ is an elementary proposition. Pp.

Now let us consider the correspondence of the formal postulates here given to certain propositions of Boolean algebra, by turning them back into the abstract terms, a, b, etc., $\oplus$, and $\otimes$:

*1.2 $\vdash : p \lor p . \supset . p$ becomes $a \oplus a \otimes a$

(Note that the implication in *1.2 is *asserted*, and is therefore rendered by $\otimes$.)

This proposition of the algebra is, of course, easily proved from $a \oplus a = a$ and $a \otimes a$. Postulate *1.2 therefore corresponds to a theorem of the algebra, and expresses in a somewhat modified form the so-called *law of tautology*.

*1.3 $\vdash : q . \supset . p \lor q$ becomes $b \otimes a \oplus b$

In the postulate-set for classes where $<$ is primitive, this proposition is employed in the definition of a sum (postulate 3). It may be termed the "principle of addition." From the postulates with $+$ and $\times$ it is deduced as theorem 18a (chap. ix, p. 229)

*1.4 $\vdash : p \lor q . \supset . q \lor p$ becomes $a \oplus b \otimes b \oplus a$

This is a weakened form of $a \oplus b = b \oplus a$ (since $=$ is mutual inclusion) and is an expression of the *commutative law*, which Whitehead and Russell choose to call the *law of permutation*.

*1.5 $\vdash : p \lor (q \lor r) . \supset . q \lor (p \lor r)$ becomes
$a \oplus (b \oplus c) . \otimes . b \oplus (a \oplus c)$

This is a weakened and somewhat modified case of the *associative law*, $a \oplus (b \oplus c) = (a \oplus b) \oplus c$, and is easily derived from it.

*1.6 $\vdash : . q \supset r . \supset : p \lor q . \supset . p \lor r$ becomes
$(-b \oplus c) \otimes [-(a \oplus b) \oplus (a \oplus c)]$

In this postulate of *Principia Mathematica*, only the second $\supset$ is asserted, and may be translated by $\otimes$; the other $\supset$'s are unasserted and must be rendered by the proper combination of - and $\oplus$. The result is a rather complicated inclusion-formula, but one that belongs to the algebra and is easily deduced.* It is known as the *principle of summation*.

As I have said in chapter ix, there are several combinations of true propositions in Boolean algebra which may be taken as "primitive," to yield deductively all the rest of the system. If we compare the postulates of *Principia Mathematica* with the Boolean postulates given in terms of $\oplus$ and $\otimes$, it will appear that the former express *all the operational laws of disjunction* (tautology, commutation, association) besides two principles (addition and summation) not assumed in the algebra as we know it.

This means that *Whitehead and Russell's formal postulates take care of all those Boolean postulates for $\oplus$ which are preceded by universal quantifiers*. The two added postulates are also of a universal character; *all the formal postulates in the calculus of elementary propositions are universal*. Those postulates which derive new elements from given elements, such as:

$$(p) \, (\exists \sim p) : \ldots$$
$$(p, q) \, (\exists p \lor q) : \ldots$$

are taken care of by the *informal* primitive propositions; and those which assert categorically the existence of certain elements,

$$(\exists 1) \, (p) : \ldots$$
$$(\exists 0) \, (p) : \ldots$$

are taken care of by the interpretation of p as a proposition, which has the property of being either true or false. (An

---

* The proof may be carried out as follows:

$$-(a \oplus b) \oplus (a \oplus c) = -a \text{ -}b \oplus (a \oplus c) \qquad \text{10a}$$
$$= (a \oplus -a \text{ -}b) \oplus c \qquad \text{11a}$$

$$a \oplus -a \text{ -}b = (a \oplus -a) \, (a \oplus -b) = 1 \, (a \oplus -b) = a \oplus -b$$
$$\text{IV\textsc{a}, V, II\textsc{b}}$$

then
$$(a \oplus -a \text{ -}b) \oplus c = (a \oplus -b) \oplus c$$
$$= a \oplus (\text{ -}b \oplus c) \qquad \text{11a}$$
$$= (-b + c) \oplus a \qquad \text{III\textsc{a}}$$
$$-b + c \ominus (\text{ -}b + c) \oplus a \qquad \text{14a}$$

hence
$$(-b \oplus c) \, [\ominus -(a \oplus b) \oplus (a \oplus c)] \qquad \text{Q.E.D.}$$

attempt is made to express this fact as a theorem, $\vdash : p . \supset . p \lor \sim p$; the theorem is valid enough, but does not express the so-called "law of thought," "Every proposition is either true or false"; that is an assumption contained in the *meaning* of "proposition.") Now, since all formal postulates (and all formal theorems) are universal, there is no need of quantifiers; where there is but one quantifier, no confusion can arise, so the universality of p, $\sim p$, q, etc., may be taken for granted. We always mean "any p," "any p and q," "any p, q, and r."

4. THE MOST IMPORTANT THEOREMS INVOLVING $\lor$, $\sim$, AND $\supset$*

In order to see how the old laws of Boolean algebra emerge from this new set of assumptions, it is necessary to know at least a few essential propositions among the hundreds of theorems which the authors of *Principia Mathematica* proceed to deduce. Some of these, expressing familiar characteristics, follow immediately from the premises, by the principle of exemplification. I shall give them their original numbers, so that the reader may be reminded that they are not strictly consecutive, but selected. Verbal translations of the symbolism may now be omitted, except where it emphasizes the import and systematic necessity of the proposition.

*2.02 $\vdash : q . \supset . p \supset q$

This expresses a peculiarity of *material* implication, that a true proposition is implied by any proposition. Note that q means "q is true." "If p is true, then, whatever q is, if q is true, p is true"; or, "If p is true, then 'q is false or p is true' holds." This is one of the cases where implication is worthless for inference because it is gratuitous; the consequent is true, anyway. The formal proof of *2.02 derives from postulate *1.3, $\vdash : q . \supset . p \lor q$, by the principle of

* Cf. *Principia Mathematica*, vol. i, *2.

application alone; for, since p means "any element," and q "any other element," let us interchange the two letters; then the postulate becomes

*1.3 $\vdash : p . \supset . q \lor p$

Also, instead of "any element q" we might have used: "any element, $\sim q$," and written:

$\vdash : p . \supset . \sim q \lor p$

By the definition of $\supset$,

$\sim q \lor p . \equiv$df. $q \supset p$

and so we have

$\vdash : p . \supset . q \supset p$,

which is the desired proposition, *2.02.

*2.03 $\vdash : p \supset \sim q . \supset . q \supset \sim p$

The proof may be effected by merely re-writing the expression

$\vdash : \sim p \lor \sim q . \supset . \sim q \lor \sim p$

which is a case covered by postulate *1.4, with $\sim p$ in place of p and $\sim q$ in place of q.

Several other forms of this principle may be given, but this is the only form which can be demonstrated without a further theorem proving that $q . \supset . \sim (\sim q)$ (*2.12).

These other forms, however, all follow the same pattern:

*2.15 $\vdash : \sim p \supset q . \supset . \sim q \supset p$
*2.16 $\vdash : p \supset q . \supset . \sim q \supset \sim p$
*2.17 $\vdash : \sim q \supset \sim p . \supset . p \supset q$

Obviously, they differ only in the choice of positive and negative terms in the first unasserted proposition. But the consequent, the second unasserted proposition, *always presents the terms in reverse order, with reversed signs*. To quote from *Principia Mathematica*: "These four analogous

propositions constitute the 'principle of transposition.' . . .
They lead to the rule that in an implication the two sides
may be interchanged by turning negative into positive and
positive into negative. They are thus analogous to the
algebraical rule that the two sides of an equation may be
interchanged by changing the signs."

*2.04 $\quad \vdash : . \, p \, . \supset . \, q \supset r : \supset : q \, . \supset . \, p \supset r$

For demonstration, use *1.5 using $\sim p$ for p, and $\sim q$ for q:

$$\vdash : \, \sim p \vee (\sim q \vee r) \, . \supset . \, \sim q \vee (\sim p \vee r)$$

In terms of $\supset$,

$$\vdash : p \supset (q \supset r) \, . \supset . \, q \supset (p \supset r)$$

Punctuating with dots,

$$\vdash : . \, p \, . \supset . \, q \supset r : \supset : q \, . \supset . \, p \supset r \qquad \text{Q.E.D.}$$

"This is called the 'commutative principle.' . . . It
states that, if r follows from q provided p is true, r follows
from p provided q is true."

Further propositions of *2 will be given without proof,
since the proofs may be found in *Principia Mathematica*,
and students should now be able to read them there.

*2.05 $\quad \vdash : . \, q \supset r \, . \supset : p \supset q \, . \supset . \, p \supset r$

The proof is very simply effected from *1.6, by using $\sim p$
in place of p $\Big($ in *Principia Mathematica* such a substitution
is indicated by writing $\dfrac{\sim p}{p}\Big)$.

*2.06 $\quad \vdash : . \, p \supset q \, . \supset : q \supset r \, . \supset . \, p \supset r$

(Use *2.04, with $\dfrac{q \supset r}{p}, \dfrac{p \supset q}{q}, \dfrac{p \supset r}{r}$. Since $q \supset r \equiv \text{df} . \, \sim q \vee r$,
and since, if $\sim q$ is an element and r is an element, $\sim q \vee r$

is an element, by *1.71, the principle of application allows the substitution $\dfrac{q \supset r}{p}$; and similarly in the two other cases).

The two theorems *2.05 and *2.06 represent the *principle of the syllogism*, the most famous principle of actual reasoning, namely *mediate reasoning*, the employment of a "middle term," q. Naturally, these two formulae and their derivatives are of utmost importance for any deductive process; in classical (i.e. Aristotelian) logic they are exalted to the rank of *the* deductive principle, and such logic is often referred to as "the logic of the syllogism" (see App. B).

*2.08 $\vdash . p \supset p$

"Every proposition implies itself." The proof of this simple fact requires several steps; the reader is referred to *Principia Mathematica*.

*2.21 $\vdash : \sim p . \supset . p \supset q$

This is the counterpart of *2.02, for it expresses that *a false proposition implies any proposition*. The proof is easy; use *1.3, with $\dfrac{p}{q}, \dfrac{q}{p}$; then use *1.4, and write $p \supset q$ for $\sim p \lor q$ when the latter form appears.

5. The Definition of Conjunction, and Some Important Theorems*

So far we have encountered only one binary operation, $\lor$, which corresponds to $\oplus$ of the algebra. In the postulate set with $\oplus$ and $\otimes$, both operations are required to define *negation*, which is said to yield a term $-a$ such that $-a \oplus a = 1$ and $-a\, a = 0$. But in the calculus of Whitehead and Russell, negation, $\sim$, is taken as primitive; consequently we may *define conjunction* in terms of disjunction and negation, as follows:

---

* Cf. *Principia Mathematica*, vol. i, *3.

$$p \cdot q \cdot \equiv \text{df.} \sim (\sim p \vee \sim q)$$

" 'p and q are both true' means 'it is false that p is false or q is false.' " In Boolean algebra, this form, here given as a *definition of* $p \cdot q$, finds its analogue in a theorem:

$$(a, b) \cdot a \otimes b = \text{-}(\text{-}a \oplus \text{-}b)$$

which follows as a corollary from De Morgan's theorem,

$$(a, b) \cdot \text{-}(a \otimes b) = \text{-}a \oplus \text{-}b$$

All the fundamental facts about $p \cdot q$ may now be expressed, for they all hold for the longer and more difficult construction, $\sim (\sim p \vee \sim q)$. If $p \vee q \cdot \supset \cdot q \vee p$ (by the principle of application, letting p mean $\sim q$ and q mean $\sim p$), $\sim q \vee \sim p \cdot \supset \cdot \sim p \vee \sim q$; hence

$$\vdash : \sim (\sim p \vee \sim q) \cdot \supset \cdot \sim (\sim q \vee \sim p)$$

which is, by definition,

$$\vdash : p \cdot q \cdot \supset \cdot q \cdot p$$

the commutative law for *logical* conjunction.* The associative law, the law of absorption, and ultimately the distributive law for $\vee$ and $\cdot$, may all be derived by operating, wherever possible, with previously derived laws for disjunction and the *disjunctive form of* $p \cdot q$, $\sim (\sim p \vee \sim q)$.

The propositions which follow, as well as the comments which accompany them, are quoted verbatim from Whitehead and Russell.

"*3.2 $\vdash : . p \cdot \supset : q \cdot \supset \cdot p \cdot q$

"I.e. 'p implies that q implies $p \cdot q$,' i.e. if each of two propositions is true, so is their logical product.

"*3.26 $\vdash : p \cdot q \cdot \supset \cdot p$
"*3.27 $\vdash : p \cdot q \cdot \supset \cdot q$

"I.e. if the logical product of two propositions is true, then each of the two propositions severally is true.

* Theorem *3.22 of *Principia Mathematica*.

"*3.3 $\vdash : . \, p \, . \, q \, . \, \supset \, . \, r : \supset : \, p \, . \, \supset \, . \, q \supset r$

"I.e. if p and q jointly imply r, then p implies that q implies r. This principle (following Peano) will be called 'exportation,' because q is 'exported' from the hypothesis. . . .

"*3.31 $\vdash : . \, p \, . \, \supset \, . \, q \supset r : \supset : \, p \, . \, q \supset r$

"This is the correlative of the above, and will be called (following Peano) 'importation.' . . .

"*3.35 $\vdash : p \, . \, p \supset q \, . \, \supset \, . \, q$

"I.e. 'if p is true, and q follows from it, then q is true.' This will be called the 'principle of assertion.' . . . It differs from *1.1 by the fact that it does not apply only when p is really true, but requires merely the hypothesis that p is true.

"*3.43 $\vdash : . \, p \supset q \, . \, p \supset r \, . \, \supset : \, p \, . \, \supset \, . \, q \, . \, r$

"I.e. if a proposition implies each of two different propositions, then it implies their logical product. This is called by Peano the 'principle of composition.' . . .

"*3.45 $\vdash : . \, p \supset q \, . \, \supset : \, p \, . \, r \, . \, \supset \, . \, q \, . \, r$

"I.e. both sides of an implication may be multiplied by a common factor. This is called by Peano the 'principle of the factor.' .

"*3.47 $\vdash : . \, p \supset r \, . \, q \supset s \, . \, \supset : \, p \, . \, q \, . \, \supset \, . \, r \, . \, s$

"I.e. if p implies r and q implies s, then p and q jointly imply r and s jointly. The law of contradiction,

$$\vdash . \sim (p \, . \sim p),$$

is proved in this number (*3.24); but in spite of its fame we have found few occasions for its use."

6. The Definition of Equivalence, and Some Important Theorems

The abstract system of Boolean algebra, when stated in terms of $\oplus$ and $\otimes$, appears as a collection of propositions most of which are *equations*. The formulae we have so far encountered in the calculus of elementary propositions have been *implications*, analogous to $\oslash$-propositions in the abstract algebra. There is, however, a logical relation, *equivalence*, which holds between two propositions if either one may always be substituted for the other; it is denoted by the symbol $\equiv$. This is strictly analogous to the relation $=$, which holds between two *elements* when one may freely replace the other. Two propositions are equivalent if and only if *each implies the other*. Just as, in the algebra, we have

$$(a, b) \cdot a = b \cdot \equiv \mathrm{df} : a \oslash b \cdot b \oslash a$$

(Def. in the formal context $K\oslash$; obvious from def. of $\oslash$ and III a, b in the formal context $K\oplus$, $\otimes$, $=$) so we have in the present calculus, the *definition of* $\equiv$:

4.01 $p \equiv q : \equiv \mathrm{df} : p \supset q \cdot q \supset p$

Wherever we can assert a *mutual* implication between two propositions, we may assert their equivalence. Either may then be substituted for the other. In a calculus of truth-values, such as the present one, any two propositions are equivalent if they have the same truth-value.

It now remains to express the principles of this system (e.g. commutivity, absorption, exportation, importation, etc.), as equivalences, instead of mere implications, and the "Boolean" form of the calculus of elementary propositions will be clearly visible. This is done by Whitehead and Russell in their fourth chapter (or "number," as they call it), which exhibits, by way of introduction, a summary of its most important contents, so that I cannot do better than to quote their account:

"The principal propositions of this number are the following:

"*4.1 $\vdash : p \supset q \cdot \equiv \cdot \sim q \supset \sim p$

"*4.11 $\vdash : p \equiv q \cdot \equiv \cdot \sim p \equiv \sim q$

* It should be noted that, just as only an *asserted* implication is a proper translation of $\oslash$, so only an *asserted* equivalence functions in place of $=$.

"These are both forms of the 'principle of transposition.'

"*4.13 $\vdash . p \equiv \sim (\sim p)$

"This is the principle of double negation, i.e. a proposition is equivalent to the falsehood of its negation.

"*4.2 $\vdash . p \equiv p$
"*4.21 $\vdash : p \equiv q . \equiv . q \equiv p$
"*4.22 $\vdash : p \equiv q . q \equiv r . \supset . p \equiv r$

"These propositions assert that equivalence is *reflexive*, *symmetrical*, and *transitive*.

"*4.24 $\vdash : p . \equiv . p . p$
"*4.25 $\vdash : p . \equiv . p \vee p$

"I.e. p is equivalent to 'p and p' and to 'p or p,' which are two forms of the *law of tautology*, and are the source of the principal differences between the algebra of symbolic logic and ordinary algebra.

"*4.3 $\vdash : p . q . \equiv . q . p$

"This is the commutative law for the product of propositions.

"*4.31 $\vdash : p \vee q . \equiv . q \vee p$

"This is the commutative law for the sum of propositions.
"The associative laws for multiplication and addition of propositions, namely:

"*4.32 $\vdash : (p . q) . r . \equiv . p . (q . r)$
"*4.33 $\vdash : (p \vee q) \vee r . \equiv . p \vee (q \vee r)$

"The distributive law in the two forms

"*4.4 $\vdash : . p . q \vee r . \equiv : p . q . \vee . p . r$
"*4.41 $\vdash : . p . \vee . q . r : \equiv . p \vee q . p \vee r$

"The second of these forms has no analogue in ordinary algebra.

"*4.71 $\vdash : . \, p \supset q . \equiv : p . \equiv . \, p . q$

"I.e. p implies q when, and only when, p is equivalent to $p . q$. This proposition is used constantly; it enables us to replace any implication by an equivalence.

"*4.73 $\vdash : . \, q . \supset : p . \equiv . \, p . q$

"I.e. a true factor may be dropped from or added to a proposition without altering the truth-value of the proposition."

Here, in outline, is the calculus of elementary propositions. Its development in *Principia Mathematica* is long and exhaustive; the summaries here cited show that it derives, step by step, all the propositions of the two-valued algebra. Its superior formulation, avoiding confusions of symbolic usage and shifts of interpretation, is, I think, clear from the foregoing sections; its superior power, both for manipulation and elaboration, which makes it applicable to really important fields of thought, will appear in the next chapter.

Summary

The two-valued algebra of propositions may be based on several alternative sets of "primitive" assumptions. One's aim in formulating an algebra is always to reach as soon as possible the greatest possible number of important propositions. Which propositions are "important" depends upon the *use* one makes of the algebra, i.e. the interpretation given to it. The postulates so far employed were originally chosen for a calculus of classes, and are important for relating classes. They do not necessarily lead most quickly to important formulae when the calculus applies to propositions. The Boolean propositional calculus has, therefore, certain formal limitations and inelegancies due to its original reference to classes.

It has also more vital weaknesses; for, the unique elements, *1* and *0*, can be interpreted only as "truth" and "falsity," an interpretation to which there are two objections: (1) "truth" and "falsity" are not propositions which have truth-value, but are themselves the truth-values which propositions have, and are not therefore "elements" in the same sense as propositions; and (2) the notion of "p is true," expressed by $p = 1$, is already *contained in the interpretation* of p as a proposition, for to utter a proposition as a whole is to assert that it is true. Consequently one concept is symbolized twice, which leads to redundancy and confusion of forms.

The distinction between elementary and logical propositions is here completely lost. Every *proposition* of the algebra becomes itself a *term* of the algebra.

In any system where the constituent relations are, by interpretation, logical relations, this loss is inevitable. But even in a propositional calculus some logical relations function as constituent ones, and some as logical ones. The latter are *asserted*, the former only considered. Whitehead and Russell have avoided confusion by using Frege's assertion-sign, $\vdash$, to indicate the total proposition which is asserted. Any proposition contained in an assertion is merely considered.

They have also given a modified meaning to "elementary proposition," namely, *one whose elements are individuals*. A negative, disjunctive, or conjunctive proposition may still be elementary, i.e. about individuals. The calculus these authors present is a calculus of elementary propositions.

A formal postulate resting on an informal notion, such as an interpretation, is necessarily fallacious. Hence $p = (p = 1)$ is an inadmissible form. "$p = 1$" is already symbolized by p. *Principia Mathematica* dispenses with any formal expression of *truth*, and substitutes a frankly informal postulate,

"Anything implied by a true proposition is true." Two other informal postulates provide for the existence of elementary propositions, such as p, the primitive notion of $\sim p$, and of $p \vee q$, all elementary propositions.

The primitive notions of the calculus are: elementary proposition, $\vdash$, $\sim$, $\vee$, and the informal notion of "truth." The *existence* of these is expressed by informal assumptions. There are three formal definitions, of $p \supset q$, $p \cdot q$, and $p \equiv q$ respectively. The first of these precedes the symbolic postulates, which assume it. All the formal postulates concern *operational rules* for $\vee$ and the defined $\supset$, so they are all universal. Where all quantifiers are universal, they may be dispensed with, as they are in the calculus of elementary propositions.

From the given postulates, all the characteristics of $\vee$, . , $\supset$, and $\equiv$, which correspond to those of $\oplus$, $\otimes$, $\ominus$, and $=$ in Boolean algebra, may be deduced. This calculus avoids the faulty interpretation, redundancy, and confusion that attend a "propositional" use of Boolean algebra, and, being formulated so as to fit the aims of a propositional system, lends itself to more important uses than the calculus designed essentially for a description of class-relations.

QUESTIONS FOR REVIEW

1. What are the formal limitations of the two-valued algebra?
2. What are its most serious weaknesses? What is the source of these weaknesses?
3. Who wrote *Principia Mathematica?* How are the weaknesses of the algebra obviated in that work?
4. What is the difference between an asserted and an unasserted proposition? How is the concept of assertion expressed?
5. What is meant, in *Principia Mathematica*, by an elementary proposition? How does this meaning compare with the one given in chapter ii of this book? In the sense of *Principia Mathematica* may $p \cdot q$ be an elementary proposition? $p \vee q$? $p \supset q$?

6. What are the primitive notions of the calculus of elementary propositions? What defined notions does it employ?
7. What are its informal postulates?
8. What are the formal postulates?
9. Why are the formal propositions of this calculus expressed without quantifiers?
10. What is the definition of $\supset$? Of . ? Of $\equiv$?
11. What theorem allows us to turn every implication into an equivalence?
12. Why is the calculus of elementary propositions based on other primitive propositions than the Boolean calculus of classes?

SUGGESTIONS FOR CLASS WORK

1. Among the following propositions, check those which are "elementary" in the sense of *Principia Mathematica*:

    Monday is Washday, and France is a Republic.

    Russell and Whitehead wrote *Principia Mathematica*.

    Russell and Whitehead say that Frege first used the "assertion sign."

    If the earth were flat, Columbus would have sailed to its edge.

    If the earth were flat, he would not have sailed, lest he might fall off its edge.

2. In the following asserted propositions, underline the asserted relationships:

    $\vdash : . \, q \supset p \, . \, r \supset p : \supset : q \vee r \, . \supset . \, p$

    $\vdash : . \, p \, . \, q \, . \supset . \, r : \supset : p \, . \supset . \, q \supset r$

    $\vdash : . \, p \supset r \, . \, q \supset s \, . \supset : p \, . \, q \, . \supset . \, r \, . \, s$

    $\vdash : : p \, . \supset . \, q \supset r : \supset : . \, p \, . \supset . \, r \supset s : \supset : p \, . \supset . \, q \supset s$

3. Give three equivalents for $p \supset q$

    Express as a conjunct, $\sim p \vee \sim q$

    Express the same as an implication and as an equivalence.

4. Express the *law of transposition* with $\supset$ and with $\equiv$.

5. In § 4 of this chapter, prove *2·05 by the indicated method. If you succeed, try *2·21.

6. Translate into terms of Boolean *class-algebra* the entire list of equivalence theorems in § 6; then, comparing them with the propositions of chapter **x**, indicate after each one its number (as postulate or theorem) in the class-calculus.

CHAPTER XIII

LOGISTICS

1. THE PURPOSE OF LOGISTICS

The field of thought to which we now want to apply symbolic logic is none less than *mathematics*. Through the ages this science has been recognized as the apotheosis of reason. It is the most developed and elaborate system of knowledge, and in the course of its wonderful evolution it has left all concrete material, all physical facts behind, and grown to be a system of purely formal relations among mere *logical properties* of things—among their shapes, magnitudes, positions, velocities, etc. All these properties might be exemplified by a thousand different things, and are therefore *abstractable*; it makes no difference whether (say) a certain magnitude is represented by one instance, or by the whole class of its possible instances. Mathematics treats of it only *in abstracto*.

For this reason, the science of number has long been regarded as the prototype and ideal of logical thought. Leibniz, in the seventeenth century, conceived the great project of making not only logic, but all philosophy a mathematical system. Greek geometry has ever been the model of all systematic demonstration, all deductive argument; Descartes and Spinoza, the outstanding protagonists of purely rational philosophy, professed to deduce their knowledge of the world *more geometrico*, from axioms and postulates, by the method of Euclid, in the hope of thus constructing a completely general, completely logical system.

The abstractness of mathematics has frequently enough been challenged, by thinkers (usually not mathematicians) who maintained that, since numbers express magnitudes and arrangements of *things*, they must ultimately represent concrete and specific things, or at least our ideas of them.

Since mathematics is first approached by the art of *counting*, the very concept of number must rest upon counting. To the more thoughtful and philosophical among the mathematicians, this challenge offered a real problem. They felt, for the most part, that their critics were confusing the *concept* of number with the normal and perhaps universal *conception* by which it is first conveyed to people; but when they tried to define the concept itself, they found themselves at a loss. In what terms could it be defined? The psychological notions of counting proved unsatisfactory, in describing anything beyond the simple manipulation of finite real numbers. All irrational, imaginary, or transfinite numbers had to be regarded as "fictions," as impossible assumptions contrary to sense and reason, which mathematicians, in some inexplicable way, found useful in their business. To the mathematicians themselves, this hypothesis did not seem very plausible. They felt, rather than knew, that the simpler and simpler terms wherein mathematical concepts might ultimately be defined were more likely to be logical than psychological; so following this instinct, they sought them in the science of formal relations.

Their efforts to define the fundamental concepts of mathematics took them to the very roots of logic. Moreover, it gave the new logic, which had but lately sprung from the fertile minds of Boole, De Morgan, Peirce, and a few others, a definite goal, namely to construct a firm and universal foundation for the immense superstructure of mathematical reasoning, to show the connection of all its branches and the justification of all its supposed "fictions."

This pursuit, being something of a special departure from general logic, has been given the name of "logistic."* For the development of symbolic logic it has been invaluable, because it has set an exacting standard, and made tre-

* French writers apply the term *logistique* to all symbolic logic, which may lead to confusion. In English and German the usage here employed is generally recognized.

mendous demands on the ingenuity and resourcefulness
of logicians—a thing which their former aim, the analysis
of discourse and rhetorical argument, certainly did not do.
It causes us to look not only for a *correct* logic, but a *powerful*
one; not only for concepts that yield a calculus, but for
such as will let us derive by definition all the necessary
notions for mathematics. That is a big order. None the
less, it was just the ambition to fill that order which led
Messrs. Whitehead and Russell to begin with their particular
version of the propositional calculus; their "calculus of
elementary propositions" is designed to meet, before long,
the notions which certain great mathematicians—notably
Peano—had arrived at as the true beginning of mathematics. How this great development from the simple logic
of elementary propositions is effected cannot possibly be
shown in an elementary book; it can only be suggested,
roughly outlined, pointed to as a distant perspective. This
final chapter is necessarily sketchy and fragmentary, but it
seeks at least to present the general ideas which carry the
system onward.

2. THE PRIMITIVE IDEAS OF MATHEMATICS

If mathematics is really to have its roots in the pure
logic of equivalent statements, in the relations of truths
and falsehoods as such, then we must be able to pass somehow from the calculus of elementary propositions to the
notions which are "lowest terms" to the mathematicians.
In order to see clearly what we are aiming to reach, let us
consider the basic concepts which Peano considers the
essential material of mathematics. These are amazingly
few. Out of them he is able to build the great structure of
arithmetic; and from arithmetic the entire edifice of mathematical science—algebra, geometry, calculus, and what-
not—can be derived by definition and deduction. If, therefore, these basic ideas, and the primitive propositions he
formulates in terms of them, may be derived by the same

methods from a system of pure logic, then the assumptions of this latter system are the real "lowest terms" of mathematics. As aforesaid, it will not be possible to demonstrate that derivation here; but I shall try to show *how the ambition to do so has affected the development of the logical system contained in Principia Mathematica.*

The special concepts Peano assumes for arithmetic are: *number, successor,* and *zero.* His primitive propositions may be cited to show, in a sketchy fashion, how he proposes to construct out of these few concepts, with the help of logic alone, the system of natural numbers which is the basis of arithmetic. In place of his own technical-looking postulates, I quote the simple and lucid paraphrase of them given by Bertrand Russell in his *Introduction to Mathematical Philosophy,** as well as some of his comments.

"The five primitive propositions which Peano assumes are:

"(1) 0 is a number.

"(2) The successor of any number is a number.

"(3) No two numbers have the same successor.

"(4) 0 is not the successor of any number.

"(5) Any property which belongs to 0, and also to the successor of any number which has the property, belongs to every number.

"The last of these is the principle of mathematical induction. . . .

"Let us consider briefly the kind of way in which the theory of the natural numbers results from these three ideas and five propositions. To begin with, we define 1 as 'the successor of 0,' 2 as 'the successor of 1,' and so on. We can obviously go on as long as we like with these definitions, since, in virtue of (2), every number that we reach will have a successor, and, in virtue of (3), this cannot be any of the numbers already defined, because, if it were, two different numbers would have the same successor; and in

* 2nd ed., London, 1920. See chap. i, especially pp. 5 and 6.

virtue of (4) none of the numbers we reach in the series of successors can be 0. Thus the series of successors gives us an endless series of continually new numbers. In virtue of (5) all numbers come in this series, which begins with 0 and travels on through successive successors: for (*a*) 0 belongs to this series, and (*b*) if a number *n* belongs to it, so does its successor, whence, by mathematical induction, every number belongs to the series."

None of the concepts here taken as primitive, i.e. *number*, *successor*, or *zero*, is a primitive notion of logic in *Principia Mathematica*. Also, to define any one of them in terms of *p*, ⊢, ∼, and ∨, is a baffling demand. Some further primitive notions would seem to be required for this purpose, but instead of taking simply the arithmetical notions themselves as primitive, we should like to have concepts which are unmistakably logical rather than mathematical. Out of what sort of *logical* material could "number," "successor" and "zero" be made?

The answer is greatly facilitated by an analysis of the concept "number," made by mathematicians themselves, notably Frege and Peano: they came to the conclusion that *numbers are classes*. The argument runs somewhat like this:

Every *instance* of a number, say the number 3, is a collection. A set of triplets, the tones of a triad, the parts of a trilogy, the Persons of the Trinity, exemplify the same number, and in this they are alike. Each set, or collection, is a class, and the *numerosity* of these classes is all they have in common. Their numerosity is 3. Now, if we could define this common element in other terms than with reference to number, we would then be *defining the number* 3.

One way of doing this is to take any two such classes, say the set of triplets, which I call A, and the tones of a triad, B, and note that *for every member of* A *there is just one member of* B. We do not need to count them to know that they are alike.

For instance, we may not know at all how many shoes

there are in a shoe-store, but if the proprietor assures us that he has no broken pairs, we know that there are just as many right shoes as left shoes, because each right is assignable to just one left. The members of the one class may be brought into *one-to-one correlation* with the members of the other. That is what logicians mean by saying the two classes are *similar*.

Suppose, now, we take a class A, which has a member *a*, i.e. which is not empty; we may say, then,

$$(\exists A)\,(\exists a)\,.\,a \,\epsilon\, A$$

Let us assume, furthermore that

$$(x) : x \,\epsilon\, A \,.\, \supset \,.\, x = a$$

Any x which is a member of A is identical with *a*. A, then, is a *unit class*. Now consider the entire class of all those collections which are similar to A. Using a Greek *a* for a variable term, whose values are classes of individuals, and "sm" for "similar," we may write the propositional form

$$a \text{ sm } A$$

as the *defining form* of the class whose members are classes similar to A. This form defines a class of classes, namely the class of all unit classes; and *this defining form is the concept* "1."

Since, however, a class in intension may always be taken in extension for practical purposes, we are brought to the odd but true conclusion that *the number 1 is the class of all classes similar to any unit class.*

By further classification, we derive the fact that "cardinal number" as such is a class of all those classes which are defined by such a form as "*a* sm A," "*β* sm F," etc., that is, "cardinal number" is the class of all cardinal numbers; and with a little ingenuity this definition may be extended to "number" as such, including ordinals as well. In this way, Peano arrived at the conclusion, epoch-making for the whole science of logistics, that *number is a class*.

I cannot here go into all the problems which undoubtedly arise in the reader's mind, such as whether there is really a distinction between "a" term and "one" term, i.e. whether $(\exists a) \cdot a \in A$ does not involve the number 1, and consequently, whether $(x) \cdot \sim (x \in A)$, which would define the concept 0, does not presuppose 0; I can only say that these matters have been most carefully weighed by Frege, Peano, Russell, and others, who have come to the conclusion that the definitions in question are sound and genuine definitions; for further explanations one has to consult their writings (see bibliography, pp. 352–5). The above explanation is intended only to show in a very sketchy and approximate way how it is possible to regard numbers as classes, and the class of numbers as a class of classes.

The next task which confronts us in logistics, then, is to bring the notion of "class" into a logic which so far deals only with propositions. Ordinary Boolean algebra allows of no such expansion of the propositional calculus; it can deal with classes only *at the expense of propositions*, namely by abandoning the interpretation $K(p, q \ldots) \vee, \cdot,$ $\supset$ for $K(a, b \ldots) +, \times, <$. What we want is a logic *which can work these two sets of concepts, these two formal contexts together*; and here the superior power of the calculus of elementary propositions becomes apparent, for with very few additional primitive notions, all of purely logical character, the combination can be effected.

3. FUNCTIONS

The first of these ideas is gained by regarding a proposition, p, as an element which has a certain *structure* itself; that is, instead of beginning the construction of logic with unanalysed propositions, we push the analysis back a little further, and consider that p is a *proposition about something*. Let p, for instance, mean "Russia is big." The proposition is *about* Russia. But that does not determine the character of the proposition, which consists in *what is said about* Russia. For instance, if someone says: "Russia is big," one might reply: *"The same thing* might be said of China," or: *"That* cannot be said of Monaco." Whether "that" can be truly asserted depends upon the subject— Russia, China, Monaco, or any other individual—the dining-table in my house, the Koh-i-noor diamond, or Mickey Mouse. This dependent part of the proposition is said to be a *function* of the subject, which means that its value (in this case, truth-value) depends on the subject. The subject is called the *argument* to the function. The term "function" is borrowed from mathematics. In a mathematical expression such as $x + 12$, the value of the sum depends upon the meaning of x, and the sum is therefore called *a function of x*. But in applying this term to propositional structures, a good deal of confusion has crept into it, which makes the introductory chapters of *Principia Mathematica* very hard reading, unless one distinguishes several meanings of "function."* For this reason, I have somewhat altered its terminology, and used "function" to

* In the first place, there is the sense of "function" here adopted, i.e. "function as opposed to argument." In this sense, a *part* of every elementary proposition or propositional form is a function of an individual (or of individuals). The other part is the argument.

In the second place, the meaning of the whole expression, "x is big," depends on the meaning of x; as soon as a value is assigned to x, the expression becomes a proposition, just as, in "$x + 12$," assigning a value to x makes the whole term a number. And just as mathematicians call the sum $x + 12$ a function of x, so the authors of *Principia Mathematica* were led *to call the propositional form ϕx a function*, namely a *"propositional function,"* with argument x. So when they speak of a "propositional function" they do not mean a part of a proposition or propositional form, namely the ϕ in ϕx or "ϕ Russia," but the propositional form itself. When they speak merely of a function, they mean ϕ.

Thirdly, the term "propositional function" is applied to a *function of propositions*, and "elementary propositional function" to a function which takes only elementary propositions for its arguments. Thus "p is true," "p is false," "p is incredible," "p implies that q

mean only "function to an argument." In this sense it is usually denoted by a Greek letter ϕ, or where two functions are to be distinguished, one by ϕ and the other by ψ (or χ, or ξ). In expressing a propositional form, it is customary to write the function first, then the argument; so we write

$$\phi x$$

for a function ϕ with argument x. If ϕ means "is big," ϕx means "x is big."

Now, since every proposition p makes a statement about some individual or individuals, and since p means *any* proposition, i.e. any ϕ about any x, then what is true about p is true of any ϕx, and what is true about p and q is true of any ϕx and ψy. Consequently the calculus of p's and q's may be expressed with functions and arguments, i.e. with *elementary propositional forms*, which must hold true wherever any elementary propositions hold true; so we may say

$$\vdash : \phi x \vee \phi x . \supset . \phi x$$
$$\vdash : \psi y . \supset . \phi x \vee \psi y$$
$$\vdash : \phi x \vee \psi y . \supset . \psi y \vee \phi x$$

and so forth; wherever p, q, r, etc., occur, we may substitute ϕx, ψy, χz, etc. There has been no change of meaning, only a change of notation; where p denoted an

is impossible," are functions of the elementary proposition p. In this sense, $\sim p$ is a function of p; and this function is in turn an elementary proposition, as we know from postulate 7.

Fourthly, the quantified propositional form, $(x) . \phi x$, is called a "propositional function." If ϕ has a specific meaning, $(x) . \phi x$ is, of course, a *general proposition*; if ϕ means "a given function," then $(x) . \phi x$ is the *form* of a general proposition. In *Principia Mathematica*, however, it is called a propositional function of one "apparent variable" ("general term"). To avoid confusion I have used "function" alone for the part of a proposition (or propositional form) denoted by ϕ (or ψ, χ, etc.); "propositional form" for ϕx; "elementary propositional form" for a form whose values are elementary propositions; "propositional function" for a function of propositions, ϕp; and "general proposition" for $(x) . \phi x$.

unanalysed proposition, ϕx denotes a proposition *as a structure*, consisting of function and argument (there might be more than one argument in an elementary proposition; for instance, in "Brown met Jones," if ϕ is "meeting" the proposition is of the form $\phi x, y$. But here we shall regard "meeting Jones" as a function of x, and treat p always as meaning ϕx).

This new notation, analysing a proposition into function and argument, has some interesting consequences. In the calculus of unanalysed propositions, p and q were either perfectly identical or entirely different. There was no way of expressing that they were distinct but *relevant* to each other. Consequently they could be related only through their truth-values, so the calculus of unanalysed propositions is merely a calculus of truth-values; and as there are only two truth-values to be calculated, the whole system is very simple, and in itself perhaps not very interesting. But with the notions here introduced we have a free field for new and important constructions; for now we can see, symbolically, the difference between relevant and irrelevant propositions in a material implication, i.e. the difference between " 'Jones is a man' implies 'Jones is mortal,' " and " 'Jones is a man' implies 'Christmas is in Winter.' " Both statements are of the form $p \supset q$; but when the propositions are analysed, we have in the one case, " 'Jones is a man' implies 'Jones is mortal,' "

$$\phi x \supset \psi x$$

and in the other,

$$\phi x \supset \psi y$$

There is an obvious structural difference between these two. The terms of the first implication *have a common ingredient,* which makes them structurally incapable of meaning simply *any* two propositions of which the former is false or the latter true. The second formula, having no common ingredient for its two elements, may mean any material implication whatever. So it appears that the new analysis of p into function and argument complicates its relations to other propositions similarly analysed; we can now distinguish between different propositions about the same thing and different propositions about things not necessarily the same, and between propositions which assert different things of the same subject, and propositions whose assertions need not be of the same nature at all. That is, in place of merely two distinct elementary propositions, p and q, we have three possible cases of two distinct elementary propositions, p and q:

$$\phi x \text{ and } \psi x$$
$$\phi x \text{ and } \phi y$$
$$\phi x \text{ and } \psi y$$

So $p \supset q$ may mean $\phi x \supset \psi x$, $\phi x \supset \phi y$, or $\phi x \supset \psi y$.

4. Assumptions for a Calculus of General Propositions

The most important consequence of analysing a proposition into function and argument is, that some functions are now found to hold true for *any* arguments assigned to them, some for *no* arguments, and some for *certain* arguments but not for others. The notion of "*any* argument" is here avowed as a new primitive idea. This one new idea, together with the analysis of p into ϕx, gives us the means of stating a *general proposition*, namely that p, alias ϕx, is true *for any value of its argument* x; in our familiar notation,

$$(x) . \phi x$$

The denial of $(x) . \phi x$ serves as a definition of another essential notion, $(\exists x)$; for to say ϕx is *not* "true with all values of x," is to say it is false for *some*. Therefore,

$$\sim [(x) . \phi x] : \equiv \text{df} . (\exists x) . \sim \phi x$$

" 'It is false that ϕx is true for every x,' is equivalent by definition to: 'For some x, ϕx is false.' "

Then

$$(\exists x) . \phi x \text{ means } \sim [(x) . \sim \phi x]$$

that is, "For some x, ϕx is true" means "It is false that for every x, ϕx is false." So the form of a simple elementary proposition, ϕx (called a "matrix" in *Principia Mathematica*) together with the new notation (x), the *defined notion* $(\exists x)$, and the primitive concept $\sim$, gives rise to all four types of general proposition:

$$(x) . \phi x$$
$$(\exists x) . \phi x$$
$$(x) . \sim \phi x$$
$$(\exists x) . \sim \phi x$$

General propositions follow all the essential laws for specific propositions. Thus,

$$\vdash : . \, (x) . \phi x . \supset : (x) . \phi x . \vee . (y) . \psi y$$
$$\vdash : . \, (\exists x) . \phi x . \supset : (\exists x) . \psi x . \vee . (\exists y) . \psi y$$
$$\vdash : . \, (x) . \phi x . \supset : (x) . \phi x . \vee . (\exists y) . \psi y$$
$$\vdash : . \, (\exists x) . \phi x . \supset : (\exists x) . \phi x . \vee . (y) . \psi y$$

and so forth, where $(x) . \phi x$ or $(\exists x) . \phi x$ stands in place of p, and $(y) . \psi y$ or $(\exists y) . \psi y$ in place of q, in the formula: $p . \supset . p \vee q$.

Of course, p or q do not *mean* $(x) . \phi x$ or $(\exists y) . \psi y$; the calculus of elementary propositions is one thing and the calculus of general propositions is another, for in the logic of *Principia Mathematica* ϕx (the analysed term p) has one place, and $(x) . \phi x$, which is derived from it, has another. *The two calculuses belong to one system*; they are not two interpretations of one abstract system, but two *analogous parts* within the *same* system. Consequently it is possible to construct formulae containing both elementary propositions and general propositions, e.g.:

$$\vdash : . \, (x) . \phi x . \vee . p : \, \equiv \, : p . \vee . (x) . \phi x$$

* 'Everything has the property ϕ, or p is true' is equivalent

to 'p is true, or everything has the property of ϕ.' " The disjunction $(x) . \phi x . \vee . p$ might mean, for instance, "All dinosaurs are dead, or I am much mistaken." But such "mixed" propositions require very careful treatment and some detailed understanding.*

The most important use of the calculus of general propositions is, that by means of it certain *functions* themselves may be related to *other functions*; that is, it allows us to relate not only two propositions to each other, but to convey the fact that one of two *functions* entails the other, or is incompatible with, or equivalent to, the other. The statement is, indeed, an indirect one; we can speak directly only about general propositions, but certain relations among these *express indirectly* relations among functions. The propositions which offer a means of relating functions themselves to each other, are *related propositions having the same argument*, and are constructed as follows:

Whenever one universal proposition implies another universal proposition, as:

$$(x) . \phi x . \supset . (y) . \psi y$$

the first quantifier, (x), covers the range of *all* individuals, and so does the second one, (y); therefore whatever value y may take in ψy, it must be one of the individuals for which ϕx holds, and *vice versa*. So the possible meanings of $(x) . \phi x . \supset . (y) . \psi y$ always include all the cases where x and y mean the same individual, where we have

$$(x) : \phi x . \supset . \psi x$$

"ϕx implies ψx, for every value of x." So we may say:

$$\vdash :: (x) . \phi x . \supset . (y) . \psi y : \supset : . (x) : \phi x . \supset . \psi x$$

* The relation between the two calculuses is treated at great length in *Principia Mathematica* under the general "theory of types," which I have purposely avoided as a subject too advanced for this introductory treatise.

This establishes a special kind of general proposition, namely *an implication between two propositions with the same argument, for any value of the argument*. Instead of two quantifiers, we have here only one, which quantifies the total assertion not an unasserted term. Instead of: " 'ϕx is true in all cases' implies 'ψy is true in all cases,' " this new proposition reads: "For any x, ϕx implies ψx"; e.g. "For any x, 'x is a man' implies 'x is mortal.' " This is called a *formal implication*. Wherever it occurs, the first-mentioned *function* entails the other, as "being a man" entails "being mortal."

If the implication between ϕx and ψx is mutual, i.e. if we have:

$$(x) :. \phi x . \supset . \psi x : \psi x . \supset . \phi x$$

then

$$(x) . \phi x . \equiv . \psi x$$

just as in the calculus of elementary propositions

$$p \supset q . q \supset p . \equiv df . p \equiv q$$

Then ϕx and ψx are said to be *formally equivalent*. This means that ϕ and ψ may always be interchanged, that they denote the same thing, i.e. that $\phi = \psi$. For instance,

$$(x) : x \text{ is mortal} . \equiv . x \text{ will die}$$

"To be mortal" is the same function as "to be destined to die." One may always be substituted for the other, with any argument.

The calculus of general propositions aims primarily at deducing *formal implications* and *formal equivalences*. Its structure is closely analogous to that of the elementary propositional calculus from which it is derived. There is no room here to expound or discuss its development; several good presentations of it may be found in the literature of logistics, notably *10 of *Principia Mathematica* itself. The point I wish to stress is that in this calculus the relations of *formal implication* and *formal equivalence* are systematically developed, and these yield, indirectly, relations of *entailment*

and *equality* among functions. The significance of the latter
will presently be shown.

5. The Definitions of "Class" and "Membership"

If we consider a formal implication as a relationship
between two functions, it is sometimes advantageous to
write these functions in such a way that the number of their
arguments is indicated, yet no argument is actually given
to them, for instance $\phi(\quad) . \supset . \psi(\quad)$. But, since the
parentheses might be imagined to contain more than one
letter, Whitehead and Russell have adopted the convention
of writing a letter for the argument, and then indicating
that it is "eclipsed" or "suppressed" by placing a cap, like
a *circonflex*, over it, i.e.

$$\phi\hat{z} . \supset . \psi\hat{z}$$

This may be read, "the function ϕ always entails ψ." The
capped letters merely indicate that we have functions of
one argument apiece; they represent empty places for arguments.*

When functions are thus abstracted from the general
propositions wherein they might figure, or the specific propositions that might exemplify them, they are treated as
pure concepts, e.g. "dying," "being mortal"; or, in logical
jargon, they are *taken in intension*. But, as a previous
chapter has explained (chap. v, § 3), every concept has an
intention, or *meaning*, and an extension, or *range of arguments
with which it holds*. Wherever the function takes a single
argument, it defines a simple class, i.e. one whose members
are all given independently of one another. *The function
taken in extension is this class.*

It is an old adage in logic that extensions are more useful
than intensions; by taking functions in extension, we find
ourselves dealing with classes. If, then, every formal impli-

* This idea comes from Frege, who gave each abstracted function
its proper number of *Argumentsstellen*.

cation or formal equivalence expresses a relation between the *functions* involved in its universal propositions, then it expresses a relation between classes, because the functions in extension *are* classes. A function $\phi\hat{z}$ taken in extension is written:

$$\hat{z} \, (\phi z)$$

"The (capped, unnamed) values with which ϕz is a true proposition."

Now, it has been shown that a formal equivalence, such as

$$(x) : \phi x \, . \equiv . \, \psi x$$

means that $\phi\hat{z} = \psi\hat{z}$; taken in extension,

$$\vdash : . \, (x) : \phi x \equiv \psi x : \equiv . \, \hat{z} \, (\phi z) = \hat{z} \, (\psi z)$$

That is, "If ϕx is equivalent to ψx for every value of x, then the class defined by $\phi\hat{z}$ is identical with that defined by $\psi\hat{z}$."

Here we have a definition of class-equality (identity) in terms of formal equivalence among propositions. On this basis, a *calculus of classes* may be constructed, which mirrors exactly the conditions of formal equivalence in the calculus of general propositions. If, by way of abbreviating our symbolism, we let $A = \hat{z} \, (\phi z)$, $B = \hat{z} \, (\psi z)$, and $C = \hat{z} \, (\chi z)$, it may be shown that

$$(x) : \phi x \, . \equiv . \, \psi x \lor \chi x \qquad \text{yields } A = B + C$$
$$(x) : \phi x \, . \equiv . \, \psi x \, . \, \chi x \qquad \text{yields } A = B \times C$$
$$(x) : \phi x \, . \supset . \, \psi x \qquad \text{yields } A < B$$

The familiar calculus of classes may thus be superimposed on the system of general propositions. Instead of taking classes as primitive terms, or ultimate elements of the system, Whitehead and Russell choose to define them in terms of propositions, and then proceed to show, by virtue of the relations which hold among propositions, the Boolean pattern that obtains among these defined entities. Their approach is, of course, much more complicated than that of the classical algebra, but it has inestimable advantages.

One of these vital advantages of the more difficult method is, that members as well as classes can be named in the present system. Just as p and $(x) . \phi x$ or $(\exists x) . \phi x$ may figure in the same proposition, so x and $\hat{z} (\phi z)$ may be related to each other; we can express the fact that an element is *a member of* a class, by defining membership, ϵ, as follows:

$$x \epsilon \hat{z} (\phi z) . \equiv . \phi x$$

" 'x is a member of the class $\hat{z} (\phi z)$' means by definition 'ϕx is true.' "

This relation, ϵ, is extremely important when we want to construct classes *whose members are classes*, such as we need for the logistic definitions of mathematical entities, for instance the *numbers* with which Peano begins his deductive system of arithmetic. Numbers, it may be remembered from § 2 of this chapter, were conceived as *classes of such classes as have certain (defined) memberships*. The memberships were defined by one-to-one correlation with the membership of a given class. All these definitions may now be seen to present purely *logical* constructions. Peano's three primitive concepts—*number*, *successor*, and *zero*—may all be made from the material of *Principia Mathematica*. Zero is the class of empty classes; 1 is the class of classes which are not empty, and whose members are all identical. "Successor of a number" is the class of those classes just one of whose members cannot be brought in one-to-one correlation with any member of a class in the given class of classes (i.e. the original number). So the more difficult view of classes, which underlies their treatment in *Principia Mathematica*, is justified by the demands of the "logistic" programme, to construct the concepts of mathematics from material purely logical.

6. The Definition of "Relation"

The Calculus of Relations is, simply and frankly, too difficult to figure in an introductory book; but a few remarks may none the less be made about the possibility and necessity of calculating how relations are related to each other. Mathematics deals almost entirely with classes that have a certain *internal order*, i.e. classes whose members are all those entities which *have certain relations to other entities*. Such classes are said to be defined by a certain *ordering relation*. That is, the *defining function* of such a class is a relation.

As an example, let us take the class of married couples. It is the class of all *pairs of individuals*, x and y, such that x is married to y. The defining function of this class is "being a married couple," and this is a function of two arguments, $\phi\hat{x}, \hat{z}$. So the class of married couples may be signified by:

$$(\hat{x}\hat{z}\,(\phi x,z)$$

But a married couple is, in turn, defined by the *relation* "marrying"; the function $\phi\hat{x},\hat{z}$ is a relation, and the class $\hat{x}\hat{z}\,(\phi x,z)$ is the *extension*, or range of validity, of a relation.

Obviously there may be formal implications or formal equivalences among propositions with two arguments apiece, as well as for propositions of single arguments; that is, we may have

$$(x, y) \,.\, \phi x,y \supset \psi x,y$$

just as well as $(x) \,.\, \phi x \supset \psi x$

Such a formal relation, quantified for two elements, expresses indirectly a relation between two functions which are relations. Let us call $\phi\hat{x},\hat{z}$, R, and $\psi\hat{x},\hat{z}$, S.

Then $\vdash : . \,(x, y) : \phi x,y \supset \psi x,y \,.\, \equiv \,.\, R = S$

As an example, we might quote the relation which holds, for numbers, between the relations: "successor of" and "greater by 1 than." Let $\phi\hat{x},\hat{z}$, or R, mean "being the successor of," and $\psi\hat{x},\hat{z}$, or S, mean "greater by 1 than."

Then $\qquad (x, y) . \phi x, y \equiv \psi x, y$

But "successor" is the same relation as "greater by 1," *because the successor of any number is greater by 1 than that number, and vice versa*; so it follows that $R = S$.

Now this is an important mathematical proposition. It tells us that the series of natural numbers is generated by adding 1 to each new number. This is not, logically, a simple idea at all, though psychologically it seems simple enough. One of the startling discoveries which Frege, Peano, and other logistic-minded mathematicians have made, is that many of our most familiar mathematical notions involve relations among relations, and are logically very complex indeed. The calculus of relations is required for all such important subjects as the study of progressions, co-ordinates, and types of order generally. But it is more complicated than either the propositional calculus or that of simple classes, and I will make no attempt to give even an introduction to it here. The only points I wish to make are (1) that *a function of two or more arguments defines a relation*, and (2) *that the class of dyads, or triads, or tetrads, etc., defined by such a function is the relation in extension.* These two ideas suffice to show how a calculus of relations is generated within the logistic system we are contemplating.

7. The Structure of *Principia Mathematica*

The system of logistics set forth in *Principia Mathematica* starts from very simple ideas, in essence a Boolean algebra, somewhat better adapted to the expression of *facts about proposition* than the modified Boolean calculus restricted to *0* and *1*. But by very ingenious manipulation and definition, and the addition of a few, well-chosen, purely logical ideas, the calculus of general propositions is derived from that of elementary propositions, the calculus of classes from that of general propositions; not by *reinterpretation* of forms abstracted from $K(p, q, r \ldots)$, $\vdash$, $\sim$, V, but by a systematic *augmentation* of the system, until we have

$$K(p, q, r \ldots), K'(\phi, \psi, \chi, \ldots x, y, z), \vdash, \mathsf{V}, \sim, (x)$$

This is a greater and more powerful system than Boolean algebra; it subsumes several systems, *each of which*, in itself, *follows Boolean laws*. In this great system we can build up propositions composed of propositions, functions whose arguments are propositions, classes whose members are classes; finally, we can define *relations* as entities, so that whole classes, or types, of relations may be studied, and *relations among relations* be established.

On this logical foundation, Whitehead and Russell rear the whole edifice of mathematics, from Cardinal Arithmetic to the several types of Geometry. The more difficult logical problems, notably the "theory of logical types," arising from the existence of certain fundamental contradictions in the construction of propositions and classes, have here been completely ignored; their consideration complicates the system somewhat more than the present sketch tends to show. What I have tried to outline here is merely the purpose, conception, and method of development of the great classic of logistic, *Principia Mathematica*: from the calculus of elementary propositions, through the calculus of general propositions, the calculus of classes, the formation of classes of classes, classes of relations, and finally the calculus of relations, to the definitions of all the concepts employed in mathematics. This is indeed a great anabasis; and anyone who still believes that the powers of logic are exhausted in the syllogistic arguments of even the greatest rhetorical debate, and that the use of symbols has not materially extended that power, is well advised to open one of the three completed volumes of *Principia Mathematica* and study the results of symbolic reasoning. If he has ever been awed by nature's miracle, namely, that "Large oaks from little acorns grow," surely he will be moved to respect a Science of Logic that derives, by rigorous proofs, all the facts of mathematics from the forms of propositions.

8. THE VALUE OF LOGIC FOR SCIENCE AND PHILOSOPHY

Many attempts have been made to treat logic as a branch of psychology or epistemology; but, great names to the contrary, it appears that the development of logic does *not* depend upon psychological findings or metaphysical views. How we think, how we learn, what experiences lead us to the discovery of forms, is quite irrelevant to the truth or falsity of logical assertions. Likewise, whether concepts are "subsistent," or "subjective," or have prototypes in the mind of God, is irrelevant to the relations of concepts to each other, which concern us in logic. It is a striking fact that the logical propositions enunciated by Leibniz, who believed his mind to be a small mirror of the Divine Mind, are perfectly acceptable to Bertrand Russell, who regards his mind (and Leibniz's) as a transient occurrence of "mnemic causations," and the Divine Mind as a subject for poetry. This uniformity of logic, despite the variety of psychological origins, and amid the eternal conflict of metaphysical doctrines, is even more impressive when we come to its most developed part, mathematics. Plato and Aristotle, St. Thomas and Duns Scotus, Newton and Spinoza, used the same mathematics, depending for possible differences only upon the degree of its development in their day. Spinoza *used* 0 as a number (though he may not have *called* it that), and Plato did not, merely because the use of 0 was introduced into European mathematics after Plato and before Spinoza; not because one believed in it and the other did not. Their philosophical positions had nothing to do with the genesis of their arithmetic, or their principles of deduction.

The converse, however, cannot be said; for the advance of logic has had a great deal to do with the growth of science, and has shifted many a philosophical point of view. There are two kinds of influence which logic constantly exercises upon all our systematic thought: one, to check the imagination by revealing implicit paradoxes, and the other, to stimulate it by showing what ingenious constructions are possible with any given material. When untrained and uncontrolled thought comes to a genuine contradiction, for instance, in science, to the fact that light is transmitted where there seems to be no medium of transmission, a logician naturally looks at all the *notions* involved in the dispute, and asks: "What are the presuppositions? What are the premises? Could one of the premises be false?—No. Then try to *reformulate* their statement. Try a substitute for the notion of 'transmitting,' that won't involve 'medium.' " It is through such *reformulations* that the great insights of science are accomplished, just as by a slight reformulation of Boolean algebra the doors are thrown open for a system of logistics. Examples could be multiplied indefinitely: the substitution of the conception of *gravitation* among heavenly bodies for that of "prescribed paths" or "supporting spheres"; the fertility of this new concept, which let it displace notions of terrestial physics, such as "seeking a proper level," as well as astronomical ones; more recently, the new concepts of *unconscious mind* and *psychological symbolism*, introduced by Freud into the study of the human mind, to replace the older ones of *association* and *reproduction* which were too weak to describe anything as amazing and vagrant as human imagination, or as complex as the life of feeling. Whatever one may think of these innovations, to a logician they are interesting exploits of constructive thought.

In philosophy, of course, logic performs the same office as in science; but here, where sense-experience does not check our errors all the time, the need for watchful analysis of concepts is ever greater. It is no exaggeration, I think, to claim that every philosopher should be not only acquainted with logic, but intimately conversant with it; for the study of logic develops the art of *seeing structures* almost to the point of habit, and reduces to a minimum the danger of getting lost amid abstract ideas.

Besides these purely methodological aids, logic also furnishes a great deal of genuinely philosophical material. The origin and status of concepts, their relation to nature and to mind, i.e. the whole problem of "universals" and "particulars"; the trustworthiness of reason; the relativity of language, logical patterns, and "facts"; these are philosophical problems, which arise directly from logical considerations, from attempts to form certain classes or assert certain propositions that meet with contradiction, the so-called "paradoxes" of logic. Furthermore, the problem of form and content, of the "viciousness" of abstractions, the relation of symbol and sense, all spring from logic, but are not themselves logical matters; whatever view we take of them, our logical practice will be unaltered, but our philosophy may be deeply affected. How a *logical formulation of material* actually generates a philosophy is too long a story for this brief note at the end of an essay; besides, I have discussed it, with various examples, in another book.* Here let it only be said that general logic is to philosophy what mathematics is to science; the realm of its possibilities, and the measure of its reason.

Summary

The purpose of logistics, a somewhat specialized department of logic, is to show that the fundamental assumptions of mathematics are all purely logical notions, and that consequently all mathematics may be deduced from a system of logic. This undertaking had a great influence upon the development of logic, which now had to aim not only at consistency, but at *fertility* of concepts and *potency* of primitive propositions as well.

* *The Practice of Philosophy*, New York, 1930 (Henry Holt and Co.), especially Part III.

All mathematics may be derived from arithmetic; therefore the notions required for arithmetic must be the aim of logistic construction. These notions, according to Peano, are *number*, *successor*, and *zero*. This is, of course, numerical o, not the o of Boolean algebra, "the empty class" or "the false."

A "number" is defined as a *class of classes having a certain membership.*" The number o is the class of all empty classes; I, the class of all classes with only identical members. The process of forming a "member" is to define the numerosity of a given class without reference to number, and then establish the class of all classes *similar* to it. Two classes are similar if the members of one may be put into *one-to-one correspondence* with the members of the other. The concept "number," itself, denotes the class of all such classes of similar classes.

These complex notions are far beyond anything that can be made within the system of classes hitherto presented. The Boolean formulation of logic is not powerful enough to support mathematics. Within its simple canons, it is not possible to talk about individuals, propositions, and classes *together*. These belong to different universes of discourse, and to pass from one to the other requires reinterpretation of the whole system. The task of logistic is, then, first of all to construct a logic wherein these various notions, all of which will presently be required for mathematics, can be used together; and where not only general propositions can be asserted, but assertions made *about general propositions*. This is the programme of *Principia Mathematica*.

After establishing the most economical formulation of propositional logic (the calculus of elementary propositions), the authors analyse the propositions, p, q, etc., into their constituent parts, *function* and *argument*. Unanalysed, they can be known only as identical or distinct, and if they are distinct, have nothing in common but their truth-value; analysed, they may have function or argument in common.

In this way they may be related more intimately than merely by material implication.

The calculus of elementary propositions is extended to general propositions by asserting that the function in an analysed proposition is true, not with a specific argument, but with *any* or *some* individual as argument. The notion of "any individual," i.e. the quantifier (x), is taken as primitive; $(\exists x)$ is defined by means of (x) and $\sim$, thus:

$$\sim [(x) \cdot \phi x] \cdot \equiv df : (\exists x) \cdot \sim \phi x$$

The calculus of general propositions is found to follow the pattern of the elementary calculus.

If an implication or an equivalence holds between two universal propositions, then it holds for any case where the argument is the *same* in both propositions; that is,

$$\vdash : . \ (x) \cdot \phi x \cdot \supset \cdot (y) \cdot \psi y : \supset : (x) \ \phi x \supset \psi x$$

and
$$\vdash : . \ (x) \cdot \phi x \cdot \equiv \cdot (y) \cdot \psi y : \supset : (x) \ \phi x \equiv \psi x$$

the implied propositions express, respectively, a *formal* implication and a *formal* equivalence. The purpose of the calculus of general propositions is to express as many formal equivalences as possible.

The importance of formal relations among propositions is, that they establish relations between the *functions* involved. Thus, $(x) : \phi x \cdot \supset \cdot \psi x$ means that $\phi \hat{z}$ entails $\psi \hat{z}$, and $(x) : \phi x \cdot \equiv \cdot \psi x$ means that the functions are identical (interchangeable).

Every function defines a class, namely the class of arguments with which it is true. This class is its extension. The function taken in extension *is* this class. A class defined by a function $\phi \hat{z}$ is written : $\hat{z} \ (\phi z)$.

Relations among functions taken in extension are, then, relations among *classes*; and such relations are asserted in every formal implication or formal equivalence. Hence a calculus of classes may be derived from the calculus of general propositions.

In a system where classes are defined through functions instead of being taken as "primitive elements," the relation of membership in a class may be defined: a member of a class which is the extension of a function, $\phi\hat{z}$, is an individual, x, such that ϕx is true. Symbolically,

$$x \in \hat{z} \, (\phi z) \; . \; =\!\!\text{df} \; . \; \phi x$$

With these concepts, the primitive ideas of Peano's arithmetic can be defined.

The greater part of mathematics, however, is concerned with *kinds of relation*: different types of series, point-sets, etc. This requires the consideration of *relations among relations*, and relations themselves must therefore be able to figure as entities, terms of other relations. This is done by regarding a relation as a certain kind of function, namely as a function of more than one argument. Taken in extension, then, a relation appears as the class of dyads, or triads, . . . m-ads, for which the function holds. Its formal definition (using R to mean "relation") is:

$$R\hat{x}\hat{z} \; . \; =\!\!\text{df} \; . \; \hat{x}\hat{z} \, (\phi x, z)$$

A calculus of relations can thus be constructed within the system of *Principia Mathematica*, but it is more complex than any calculus treated in this book.

The system of logistics set forth in *Principia Mathematica* is a great structure whose parts are separate systems, but so connected by definitions and step-wise derivations that their elements may be utilized for one great science, mathematics. Transitions from one sub-system to another have created some difficulties, which the authors meet by the "theory of logical types"; but this difficult doctrine is a subject for more advanced study than this book presents.

The value of logic for science is patent enough from its close relation to mathematics, the very framework of science. Methodologically, its exploration of unobvious forms furnishes many suggestions for the solution of scientific dilemmas. For philosophy, logic is indispensable, because analysis of concepts is practically our only check on philosophical errors. Also it offers a great deal of direct philosophical material, although the science of logic itself is independent of metaphysical views or psychological origins.

QUESTIONS FOR REVIEW

1. What is meant by "logistics"?
2. How has the conception of a science of logistics affected the development of symbolic logic in general?
3. What does Peano regard as the primitive notions of arithmetic?
4. What logical concepts does he require for the definition of number?
5. What is meant by calling two classes "similar"?
6. What limitation of Boolean logic does *Principia Mathematica* set out to transcend? Do you think it is successful?
7. What are the constituents of propositions? What is gained by analysing p and q into their constituents?
8. What primitive notion is added to the system to construct the calculus of general propositions?
9. What is meant by "formal implication" and "formal equivalence"? Why are these notions important?
10. How are classes derived from propositions? What is the advantage of defining classes, rather than taking them as primitive elements?
11. How may individuals and classes be related?
12. How are relations defined, when they are taken as *entities*? What is meant by "a relation in extension"?

SUGGESTIONS FOR CLASS WORK

1. Write out the five formal postulates of the calculus of elementary propositions with *analysed* propositions.
2. Express symbolically:
   Everything is subject to change, or the pyramids will stand for ever.
   All men are mortal, and Socrates is a man.
   To sleep is always to dream.
   Every sleeper dreams.

3. Complete these definitions:

$$p \cdot q \cdot \equiv df \cdot \text{.....................}$$
$$p \supset q \cdot \equiv df \cdot \text{.....................}$$
$$p \equiv q \cdot \equiv df \cdot \text{.....................}$$
$$(\exists x) \cdot \phi x \cdot \equiv df \cdot \text{.............}$$
$$\phi \hat{z} = \psi \hat{z} \cdot \equiv df : \text{.............}$$
$$x \in \hat{z} (\phi z) \cdot \equiv df : \text{.............}$$

4. Using N for "number," $x +$ for "successor of x," and ϕ for a "property," express the five postulates for arithmetic symbolically.

5. Symbolize:

   a. There are Atlanteans.

   The function of "being an Atlantean" (in intension).

   The class of "Atlanteans."

   b. Everybody is somebody's descendant.

   The function "descendant of" (in intension).

   The class of "descendants."

APPENDIX A

SYMBOLIC LOGIC AND THE LOGIC OF THE SYLLOGISM

FOR those readers who are acquainted with the traditional logic of the syllogism, it may be interesting to view it in relation to the "symbolic logic" here presented. The older logic is a proper part of the new; and it is apt to be a matter of some surprise to find how very small a part it is. In general, it may be said that the categorical syllogism is a fragment of the calculus of classes, and the disjunctive and hypothetical syllogisms are contained in the calculus of elementary propositions.

First, consider the expression of the four categorical propositions that make up the "square of opposition":

All S is P ————————————A
No S is P ——————————— —E
Some S is P ——————————— —I
Some S is not P———————————O

The first says that the class S is *entirely included* in the class P, or: all S's are P's; the second, that the class S is *entirely excluded* from P, or: no S's are P's; the third, that S is *partially included* in P, or: some S's are P's, i.e. S and P *overlap*; and the fourth, that S is *partially excluded* from P, or: some S's are not P's. There are several ways of symbolizing these relationships in Boolean algebra:*

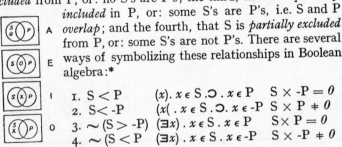

A	1.	S < P	$(x) . x \epsilon S . \supset . x \epsilon P$	$S \times -P = 0$
E	2.	S < -P	$(x(. x \epsilon S . \supset . x \epsilon -P$	$S \times P \neq 0$
I	3.	$\sim (S > -P)$	$(\exists x) . x \epsilon S . x \epsilon P$	$S \times P = 0$
O	4.	$\sim (S < P$	$(\exists x) . x \epsilon S . x \epsilon -P$	$S \times -P \neq 0$

FIG. 23

* The equivalence: $(a, b) . a < b . \equiv . a -b = 0$ is established in chapter ix as theorem 20. Here its usefulness becomes apparent. By the principle of transposition we may derive

$$(a, b) : \sim (a < b) . \equiv . \sim (a -b = 0)$$

used in 3 and 4 above.

It is obvious upon inspection that 1 and 4, 2 and 3, are each other's contradictories, as the "square of opposition" shows:

The relation which makes a product equal or unequal to *0* is the easiest to use, so I shall adopt it for the rest of this exposition, though sometimes the proposition with < may also be given, where it is psychologically closer to the verbal form. Since the ε-form is to be dropped, and the classes S, P, etc., to be taken in general, I shall henceforth use lower-case italics, but in deference to traditional logic write *s*, *p*, and *m* respectively, for "subject-class," "predicate-class," and the class which is the "middle term."

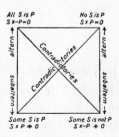

FIG. 24

A syllogism consists of three assertions, each of type A, E, I, or O; in a valid syllogism, the product of the first and second propositions implies the third. This is possible only if at least one of the premises is a universal proposition. Since all syllogisms can be reduced to the "first figure," the six valid moods of this figure comprise all valid syllogisms. It would, of course, be just as easy to reduce the whole array of combinations to any other figure, by conversion or obversion of terms, and inversion of premises. The reason for this reducibility of any figure to any other rests upon three facts well-known in symbolic logic: (1) that it is always legitimate to exchange the *premises*, because they are conjoined propositions of the form $p . q$, and by the commutative law for propositions, $p . q \equiv q . p$; (2) that in a class-inclusion, such as the premises assert, the order of the terms may be inverted with changed signs, by the law of transposition, i.e. $(a, b) : a < b . \equiv . -b < -a$; consequently the "middle term," on whose position in the premises the figure depends, may be put into any position we choose, provided the appropriate negatives are used; and (3) that by the commutative law for classes, the terms of a class-conjunct may also be exchanged, because $(a, b) : a . b = b . a$. If, therefore, we wish to reduce a syllogism of (say) the second figure,

$$\text{No } p \text{ is } m$$
$$\text{All } s \text{ is } m$$
$$\overline{\text{No } s \text{ is } p}$$

to the first figure, the simplest procedure is to express the above implication symbolically,

$$p < -m$$
$$s < m$$
$$\overline{\phantom{s < -p}}$$
$$s < -p$$

and then, in equivalent language, with products and equations:

$$pm = 0$$
$$s\,{-}m = 0$$
$$\overline{}$$
$$sp = 0$$

In the first formula, $p < -m\,.\, \equiv\,.\, m < -p$; so the position of the middle term, m, is changed, and the syllogism thereby cast in the first figure. To prove its equivalence to the previous form, translate it into products

$$m < -p\,.\, \equiv\,.\, mp = 0$$
$$mp = pm$$

therefore $m < -p\,.\, \equiv\,.\, pm = 0$

So we arrive at the formula above:

$$pm = 0$$
$$s\,{-}m = 0$$
$$\overline{}$$
$$sp = 0$$

These three principles—the commutative laws for propositions and for classes, and the law of transposition for classes—govern the entire art of reduction: inversion, full or partial, conversion, simple or by limitation, and obversion.

The next question is what laws, assumed or deduced in symbolic logic, guarantee the conclusiveness of the "valid moods" and inconclusiveness of the "invalid" ones. The only law required for this purpose is the *law of transitivity*, which is expressible either in terms of $<$ or of $=$:

$$(a, b, c) : a < b\,.\, b < c\,.\, \supset\,.\, a < c$$

or: $(a, b, c) :.\, a\,{-}b = 0\,.\, b\,{-}c\,.\, = 0\,.\, \supset :\, a\,{-}c = 0$

This is the formula for all valid syllogisms of universal premises and universal conclusion. It is the familiar transitivity-formula of Boolean algebra, and as it stands, it expresses a syllogism in the first figure with the premises exchanged: obviously, if we want the middle-term to stand first, we may just as well write:

$$(a, b, c) : b \text{-} c = 0 \ . \ a \text{-} b = 0 \ . \supset . \ a \text{-} c = 0$$

As for syllogisms with a particular premise, they are not so readily expressed with $<$, for which reason I have given preference to the other notation. Whenever we have a particular proposition, "Some S is P," we have a partial inclusion, or overlapping; but $<$ expresses total inclusions, and can render "overlapping" of a and b only as:

$$(\exists c) \ . \ c < a \ . \ c < b \ . \ c \neq 0$$

Of course it is much easier to write:

$$ab \neq 0$$

Let us take a syllogism in the mood A I I, in the first figure:

> All steel structures are fireproof
> Some garages are steel structures
> _____
> Some garages are fireproof.

In terms of products of classes, this becomes

$$b \text{-} c = 0$$
$$ab \neq 0$$
$$\overline{}$$
$$a c \neq 0$$
$$b \text{-} c = 0 \ . \ ab \neq 0 \ . \supset . \ ac \neq 0$$

The proof of this inequality is simple.

$$ab \neq 0 \ . \supset . \ a \neq 0 \ . \ b \neq 0$$
$$b = bc + b \text{-} c = bc + 0 = bc$$
$$ab \neq 0 \ . \ b = bc \ . \supset . \ abc \neq 0$$
$$abc < ac$$
Hence
$$abc \neq 0 \ . \supset . \ ac \neq 0 \qquad \qquad \text{Q.E.D.}$$

Since all negative statements may be expressed as positive statements about negative terms—e.g., "Some S is not P" may be expressed as "Some S is -P," and negative terms behave in the calculus exactly like their positive complements, *all* syllogisms with a particular premise are expressible by the above formula, which is a corollary to the law of transitivity.

Two problems of the categorical syllogism remain: (1) the treatment of "singular propositions," and (2) the "weakened cases" of the syllogism.

The first of these is easily disposed of. Take, for example, the most orthodox of all traditional arguments:

> All men are mortal
> Socrates is a man
> _____
>
> Socrates is mortal.

If we regard the minor premise as a singular proposition, then "is" here denotes a different relation from "are" in the major premise; then we have, really,

> Men < mortals
> Socrates ϵ man
> _____

from which it follows that Socrates ϵ mortal. Since "Men < mortals" means "(x) : x ϵ man . ⊃ . x ϵ mortal," this interpretation is permissible. But if we would avoid a dangerous trick of language, namely letting "is" (or "are") mean sometimes ϵ and sometimes <, we may regard "Socrates" not as the name of an individual, but of a *unit class*; then the class of Socrateses, which has but one member, is included in that of men, and therefore in that of mortals; and the "singular" premise is simply a universal one, asserting that all Socrateses are men, and the syllogism is of the form A A A; even though there happens to be only one Socrates.

The second problem, namely how to account for the "weakened cases" of the syllogism—A A I and E A O in the first figure, E A O and A E O in the second, and A E O in the fourth— arises from a special condition assumed in Aristotelian logic, which the syllogistic formulae of Boolean algebra do not express: namely, that *in asserting a class-inclusion, it is always taken for granted that neither of the classes is empty*. Take, for instance, a syllogism in the mood A A I in the first figure:

> All cats are animals
> All animals have feelings
> _____
>
> *Some* cats have feelings

This is true, *if we grant that there are cats*. If the example had been:

$$\text{All griffins are animals}$$
$$\text{All animals have feelings}$$

the conclusion, "Some griffins have feelings," would not have followed, since the class of griffins is *0*, and A A I is of the form:

$$a \text{ -} b = 0$$
$$b \text{ -} c = 0$$
$$\overline{}$$
$$ac \neq 0$$

which is valid only if $a \neq 0$. Therefore it may be said that the "weakened cases" are valid if, and only if, the minor term is not an empty class.

From this brief account, it may be seen that the categorical syllogism is a small part of the algebra of classes, namely, a sub-system limited to three terms, other than *0* or *1*, and their respective complements, and setting forth the relations of inclusion (partial or total) among these. Thousands of men, through thousands of years, have had millions of headaches over the 24 valid and 40 invalid combinations of theses terms, arranging, relating, and naming them. Symbolic logic proves them all equivalent to just three forms of a much greater system:

1. $a \text{ -} b = 0 \cdot b \text{ -} c = 0 \cdot \supset \cdot a \text{ -} c = 0$
2. $b \text{ -} c = 0 \cdot ab \neq 0 \cdot \supset \cdot ac \neq 0$
3. $a \neq 0 \cdot a \text{ -} b = 0 \cdot b \text{ -} c = 0 \cdot \supset \cdot ac \neq 0$

For a true Aristotelian, this exhausts the abstract system of logic. Later generations of scholars, however, have added to the Aristotelian structure the two syllogisms of compound propositions, known respectively as the *hypothetical* and the *disjunctive*. Consider, first, the forms of the hypothetical syllogism:

MIXED HYPOTHETICAL

Modus ponens	*Modus tollens*
If A is B, C is D;	If A is B, C is D
A is B	C is not D
C is D	A is not B

PURE HYPOTHETICAL

Modus ponens	*Modus tollens*
If A is B, C is D;	If A is B, C is D;
If C is D, E is F:	If C is D, E is not F
———————————	———————————
If A is B, E is F	If E is F, A is not B

The major premise in the mixed hypothetical forms is an implication of one proposition by another; the minor is a categorical
assertion, and so is the conclusion. The whole argument is of the
form:*

$$\vdash . p \supset q$$
$$\vdash . p$$
$$\overline{\qquad}$$
$$\vdash . q$$

$$\vdash . p \supset q$$
$$\vdash . \sim q$$
$$\overline{\qquad}$$
$$\vdash . \sim p$$

In the calculus of elementary propositions, we meet with the
formula:

*3.35 $\vdash : p . p \supset q . \supset . q$, or equivalently:

$\vdash : p \supset q . p . \supset . q$, which states exactly the mixed hypothetical
syllogism in *modus ponens*.

Since $p \supset q . \supset . \sim q . \supset . \sim p$, (*2.16), it is easy enough to
derive the formula also in *modus tollens*:

$$\vdash : p \supset q . \sim q . \supset . \sim p$$

As for the pure hypothetical in *modus ponens*, let "A is B"
$= p$, "C is D" $= q$, "E is F" $= r$; then the whole statement
reads:

$$\vdash : p \supset q . q \supset r . \supset . p \supset r$$

which is *3.33 of *Principia Mathematica*, the most familiar form
of the law of transitivity for $\supset$. *Modus tollens*, then, would be:

$$\vdash : p \supset q . q \supset \sim r . \supset . r \supset \sim p$$

which is easy to derive by use of the same principle as above,
namely *2.16.

* Note that p here is a symbol for any *proposition*, not for any
predicate-class.

Any standard logic shows that all *hypothetical* syllogisms may be reduced to these forms, for instance:

> If A is B, E is F
> If C is D, E is not F
> _____
> If A is B, C is not D

This argument reads:

$$\vdash : p \supset r \cdot q \supset \sim r \cdot \supset \cdot p \supset \sim q$$

In the calculus, this proposition is easily proved, of course, from the fact that if $p \supset r$, then $\sim r \supset \sim p$; hence, if $q \supset \sim r$, and $\sim r \supset \sim p$, then $q \supset \sim p$; and if $q \supset \sim p$, then $p \supset \sim q$, which is the conclusion of the syllogism. This is only one example of the transmutations which are possible in the hypothetical syllogism; the terms of the two implications in the premises may always be exchanged by changing their qualities, the premises themselves may be exchanged, just as the "syllogism" prescribes; but all these variants are expressible as corollaries of one theorem of the calculus of elementary propositions, namely

*3.33 $\qquad \vdash : p \supset q \cdot q \supset r \cdot \supset \cdot p \supset r$

being all derived by one principle,

*2.16 $\qquad \vdash : p \supset q \cdot \supset \cdot \sim q \supset \sim p$

These two propositions, therefore, constitute the *basic forms* of the hypothetical syllogism.

The disjunctive syllogism, we are told, has two moods, each of which presents two cases, in that *by denying either term, we assert the other*, (*modus tollendo ponens*) and *by asserting either term we deny the other* (*modus ponendo tollens*). This would give us the following four forms:

Modus tollendo ponens

$\vdash : p \vee q \cdot \sim q \cdot \supset \cdot p \qquad\qquad \vdash : p \vee q \cdot \sim p \cdot \supset \cdot q$

Modus ponendo tollens

$\vdash : p \vee q \cdot p \cdot \supset \cdot \sim q \qquad\qquad \vdash : p \vee q \cdot q \cdot \supset \cdot \sim p$

The propositions of the first mood are easily proved in the

calculus of elementary propositions; for, since $p \lor q . \equiv . \sim p \supset q$ (i.e. $\sim (\sim p) \lor q$), they become respectively,

$$\vdash : \sim p \supset q . \sim q . \supset . p$$

Dem: $\sim p \supset q . \supset . \sim q \supset p$ $(*2.15)$

$\sim p \supset q . \sim q . \supset . \sim q$ $(*3.27)$ $\text{-}p$

———————

$\sim p \supset q$

therefore $\sim p \supset q . \sim q . \supset . p$ Q.E.D.

and: $\vdash : \sim p \supset q . \sim p . \supset . q$

which is $*3.35$, writing $\sim p$ for p throughout. But the propositions of the second mood do not appear in the system of *Principia Mathematica*; the implication is not valid by its rules. The reason for this is that, just as the categorical syllogism made an assumption about classes which the class-calculus did not (namely, that the initially given classes were never empty), so the hypothetical syllogism makes an assumption which the calculus of elementary propositions does not: namely, that disjunction means exclusive disjunction, *either . . . or, but not both.* Traditional logic books, from the *Port Royal Logic* down, have taken for granted that *either . . . or* meant *one and only one of the two.* In symbolic logic we have abandoned the tacit acceptance of this meaning: and if we wish to adopt it openly, we have to write *modus ponendo tollens:*

$$\vdash : . p \lor q . \sim (p . q) . p : \supset . \sim q \qquad \vdash : p \lor q . \sim (p . q) . q . \supset . \sim p$$

These forms are perfectly valid; but, since $p \supset p \lor q$, and $q . \supset . p \lor q$, the disjunction may be deleted, and only the denial of the conjunction, together with the assertion of p (or of q) be written:

$$\vdash : \sim (p . q) . p . \supset . \sim q \qquad \vdash : \sim (p . q) . q . \supset . \sim p$$

These propositions are perfectly acceptable; for, since

$$\sim (p . q) . \equiv \mathrm{df} . \sim p \lor \sim q$$

the first becomes:

$$\vdash : \sim p \lor \sim q . p . \supset . \sim q$$

or: $$\vdash : p \supset \sim q . p . \supset . \sim p$$

and the second:

$$\vdash : \sim p \lor \sim q . q . \supset . \sim p$$

or: $$\vdash : p \supset \sim q . q . \supset . \sim p$$

which are all familiar or easily demonstrable theorems.

It is hardly necessary to point out that a pure disjunctive syllogism may always be reduced to a pure hypothetical one, in one mood or the other; that consequently all "compound syllogisms" may be formulated in terms of the propositional calculus; that they constitute only a very small portion of this calculus, being restricted to the following propositions and their corrollaries:

$*2.16$ $\vdash : p \supset q . \supset . \sim q \supset \sim p$

$*3.33$ $\vdash : p \supset q . q \supset r . \supset . p \supset r$

$*3.35$ $\vdash : p \supset q . p . \supset . q$

cor. $\vdash : p \supset q . \sim q . \supset . \sim p$

together with the two definitions,

$$p \supset q . \equiv \mathrm{df} . \sim p \lor q$$
$$p . q . \equiv \mathrm{df} . \sim (\sim p \lor \sim q)$$

which account for the interchangeability of forms sanctioned by the "laws" of the syllogism. All the "laws" of syllogistic logic are generalized in symbolic logic; instead of making each new exemplification a new and special rule, symbolic logic collects the various analogous cases into one formula, that determines at once which combinations of terms (positive or negative) are valid, which invalid; and having disposed of the syllogism, we are free to construct far more elaborate systems, beyond the scope of rhetorical thinking, even touching the abstract heavens of mathematics.

PROOFS OF THEOREMS 11a AND 11b

THESE are the proofs of theorems 11a and 11b, the associative laws for $+$ and $\times$ respectively, not given in the text (chap. ix, § 4) because of their length and difficulty. The proof of 11a was given by Huntington, following his postulate-set for $K(a, b \ldots) +, \times$ (as theorem 13a).

Theorem 11a

$$(a, b, c) : (a + b) + c = a + (b + c)$$

Dem.

Let $\quad (a + b) + c = x$, and $a + (b + c) = y$

Then $\quad -x = (-a - b) \, \text{-}c$ \hfill Th. 10a

To prove that $x = y$, it is sufficient to show that $-x + y = 1$ and $-xy = 0$.

Lemma 1

$$y + \text{-}a = y + \text{-}b = y + \text{-}c = 1$$

Dem.

$$y + \text{-}a = \text{-}a + [a + (b + c)] = 1$$

Lemma 1 of 10a

$$y + \text{-}b = 1 \, (\text{-}b + y) = (\text{-}b + b) \, (\text{-}b + y)$$
$$= \text{-}b + by \qquad \qquad \text{IIB, V, IVA}$$

$$by = b \, [a + (b + c)] = (ba) + [b \, (b + c)]$$
$$= [(ba) + (bb + bc)] = ba + b = b$$

hence $\quad y + \text{-}b = \text{-}b + b = 1$

Similarly, $\quad y + \text{-}c = 1$

Lemma 2

$$-xa = -xb = -xc = 0$$

Dem.

$$-xa = 0 + \text{-}xa = \text{-}aa + \text{-}xa = a \, \text{-}a$$
$$+ \, a \, \text{-}x = a \, (\text{-}a + \text{-}x)$$

$$a \, (\text{-}a + \text{-}x) = a \, [\text{-}a + (\text{-}a \, \text{-}b) \, \text{-}c]$$
$$= a \, [(\text{-}a + \text{-}ab) \, (\text{-}a + \text{-}c)]$$

$$a \, [\text{-}a \, (\text{-}a + \text{-}c)] = a \, \text{-}a = 0$$

4a

Similarly, $-xb = 0 \cdot -xc = 0$

Lemma 3

$$y + -x = 1 \cdot y -x = 0$$

Dem.

$$y + -x = y + [(-a -b) -c] = [(y + -a)$$
$$(y + -b) (y + -c) = (1 \times 1) 1 = 1$$

$$y -x = -x [a + (b + c)] = -xa +$$
$$(-xb + -xc) = 0 + (0 + 0) = 0$$

Therefore, $y + -x = 1 \cdot y -x = 0$, or: $-x = -y$,
or: $x = y$ Q.E.D.

Theorem 11b

$$(a, b, c) : (ab) c = a(bc)$$

Dem.

$$(ab) c = -[(-a + -b) + -c]$$ 10b

$$a (bc) = -[- a + (-b + -c)]$$
$$(-a + -b) + -c = -a + (-b + -c)$$ 11a

hence $-[(-a + -b) + -c] = -[-a + (-b + -c)]$

or: $(ab) c = a(bc)$ Q E.D.

APPENDIX C

THE CONSTRUCTION AND USE OF TRUTH-TABLES

EVERY proposition is either true or false. A calculus of truth-values begins with propositions assumed to be true, or assumed to be false; what one "calculates" by the very exposition of such a system is the truth-value of propositions determined by the truth values of the elements (propositions) originally assumed. For instance, if p is assumed to be true, $\sim p$ is false; but for any q that does not involve p in its makeup (as it would, if q were $\sim p$, or $r \cdot p$, or $r \vee p$) no truth-value is determined by the fact that p is true. If, however, q is obtained wholly or partly by an operation on p, the truth-value of q depends wholly or partly on that of p. For instance: if p is true, and $q = \sim p$, q is false; if p is true, than $p \vee q$ is true no matter what q is; if p is true, $p \supset q$ is true if and only if q is true; if p is true, $q \supset p$ is true no matter what q is.

In a complete truth-value system, the truth-values of all operationally constructed elements are determined by those of their constituents. If, then, we wish to know what, under various circumstances, would be the truth-value of the elementary proposition $p \vee q$, we can exhibit those circumstances in a "truth-table," or graph, of all the possible truth-relations among p, q, and $p \vee q$, as follows (using T for "is true" and F for "is false," and taking the values of the elements preceding the double-bar as arbitrarily given and varied):

p	q	$p \vee q$
T	T	T
T	F	T
F	T	T
F	F	F

The simplest table is, of course, that which involves only two elements, p and $\sim p$:

$$p \qquad \sim p$$

T	F
F	T

The operation $\sim$ is unary, $\vee$ and . are binary; there are no relations of higher degree in the calculus. Forms like $p \vee q \vee r$ may always be treated as $(p \vee q) \vee r$, $p \vee (q \vee r)$, the truth-values of which are equivalent, as the following table shows:

p	q	r	$p \vee q$	$q \vee r$	$(p \vee q) \vee r$	$p \vee (q \vee r)$
T	T	T	T	T	T	T
T	T	F	T	T	T	T
T	F	T	T	T	T	T
T	F	F	T	F	T	T
F	T	T	T	T	T	T
F	T	F	T	T	T	T
F	F	T	F	T	T	T
F	F	F	F	F	F	F

The table shows that $(p \vee q) \vee r$ and $p \vee (q \vee r)$ are equivalent elements in this truth-value system, because their truth-values are alike under all conditions.

The truth-values of all possible elements in the two-valued calculus of propositions may be determined, therefore, by arbitrarily assuming and varying the values of just two original elements. Since negation yields new elements that look as simple as their progenitors it may appear as though we should list four determining elements, p, $\sim p$, q, and $\sim q$; but if we assume a value for $\sim p$—say, T—then that of p is F; one of the pair is automatically determined whenever the value of the other is arbitrarily assumed. So we may start with the maximum number of terms that any of the operations require, namely two, to determine unambiguously the truth-value of any constructed element; and the systematic nature of the operations may be surveyed in one table:

p	q	$\sim p$	$\sim q$	$p \vee q$	$p \cdot q$
T	T	F	F	T	T
T	F	F	T	T	F
F	T	T	F	T	F
F	F	T	T	F	F

The most prominent operation in the calculus, however, is ⊃, because it is the operation which, on the logical level, permits inference; so, by way of illustrating how a truth-table may be constructed to test the legitimacy of a defined operation, let us look at the conditions under which the elementary proposition $p \supset q$ holds or fails (remember that $p \supset q . = \mathrm{df} . \sim p \vee q$):

p	q	$\sim p$	$\sim p \vee q$
T	T	F	T
T	F	F	F
F	T	T	T
F	F	T	T

It appears from the table that $p \supset q$ always holds except in the case that p is true and q is false, which satisfies the condition for material implication. There are, moreover, no indeterminable cases; the defined operation, ⊃, is legitimate in the calculus, for it yields new elements with determinate truth-values.

A truth-table presents the essential scope of an operation, and may be constructed to show the scope of an entire propositional system, wherefore it is sometimes called the "matrix" of such a system. It shows up inconsistency in the system (if two values are assignable to the same element), incompleteness (if none is assignable in some cases), and incoherence (if it applies to less than all elements).

Some logicians have constructed propositional algebras which either do not admit the dichotomy of "true" and "false," i.e. the law:

$$(p): p = 1 \,.\, \mathbf{V} \,.\, p = 0,$$

or have added further values, such as "p is possible," "p is necessary"; their truth-tables are, in the first case, incomplete, in the second much more complex (which is not a logical fault, only a pedagogical misfortune). A full and excellent treatment of the whole subject of truth-tables and their uses may be found in the *Symbolic Logic* of Lewis and Langford, Chapter VII, to which the student is advised to turn for more detailed study.

SUGGESTIONS FOR FURTHER STUDY

AFTER reading the present Introduction, serious students will probably find themselves drawn to different special fields within the scope of Symbolic Logic. A certain amount of further general reading is highly desirable, and should be undertaken first; after that, the reader should be able to strike out in whatever direction he chooses, pursuing logistics, or postulational theory, or the history of symbolic logic, according to his tastes. The following bibliography is restricted to works available in English. An attempt has been made to list suitable readings in order of exposition, or, where this is patently impossible, in order of difficulty; but of course neither arrangement has been entirely feasible. Anyone who is in need of a more complete bibliography may be referred to the one appended to Lewis's *Survey of Symbolic Logic*, which lists the literature to 1918, and to the *Journal of Symbolic Logic*, Vol. I, No. 4, which consists entirely of a bibliography, from the beginnings of the subject to 1935. (This number may be purchased separately, and may be obtained by addressing Professor Alonzo Church at Princeton University, Princeton, N.J., U.S.A.)

The following works are especially recommended for further study:

GENERAL

1. RUSSELL, B.: "Logic as the Essence of Philosophy," in *Mysticism and Logic*. London: George Allen & Unwin, Ltd., 1918. A general discussion of "logical form" *versus* "content," and its importance for philosophical thinking.

2. ROYCE, J.: "Principles of Logic," in Windelband and Ruge's *Encyclopaedia of the Philosophical Sciences*, Vol. I, Eng. transl. London, 1913. An essay treating logic as the science of forms.

3. LEWIS, C. I.: *Survey of Symbolic Logic*. Berkeley, California. 1918. Out of print, but often available in libraries. Covers in greater detail the systems here set forth, as well as certain systems I have not touched upon.

4. RUSSELL, B.: *The Principles of Mathematics*, Vol. I. Cambridge, 1903. Also out of print, but often available in libraries. Part I, which deals with symbolic logic, is the only part here recommended. Later parts deal entirely with the derivation of mathematics.

5. LEWIS, C. I., and LANGFORD, C. H.: *Symbolic Logic*. New York, 1932. Contains the completed version of the "system of strict implication" introduced in Lewis's *Survey of Symbolic Logic*, as well as some new ventures in logical theory.

6. WHITEHEAD, A. N., and RUSSELL, B.: *Principia Mathematica*, Vol. I, 1st ed. Cambridge, 1910, 2nd ed. 1925. Sections A and B of this great work should now be attempted.

LOGISTICS

1. RUSSELL, B.: "The Theory of Continuity," "The Problem of Infinity," "The Positive Theory of Infinity": all in *Our Knowledge of the External World*. (London: George Allen & Unwin, Ltd., and New York.) These are very readable essays, and therefore a good initiation to the difficult problems of mathematics. Since Russell has been the most active and prolific English writer on logistics, it is natural that the next works to be recommended are also his.

2. —— *Introduction to Mathematical Philosophy*. London: George Allen & Unwin, Ltd., 1919. A brief but masterly presentation.

3. —— *The Principles of Mathematics*, Vol. I (no later volume has appeared). The later parts may now be read.

4. DEDEKIND, R.: *Essays on the Theory of Numbers*. Eng. transl. Chicago, 1909. Two contributions by one of the German pioneers in logistics.

5. LEWIS, C. I.: "Types of Order and the System Σ" (among *Papers in Honour of Josiah Royce on his Sixtieth Birthday*), *Philosophical Review*, 1916. Expounds the logic of Royce.

6. QUINE, W. V. O.: *A System of Logistic*. Cambridge, Mass., 1934. A difficult but significant little book.

POSTULATE THEORY

1. YOUNG, J. W.: *Lectures on the Fundamental Concepts of Algebra and Geometry*. New York, 1911. This book, though from its title one would expect to find it under LOGISTICS, is a clear and not too difficult introduction to the technique of choosing postulates and deducing theorems, i.e. of constructing deductive systems.

2. HUNTINGTON, E. V.: "Sets of Independent Postulates for the Algebra of Logic," in *Transactions of the American Mathe-*

matical Society, Vol. 5, pp. 288–309 (1904). This is the paper from which the postulate-sets for Boolean algebra, employed in this book, have been taken.

3. HUNTINGTON, E. V: "Postulates for Assertion, Conjunction, Negation, and Equality." *Proc. Am. Acad. of Arts and Science*, Vol. 72, No. 1 (1937).

4. HILBERT, D.: *Foundations of Geometry*. Chicago, 1910. A discussion of postulate-technique by an eminent mathematician and mathematical logician.

5. HUNTINGTON, E. V.: *The Continuum as a Type of Order*. Cambridge, Mass., 1917.

Further postulate-sets worthy of study are:

SHEFFER, H. M.: "A Set of Five Independent Postulates for Boolean Algebras, with Application to Logical Constants." *Trans. Amer. Math. Soc.*, Vol. 14 (1913). This paper is important for the introduction of the "stroke function," adopted by Whitehead and Russell in their second edition of *Principia Mathematica*.

BERNSTEIN, B. A.: "A Set of Four Independent Postulates for Boolean Algebras." *Trans. Amer. Math. Soc.*, Vol. 17 (1916).

HUNTINGTON, E. V.: "A Set of Independent Postulates for Cyclic Order." *Proc. Nat. Acad. Sci.*, Vol. 2 (1916), No. 11.

—— "Complete Existential Theory of the Postulates for Serial Order." *Amer. Math. Soc. Bull.*, Vol. 23 (1917).

—— "New Sets of Independent Postulates." *Trans. Amer. Math. Soc.*, Vol. 35 (1933).

HUNTINGTON, E. V., and KLINE, J. R.: "Sets of Independent Postulates for Betweenness." *Trans. Amer. Math. Soc.*, Vol. 18 (1917).

—— "A New Set of Postulates for Betweenness." *Trans. Amer. Math. Soc.*, Vol. 25 (1924).

CHURCH, A.: "On Irredundant Sets of Postulates." *Trans. Amer. Math. Soc.*, Vol. 27 (1925).

HISTORICAL

1. SHEARMAN, A. T.: *The Development of Symbolic Logic*. London, 1906. A general history, brief and readable.

2. LEWIS, C. I.: *Survey of Symbolic Logic*, Chap. 1. More detailed study of really significant phases of, and the chief contributors to, symbolic logic.

After these introductory readings, the student may be referred to the chief historical sources (such as are available in English):

3. DE MORGAN, A.: *Formal Logic*. London, 1847.

4. BOOLE, G.: *An Investigation of the Laws of Thought*. London, 1857. Reprinted as Vol. 2 of Boole's *Collected Logical Works*, Chicago, 1916. This is the original presentation of the "Algebra of Logic," from which symbolic logic may be said to have sprung.

5. MACCOLL, H.: *Symbolic Logic and Its Applications*. London, 1906. Presents a system of logic which is not a "Boolean" system.

6. LADD-FRANKLIN, C.: "On the Algebra of Logic,"

7. MITCHELL, O. H.: "On a New Algebra of Logic,"

8. PEIRCE, C. S.: "The Logic of Relatives."

   All three in *Studies in Logic* by Members of Johns Hopkins University, Boston, 1883. These three papers, besides being of considerable intrinsic interest as so many experiments in the formulation of "logical algebras," afford excellent practice in reading a variety of symbolisms.

9. FREGE, G.: Translated Portions of his Works in *The Monist*, Vols. 25 (1915), 26 (1916), 27 (1917). One of Russell's most important sources, not easily available. Hard to read because of unfortunate symbolism.

10. COUTURAT, L.: *The Algebra of Logic*. Eng. Transl. Chicago, 1914. A summing-up of the "Boole-Schroeder Algebra," inclusive of the two-valued algebra of propositions. Couturat uses $<$ both for inclusion and implication, in the same proposition. The task of distinguishing its "constituent" uses from its "logical" ones affords a good exercise.

ADDENDA, 1952

The following books, valuable to students of this Introduction, have appeared since its original publication:

1. COOLEY, JOHN C.: *A Primer of Formal Logic*. N.Y.: The Macmillan Co., 1946. A useful, straightforward textbook.

2. REICHENBACH, HANS: *Elements of Symbolic Logic*. N.Y.: The Macmillan Co., 1947.

3. TARSKI, ALFRED: *Introduction to Logic, and to the Methodology of the Deductive Sciences*. Transl. by Olaf Helmer. N.Y.: Oxford University Press, 1941. An authoritative work, not

easy, but rewarding; discusses the bases of arithmetical operations, and offers many exercises.

4. QUINE, WILLARD V. O.: *Methods of Logic.*

5. CARNAP, RUDOLF: *Foundations of Logic and Mathematics.* Chicago: University of Chicago Press, 1939 (fifth impression 1949). Vol. I, No. 3, of the International Encyclopaedia of Unified Science. A semantic treatment of logic.

6. WOODGER, J. H.: *The Technique of Theory Construction.* Chicago: University of Chicago Press, 1939 (second impression 1947). Vol. II, No. 5, of the International Encyclopaedia of Unified Science.

7. ROSENBLOOM, PAUL: *The Elements of Mathematical Logic.* N.Y.: Dover Publications, 1950. A book for mathematicians who wish to be introduced to symbolic logic.

INDEX

Absorption: *see under* Law

Abstraction: and generalization, 17, 240 f.; nature of, 33 ff., 38, 42 f.; fear of, 34, 43; and interpretation, chap. X, *passim*; how attained, 245, 262

Addition, Principle of: 298

Adinity: 50 n.

Algebra: kinds of, 17; and abstraction, 34; definition of, 207; *see also* Boolean algebra

Analogy: chap. I, sect. 5, *passim*; as common form, 29, 258 f.; as "logical picture," 29 ff.; and representation, 30 ff., 42; among propositions, 84, 301 f.

Application, Principle of: 210, 236, 300 f.

Argument: to a function, 319 ff., 335

ARISTOTLE: *see* Traditional logic

Assertion: of relationships, 51; understood, 52, 61; joint, *see* Conjunction; total, 86; about assertions, 291, 309; as primitive idea, 292, 296, 306 n., 309; sign of, 293 f.; principle of, 305

Axiom: 184 f.

BOOLE, GEORGE: 90, 208, 254, 313

Boolean Algebra: 17 f., 174, 208, 236; abstract, 253 ff., 264, 305 f.; interpretations for, 255; two-valued, 260 ff., 264, 270, 282; and logistic, 294 f., 335; and traditional logic, Appendix A, *passim*

Boole-Schroeder Algebra: *see* Boolean algebra

Calculus: nature of, 199 f., 235; of classes, 200, 203, 235 f.; formality of, 235, 238; of propositions, chap. XI, *passim*, 287; of elementary propositions, 295–308, *passim*, 309, 314, 335; of truth-values, *see* Truth-values; of general propositions, 322-326, *passim*, 335; of relations, 329 f., 337

CARNAP, RUDOLPH: 18

CHAPMAN, F. MILLER: 259

Class: symbol for, 69, 327; nature of, 114 f.; and concept, 115 f., 130; sub-, 117 ff., 130; unit-, 119, 131, 317; null-, 122 f., 128, 131, 144, 147, 169, 172, 344; universe-, 123, 127, 131, 144, 170 f., 172; intension of, 125, 153; extension of, 125 f., 153, 330; identity of —es, 125 ff., 131, 327; complementary, 143 f., 147 ff., 154, 194, 218, 223; sums and products of —es, 138 f., 153 f., 194, 223 f., 327; in traditional logic, 160; as constructs, 160 f., 166, 326, 336; as primitive concept, 167, 170, 179; similar —es, 317, 335; and predicates, 159 f., 164 f., 177

Tautology: *see under* Law

Terms: *see* Element

Theorems: nature of, 186 f., 202; elementary, 211; of *Principia Mathematica*, 300

Proof of: 1a, 213; 2b, 214; 3a, 215; 4b, 217; 5a, 218; 6, 219; 7, 219; 11a, 350 f.; 11b, 351; 10a, 221 f.; 12, 126; 13, 227; 14a, 228; 15a, 228; 16, 228 f.; 17a, 229; 18b, 229; 19, 229 f.; 21, 231; *1.6, 299 n.; *2.02, 300 f.; *2.04, 302; *2.05, 302; *2.06, 302 f.; *2.21, 303

Theory of Types: 324 n.

Traditional Logic: sympolic expression of, 17; typical propositions of, 106 f.; dichotomy in, 142; predicates in, 157, 160; and classes, 160; and Boolean algebra, 262, Appendix A, *passim*; and syllogism, 303

Transitivity: 247 f., 251, 263

Transposition: *see* Contraposition *under* Law

Truth: and falsity, 71, 73, 76, 80, 90 f., 108, 270, 296, 309; of premises, 184 f., 202; and validity, 188 f., 202

Truth-value: meaning of, 71, 73, 80; granted, 82; consistent —s, 76; and propositions, 90, 97, 306; of postulates and theorems, 188; calculus of —s, 273 ff., 284, 288, 321

Universe of Discourse: 68 f., 70, 79, 82 f., 101; generalized, 103; dichotomy of, 142 ff., 153; confusion with 1, 170 f.; greatest, 242 f.

Value: for variable, 87 ff., 108 f., 117 f., 121, 130, 177, 260; for propositional form, *see* Propositional form; exemplary, 261; interpretational, 261

Variable: 85–93, *passim*, 108 f., 207; relation-, 244, 264; *see also* Value

VENN, JOHN: 170

Verbs: as names of relations, 50 f.; double function of, 51; auxiliary, 51, 56; and assertions, 293

WHITEHEAD, ALFRED N.: 90

WHITEHEAD and RUSSELL: *Principia Mathematica* of, 18, 90, 135 n., 282, 285, chap. XII, *passim*, 314 f., 330 ff., 337; cited, 304 f., 306 f.

YOUNG, JOHN W.: 207

CATALOG OF DOVER BOOKS

BOOKS EXPLAINING SCIENCE AND MATHEMATICS

THE COMMON SENSE OF THE EXACT SCIENCES, W. K. Clifford. Introduction by James Newman, edited by Karl Pearson. For 70 years this has been a guide to classical scientific and mathematical thought. Explains with unusual clarity basic concepts, such as extension of meaning of symbols, characteristics of surface boundaries, properties of plane figures, vectors, Cartesian method of determining position, etc. Long preface by Bertrand Russell. Bibliography of Clifford. Corrected, 130 diagrams redrawn. 249pp. 5⅜ x 8.
T61 Paperbound **$1.60**

SCIENCE THEORY AND MAN, Erwin Schrödinger. This is a complete and unabridged reissue of SCIENCE AND THE HUMAN TEMPERAMENT plus an additional essay: "What is an Elementary Particle?" Nobel Laureate Schrödinger discusses such topics as nature of scientific method, the nature of science, chance and determinism, science and society, conceptual models for physical entities, elementary particles and wave mechanics. Presentation is popular and may be followed by most people with little or no scientific training. "Fine practical preparation for a time when laws of nature, human institutions . . . are undergoing a critical examination without parallel," Waldemar Kaempffert, N. Y. TIMES. 192pp. 5⅜ x 8.
T428 Paperbound **$1.35**

PIONEERS OF SCIENCE, O. Lodge. Eminent scientist-expositor's authoritative, yet elementary survey of great scientific theories. Concentrating on individuals—Copernicus, Brahe, Kepler, Galileo, Descartes, Newton, Laplace, Herschel, Lord Kelvin, and other scientists—the author presents their discoveries in historical order adding biographical material on each man and full, specific explanations of their achievements. The clear and complete treatment of the post-Newtonian astronomers is a feature seldom found in other books on the subject. Index. 120 illustrations. xv + 404pp. 5⅜ x 8.
T716 Paperbound **$1.50**

THE EVOLUTION OF SCIENTIFIC THOUGHT FROM NEWTON TO EINSTEIN, A. d'Abro. Einstein's special and general theories of relativity, with their historical implications, are analyzed in non-technical terms. Excellent accounts of the contributions of Newton, Riemann, Weyl, Planck, Eddington, Maxwell, Lorentz and others are treated in terms of space and time, equations of electromagnetics, finiteness of the universe, methodology of science. 21 diagrams. 482pp. 5⅜ x 8.
T2 Paperbound **$2.00**

THE RISE OF THE NEW PHYSICS, A. d'Abro. A half-million word exposition, formerly titled THE DECLINE OF MECHANISM, for readers not versed in higher mathematics. The only thorough explanation, in everyday language, of the central core of modern mathematical physical theory, treating both classical and modern theoretical physics, and presenting in terms almost anyone can understand the equivalent of 5 years of study of mathematical physics. Scientifically impeccable coverage of mathematical-physical thought from the Newtonian system up through the electronic theories of Dirac and Heisenberg and Fermi's statistics. Combines both history and exposition; provides a broad yet unified and detailed view, with constant comparison of classical and modern views on phenomena and theories. "A must for anyone doing serious study in the physical sciences," JOURNAL OF THE FRANKLIN INSTITUTE. "Extraordinary faculty . . . to explain ideas and theories of theoretical physics in the language of daily life," ISIS. First part of set covers philosophy of science, drawing upon the practice of Newton, Maxwell, Poincaré, Einstein, others, discussing modes of thought, experiment, interpretations of causality, etc. In the second part, 100 pages explain grammar and vocabulary of mathematics, with discussions of functions, groups, series, Fourier series, etc. The remainder is devoted to concrete, detailed coverage of both classical and quantum physics, explaining such topics as analytic mechanics, Hamilton's principle, wave theory of light, electromagnetic waves, groups of transformations, thermodynamics, phase rule, Brownian movement, kinetics, special relativity, Planck's original quantum theory, Bohr's atom, Zeeman effect, Broglie's wave mechanics, Heisenberg's uncertainty, Eigen-values, matrices, scores of other important topics. Discoveries and theories are covered for such men as Alembert, Born, Cantor, Debye, Euler, Foucault, Galois, Gauss, Hadamard, Kelvin, Kepler, Laplace, Maxwell, Pauli, Rayleigh, Volterra, Weyl, Young, more than 180 others. Indexed. 97 illustrations. ix + 982pp. 5⅜ x 8.
T3 Volume 1, Paperbound **$2.00**
T4 Volume 2, Paperbound **$2.00**

CONCERNING THE NATURE OF THINGS, Sir William Bragg. Christmas lectures delivered at the Royal Society by Nobel laureate. Why a spinning ball travels in a curved track; how uranium is transmuted to lead, etc. Partial contents: atoms, gases, liquids, crystals, metals, etc. No scientific background needed; wonderful for intelligent child. 32pp. of photos, 57 figures. xii + 232pp. 5⅜ x 8.
T31 Paperbound **$1.35**

THE UNIVERSE OF LIGHT, Sir William Bragg. No scientific training needed to read Nobel Prize winner's expansion of his Royal Institute Christmas Lectures: Insight into nature of light, methods and philosophy of science. Explains lenses, reflection, color, resonance, polarization, x-rays, the spectrum, Newton's work with prisms, Huygens' with polarization, Crookes' with cathode ray, etc. Leads into clear statement of 2 major historical theories of light, corpuscle and wave. Dozens of experiments you can do. 199 illus., including 2 full-page color plates. 293pp. 5⅜ x 8.
S538 Paperbound **$1.85**

TEACH YOURSELF books. For adult self-study, for refresher and supplementary study.

The most effective series of home study mathematics books on the market! With absolutely no outside help, they will teach you as much as any similar college or high-school course, or will helpfully supplement any such course. Each step leads directly to the next, each question is anticipated. Numerous lucid examples and carefully-wrought practice problems illustrate meanings. Not skimpy outlines, not surveys, not usual classroom texts, these 204- to 380-page books are packed with the finest instruction you'll find anywhere for adult self-study.

TEACH YOURSELF ALGEBRA, P. Abbott. Formulas, coordinates, factors, graphs of quadratic functions, quadratic equations, logarithms, ratio, irrational numbers, arithmetical, geometrical series, much more. 1241 problems, solutions. Tables. 52 illus. 307pp. 6⅞ x 4¼.
Clothbound **$2.00**

TEACH YOURSELF GEOMETRY, P. Abbott. Solids, lines, points, surfaces, angle measurement, triangles, theorem of Pythagoras, polygons, loci, the circle, tangents, symmetry, solid geometry, prisms, pyramids, solids of revolution, etc. 343 problems, solutions. 268 illus. 334pp. 6⅞ x 4¼.
Clothbound **$2.00**

TEACH YOURSELF TRIGONOMETRY, P. Abbott. Geometrical foundations, indices, logarithms, trigonometrical ratios, relations between sides, angles of triangle, circular measure, trig. ratios of angles of any magnitude, much more. Requires elementary algebra, geometry. 465 problems, solutions. Tables. 102 illus. 204pp. 6⅞ x 4¼. Clothbound **$2.00**

TEACH YOURSELF THE CALCULUS, P. Abbott. Variations in functions, differentiation, solids of revolution, series, elementary differential equations, areas by integral calculus, much more. Requires algebra, trigonometry. 970 problems, solutions. Tables. 89 illus. 380pp. 6⅞ x 4¼.
Clothbound **$2.00**

TEACH YOURSELF THE SLIDE RULE, B. Snodgrass. Fractions, decimals, A-D scales, log-log scales, trigonometrical scales, indices, logarithms. Commercial, precision, electrical, dualistic, Brighton rules. 80 problems, solutions. 10 illus. 207pp. 6⅞ x 4¼.   Clothbound **$2.00**

See also: **TEACH YOURSELF ELECTRICITY, C. W. Wilman; TEACH YOURSELF HEAT ENGINES, E. De Ville; TEACH YOURSELF MECHANICS, P. Abbott.**

$$* \qquad * \qquad *$$

HOW DO YOU USE A SLIDE RULE? by A. A. Merrill. Not a manual for mathematicians and engineers, but a lucid step-by-step explanation that presents the fundamental rules clearly enough to be understood by anyone who could benefit by the use of a slide rule in his work or business. This work concentrates on the 2 most important operations: multiplication and division. 10 easy lessons, each with a clear drawing, will save you countless hours in your banking, business, statistical, and other work. First publication. Index. 2 Appendixes. 10 illustrations. 78 problems, all with answers. vi + 36pp. 6⅛ x 9¼.   T62 Paperbound **60¢**

THEORY OF OPERATION OF THE SLIDE RULE, J. P. Ellis. Not a skimpy "instruction manual", but an exhaustive treatment that will save you uncounted hours throughout your career. Supplies full understanding of every scale on the Log Log Duplex Decitrig type of slide rule. Shows the most time-saving methods, and provides practice useful in the widest variety of actual engineering situations. Each operation introduced in terms of underlying logarithmic theory. Summary of prerequisite math. First publication. Index. 198 figures. Over 450 problems with answers. Bibliography. 12 Appendices. ix + 289pp. 5⅜ x 8.
S727 Paperbound **$1.50**

ARITHMETICAL EXCURSIONS: AN ENRICHMENT OF ELEMENTARY MATHEMATICS, H. Bowers and J. Bowers. For students who want unusual methods of arithmetic never taught in school; for adults who want to increase their number sense. Little known facts about the most simple numbers, arithmetical entertainments and puzzles, figurate numbers, number chains, mysteries and folklore of numbers, the "Hin-dog-abic" number system, etc. First publication. Index. 529 numbered problems and diversions, all with answers. Bibliography. 50 figures. xiv + 320pp. 5⅜ x 8.   T770 Paperbound **$1.65**

APPLIED MATHEMATICS FOR RADIO AND COMMUNICATIONS ENGINEERS, C. E. Smith. No extraneous material here!—only the theories, equations, and operations essential and immediately useful for radio work. Can be used as refresher, as handbook of applications and tables, or as full home-study course. Ranges from simplest arithmetic through calculus, series, and wave forms, hyperbolic trigonometry, simultaneous equations in mesh circuits, etc. Supplies applications right along with each math topic discussed. 22 useful tables of functions, formulas, logs, etc. Index. 166 exercises, 140 examples, all with answers. 95 diagrams. Bibliography. x + 336pp. 5⅜ x 8.   S141 Paperbound **$1.75**

HIGHER MATHEMATICS FOR STUDENTS OF CHEMISTRY AND PHYSICS, J. W. Mellor. Not abstract but practical, building its problems out of familiar laboratory material, this covers differential calculus, coordinate, analytical geometry, functions, integral calculus, infinite series numerical equations, differential equations, Fourier's theorem, probability, theory of errors calculus of variations, determinants. "If the reader is not familiar with this book, it will repay him to examine it," CHEM. & ENGINEERING NEWS. 800 problems. 189 figures. Bibliography. xxi + 641pp. 5⅜ x 8. S193 Paperbound **$2.2**

TRIGONOMETRY REFRESHER FOR TECHNICAL MEN, A. Albert Klaf. 913 detailed questions and answers cover the most important aspects of plane and spherical trigonometry. They will help you to brush up or to clear up difficulties in special areas. The first portion of this book covers plane trigonometry, including angles, quadrants, trigonometrical functions, graphical representation, interpolation, equations, logarithms, solution of triangle, use of the slide rule and similar topics. 188 pages then discuss application of plane trigonometry to special problems in navigation, surveying, elasticity, architecture, and various fields of engineering Small angles, periodic functions, vectors, polar coordinates, de Moivre's theorem are fully examined. The third section of the book then discusses spherical trigonometry and the solution of spherical triangles, with their applications to terrestrial and astronomical problems. Methods of saving time with numerical calculations, simplification of principal functions of angle, much practical information make this a most useful book. 913 questions answered. 1738 problems, answers to odd numbers. 494 figures. 24 pages of useful formulae functions. Index. x + 629pp. 5⅜ x 8. T371 Paperbound **$2.0**

CALCULUS REFRESHER FOR TECHNICAL MEN, A. Albert Klaf. This book is unique in English as a refresher for engineers, technicians, students who either wish to brush up their calculus or to clear up uncertainties. It is not an ordinary text, but an examination of most important aspects of integral and differential calculus in terms of the 756 question most likely to occur to the technical reader. The first part of this book covers simple differential calculus, with constants, variables, functions, increments, derivatives, differentiation logarithms, curvature of curves, and similar topics. The second part covers fundamental ideas of integration, inspection, substitution, transformation, reduction, areas and volumes mean value, successive and partial integration, double and triple integration. Practical aspects are stressed rather than theoretical. A 50-page section illustrates the application of calculus to specific problems of civil and nautical engineering, electricity, stress and strain, elasticity, industrial engineering, and similar fields.—756 questions answered. 56 problems, mostly answered. 36 pages of useful constants, formulae for ready reference Index. v + 431pp. 5⅜ x 8. T370 Paperbound **$2.0**

TEXTBOOK OF ALGEBRA, G. Chrystal. One of the great mathematical textbooks, still about the best source for complete treatments of the topics of elementary algebra; a chief reference work for teachers and students of algebra in advanced high school and university courses, or for the mathematician working on problems of elementary algebra or looking for a background to more advanced topics. Ranges from basic laws and processes to extensive examination of such topics as limits, infinite series, general properties of integral numbers, and probability theory. Emphasis is on algebraic form, the foundation of analytical geometry and the key to modern developments in algebra. Prior course in algebra is desirable, but not absolutely necessary. Includes theory of quotients, distribution of products, arithmetical theory of surds theory of interest, permutations and combinations, general expansion theorems, recurring fractions, and much, much more. Two volume set. Index in each volume. Over 1500 exercises approximately half with answers. Total of xlviii + 1187pp. 5⅜ x 8.
S750 Vol I Paperbound **$2.3**
S751 Vol II Paperbound **$2.3**
The set **$4.7**

COLLEGE ALGEBRA, H. B. Fine. Standard college text that gives a systematic and deductive structure to algebra; comprehensive, connected, with emphasis on theory. Discusses the commutative, associative, and distributive laws of number in unusual detail, and goes on with undetermined coefficients, quadratic equations, progressions, logarithms, permutations probability, power series, and much more. Still most valuable elementary-intermediate text on the science and structure of algebra. Index. 1560 problems, all with answers. x + 631pp. 5⅜ x 8. T211 Paperbound **$2.00**

THE CONTINUUM AND OTHER TYPES OF SERIAL ORDER, E. V. Huntington. This famous book gives a systematic elementary account of the modern theory of the continuum as a type of serial order. Based on the Cantor-Dedekind ordinal theory, which requires no technical knowledge of higher mathematics, it offers an easily followed analysis of ordered classes, discrete and dense series, continuous series, Cantor's transfinite numbers. 2nd edition. Index. viii + 82pp. 5⅜ x 8.
S129 Clothbound **$2.75**
S130 Paperbound **$1.00**

A TREATISE ON PLANE AND ADVANCED TRIGONOMETRY, E. W. Hobson. Extraordinarily wide coverage, going beyond usual college level trig, one of the few works covering advanced trig in full detail. By a great expositor with unerring anticipation and lucid clarification of potentially difficult points. Includes circular functions; expansion of functions of multiple angle; trig tables; relations between sides and angles of triangle; complex numbers; etc. Many problems solved completely. "The best work on the subject." Nature. Formerly entitled "A Treatise on Plane Trigonometry." 689 examples. 6 figures. xvi + 383pp. 5⅜ x 8.
S353 Paperbound **$1.95**

FAMOUS PROBLEMS OF ELEMENTARY GEOMETRY, Felix Klein. Expanded version of the 1894 Easter lectures at Göttingen. 3 problems of classical geometry, in an excellent mathematical treatment by a famous mathematician: squaring the circle, trisecting angle, doubling cube. Considered with full modern implications: transcendental numbers, pi, etc. Notes by R. Archibald. 16 figures. xi + 92pp. 5⅜ x 8.   T348 Clothbound **$1.50**
                                                                        T298 Paperbound **$1.00**

*   *   *

ELEMENTARY MATHEMATICS FROM AN ADVANCED STANDPOINT, Felix Klein.

This classic text is an outgrowth of Klein's famous integration and survey course at Göttingen. Using one field of mathematics to interpret, adjust, illuminate another, it covers basic topics in each area, illustrating its discussion with extensive analysis. It is especially valuable in considering areas of modern mathematics. "Makes the reader feel the inspiration of . . . a great mathematician, inspiring teacher . . . with deep insight into the foundations and interrelations," BULLETIN, AMERICAN MATHEMATICAL SOCIETY.

Vol. 1. ARITHMETIC, ALGEBRA, ANALYSIS. Introducing the concept of function immediately, it enlivens abstract discussion with graphical and geometrically perceptual methods. Partial contents: natural numbers, extension of the notion of number, special properties, complex numbers. Real equations with real unknowns, complex quantities. Logarithmic, exponential functions, goniometric functions, infinitesimal calculus. Transcendence of e and pi, theory of assemblages. Index. 125 figures. ix + 274pp . 5⅜ x 8.   S150 Paperbound **$1.75**

Vol. 2. GEOMETRY. A comprehensive view which accompanies the space perception inherent in geometry with analytic formulas which facilitate precise formulation. Partial contents: Simplest geometric manifolds: line segment, Grassmann determinant principles, classification of configurations of space, derivative manifolds. Geometric transformations: affine transformations, projective, higher point transformations, theory of the imaginary. Systematic discussion of geometry and its foundations. Indexes. 141 illustrations. ix + 214pp. 5⅜ x 8.
                                                                        S151 Paperbound **$1.75**

*   *   *

COORDINATE GEOMETRY, L. P. Eisenhart. Thorough, unified introduction. Unusual for advancing in dimension within each topic (treats together circle, sphere; polar coordinates, 3-dimensional coordinate systems; conic sections, quadric surfaces), affording exceptional insight into subject. Extensive use made of determinants, though no previous knowledge of them is assumed. Algebraic equations of 1st degree, 2 and 3 unknowns, carried further than usual in algebra courses. Over 500 exercises. Introduction. Appendix. Index. Bibliography. 43 illustrations. 310pp. 5⅜ x 8.   S600 Paperbound **$1.65**

MONOGRAPHS ON TOPICS OF MODERN MATHEMATICS, edited by J. W. A. Young. Advanced mathematics for persons who haven't gone beyond or have forgotten high school algebra. 9 monographs on foundation of geometry, modern pure geometry, non-Euclidean geometry, fundamental propositions of algebra, algebraic equations, functions, calculus, theory of numbers, etc. Each monograph gives proofs of important results, and descriptions of leading methods, to provide wide coverage. New introduction by Prof. M. Kline, N. Y. University. 100 diagrams. xvi + 416pp. 6⅛ x 9¼.   S289 Paperbound **$2.00**

MATHEMATICS, INTERMEDIATE TO ADVANCED

Geometry

THE FOUNDATIONS OF EUCLIDEAN GEOMETRY, H. G. Forder. The first rigorous account of Euclidean geometry, establishing propositions without recourse to empiricism, and without multiplying hypotheses. Corrects many traditional weaknesses of Euclidean proofs, and investigates the problems imposed on the axiom system by the discoveries of Bolya and Lobatchefsky. Some topics discussed are Classes and Relations; Axioms for Magnitudes; Congruence and Similarity; Algebra of Points; Hessenberg's Theorem; Continuity; Existence of Parallels; Reflections; Rotations; Isometries; etc. Invaluable for the light it throws on foundations of math. Lists: Axioms employed, Symbols, Constructions. 295pp. 5⅜ x 8.
                                                                        S481 Paperbound **$2.00**

ADVANCED EUCLIDEAN GEOMETRY, R. A. Johnson. For years the standard textbook on advanced Euclidean geometry, requires only high school geometry and trigonometry. Explores in unusual detail and gives proofs of hundreds of relatively recent theorems and corollaries, many formerly available only in widely scattered journals. Covers tangent circles, the theorem of Miquel, symmedian point, pedal triangles and circles, the Brocard configuration, and much more. Formerly "Modern Geometry." Index. 107 diagrams. xiii + 319pp. 5⅜ x 8.
                                                                        S669 Paperbound **$1.65**

NON-EUCLIDEAN GEOMETRY, Roberto Bonola. The standard coverage of non-Euclidean geometry. It examines from both a historical and mathematical point of view the geometries which have arisen from a study of Euclid's 5th postulate upon parallel lines. Also included are complete texts, translated, of Bolyai's THEORY OF ABSOLUTE SPACE, Lobachevsky's THEORY OF PARALLELS. 180 diagrams. 431pp. 5⅜ x 8.   S27 Paperbound **$1.95**

ELEMENTS OF NON-EUCLIDEAN GEOMETRY, D. M. Y. Sommerville. Unique in proceeding step-by-step, in the manner of traditional geometry. Enables the student with only a good knowledge of high school algebra and geometry to grasp elementary hyperbolic, elliptic, analytic non-Euclidean geometries; space curvature and its philosophical implications; theory of radical axes; homothetic centres and systems of circles; parataxy and parallelism; absolute measure; Gauss' proof of the defect area theorem; geodesic representation; much more, all with exceptional clarity. 126 problems at chapter endings provide progressive practice and familiarity. 133 figures. Index. xvi + 274pp. 5⅜ x 8.   S460 Paperbound **$1.50**

HIGHER GEOMETRY: AN INTRODUCTION TO ADVANCED METHODS IN ANALYTIC GEOMETRY, F. S. Woods. Exceptionally thorough study of concepts and methods of advanced algebraic geometry (as distinguished from differential geometry). Exhaustive treatment of 1-, 2-, 3-, and 4-dimensional coordinate systems, leading to n-dimensional geometry in an abstract sense. Covers projectivity, tetracyclical coordinates, contact transformation, pentaspherical coordinates, much more. Based on M.I.T. lectures, requires sound preparation in analytic geometry and some knowledge of determinants. Index. Over 350 exercises. References. 60 figures. x + 423pp. 5⅜ x 8.   S737 Paperbound **$2.00**

ELEMENTS OF PROJECTIVE GEOMETRY, L. Cremona. Outstanding complete treatment of projective geometry by one of the foremost 19th century geometers. Detailed proofs of all fundamental principles, stress placed on the constructive aspects. Covers homology, law of duality, anharmonic ratios, theorems of Pascal and Brianchon, foci, polar reciprocal figures, etc. Only ordinary geometry necessary to understand this honored classic. Index. Over 150 fully worked out examples and problems. 252 diagrams. xx + 302pp. 5⅜ x 8.   S668 Paperbound **$1.75**

A TREATISE ON THE DIFFERENTIAL GEOMETRY OF CURVES AND SURFACES, L. P. Eisenhart. Introductory treatise especially for the graduate student, for years a highly successful textbook. More detailed and concrete in approach than most more recent books. Covers space curves, osculating planes, moving axes, Gauss' method, the moving trihedral, geodesics, conformal representation, etc. Last section deals with deformation of surfaces, rectilinear congruences, cyclic systems, etc. Index. 683 problems. 30 diagrams. xii + 474pp. 5⅜ x 8.
                                                            S667 Paperbound **$2.75**

A TREATISE ON ALGEBRAIC PLANE CURVES, J. L. Coolidge. Unabridged reprinting of one of few full coverages in English, offering detailed introduction to theory of algebraic plane curves and their relations to geometry and analysis. Treats topological properties, Riemann-Roch theorem, all aspects of wide variety of curves including real, covariant, polar, containing series of a given sort, elliptic, polygonal, rational, the pencil, two parameter nets, etc. This volume will enable the reader to appreciate the symbolic notation of Aronhold and Clebsch. Bibliography. Index. 17 illustrations. xxiv + 513pp. 5⅜ x 8. S543 Paperbound **$2.45**

AN INTRODUCTION TO THE GEOMETRY OF N DIMENSIONS, D. M. Y. Sommerville. An introduction presupposing no prior knowledge of the field, the only book in English devoted exclusively to higher dimensional geometry. Discusses fundamental ideas of incidence, parallelism, perpendicularity, angles between linear space; enumerative geometry; analytical geometry from projective and metric points of view; polytopes; elementary ideas in analysis situs; content of hyper-spacial figures. Bibliography. Index. 60 diagrams. 196pp. 5⅜ x 8.
                                                            S494 Paperbound **$1.50**

GEOMETRY OF FOUR DIMENSIONS, H. P. Manning. Unique in English as a clear, concise introduction. Treatment is synthetic, and mostly Euclidean, although in hyperplanes and hyperspheres at infinity, non-Euclidean geometry is used. Historical introduction. Foundations of 4-dimensional geometry. Perpendicularity, simple angles. Angles of planes, higher order. Symmetry, order, motion; hyperpyramids, hypercones, hyperspheres; figures with parallel elements; volume, hypervolume in space; regular polyhedroids. Glossary. 78 figures. ix + 348pp. 5⅜ x 8.   S182 Paperbound **$1.95**

ELEMENTARY CONCEPTS OF TOPOLOGY, P. Alexandroff. First English translation of the famous brief introduction to topology for the beginner or for the mathematician not undertaking extensive study. This unusually useful intuitive approach deals primarily with the concepts of complex, cycle, and homology, and is wholly consistent with current investigations. Ranges from basic concepts of set-theoretic topology to the concept of Betti groups. "Glowing example of harmony between intuition and thought," David Hilbert. Translated by A. E. Farley. Introduction by D. Hilbert. Index. 25 figures. 73pp. 5⅜ x 8.   S747 Paperbound **$1.00**

THE WORKS OF ARCHIMEDES, edited by T. L. Heath. All the known works of the great Greek mathematician are contained in this one volume, including the recently discovered Method of Archimedes. Contains: On Sphere & Cylinder, Measurement of a Circle, Spirals, Conoids, Spheroids, etc. This is the definitive edition of the greatest mathematical intellect of the ancient world. 186-page study by Heath discusses Archimedes and the history of Greek mathematics. Bibliography. 563pp. 5⅜ x 8.   S9 Paperbound **$2.00**

THE THIRTEEN BOOKS OF EUCLID'S ELEMENTS, edited by **Sir Thomas Heath.** Definitive edition of one of the very greatest classics of Western world. Complete English translation of Heiberg text, together with spurious Book XIV. Detailed 150-page introduction discussing aspects of Greek and Medieval mathematics. Euclid, texts, commentators, etc. Paralleling the text is an elaborate critical apparatus analyzing each definition, proposition, postulate, covering textual matters, mathematical analysis, commentators of all times, refutations, supports, extrapolations, etc. This is the FULL EUCLID. Unabridged reproduction of Cambridge U. 2nd edition. 3 volumes. Total of 995 figures, 1426pp. 5⅜ x 8.
$88,89,90, 3 volume set, paperbound **$6.00**

THE GEOMETRY OF RENE DESCARTES. With this book Descartes founded analytical geometry. Excellent Smith-Latham translation, plus original French text with Déscartes' own diagrams. Contains Problems the Construction of Which Requires Only Straight Lines and Circles; On the Nature of Curved Lines; On the Construction of Solid or Supersolid Problems. Notes. Diagrams. 258pp. 5⅜ x 8.
S68 Paperbound **$1.50**

See also: **FOUNDATIONS OF GEOMETRY,** B. Russell; **THE PHILOSOPHY OF SPACE AND TIME,** H. Reichenbach; **FAMOUS PROBLEMS OF ELEMENTARY GEOMETRY,** F. Klein; **MONOGRAPHS ON TOPICS OF MODERN MATHEMATICS,** ed. by J. W. Young.

Calculus and function theory, Fourier theory, real and complex functions, determinants

A COLLECTION OF MODERN MATHEMATICAL CLASSICS, edited by **R. Bellman.** 13 classic papers, complete in their original languages, by Hermite, Hardy and Littlewood, Tchebychef, Fejér, Fredholm, Fuchs, Hurwitz, Weyl, van der Pol, Birkhoff, Kellogg, von Neumann, and Hilbert. Each of these papers, collected here for the first time, triggered a burst of mathematical activity, providing useful new generalizations or stimulating fresh investigations. Topics discussed include classical analysis, periodic and almost periodic functions, analysis and number theory, integral equations, theory of approximation, non-linear differential equations, and functional analysis. Brief introductions and bibliographies to each paper. xii + 292pp. 6 x 9.
S730 Paperbound **$2.00**

MATHEMATICS OF MODERN ENGINEERING, E. G. Keller and R. E. Doherty. Written for the Advanced Course in Engineering of the General Electric Corporation, deals with the engineering use of determinants, tensors, the Heaviside operational calculus, dyadics, the calculus of variations, etc. Presents underlying principles fully, but purpose is to teach engineers to deal with modern engineering problems, and emphasis is on the perennial engineering attack of set-up and solve. Indexes. Over 185 figures and tables. Hundreds of exercises, problems, and worked-out examples. References. Two volume set. Total of xxxiii + 623pp. 5⅜ x 8.
S734 Vol I Paperbound **$1.65**
S735 Vol II Paperbound **$1.65**
The set **$3.30**

MATHEMATICAL METHODS FOR SCIENTISTS AND ENGINEERS, L. P. Smith. For scientists and engineers, as well as advanced math students. Full investigation of methods and practical description of conditions under which each should be used. Elements of real functions, differential and integral calculus, space geometry, theory of residues, vector and tensor analysis, series of Bessel functions, etc. Each method illustrated by completely-worked-out examples, mostly from scientific literature. 368 graded unsolved problems. 100 diagrams. x + 453pp. 5⅜ x 8⅜.
S220 Paperbound **$2.00**

THEORY OF FUNCTIONS AS APPLIED TO ENGINEERING PROBLEMS, edited by R. Rothe, F. Ollendorff, and K. Pohlhausen. A series of lectures given at the Berlin Institute of Technology that shows the specific applications of function theory in electrical and allied fields of engineering. Six lectures provide the elements of function theory in a simple and practical form, covering complex quantities and variables, integration in the complex plane, residue theorems, etc. Then 5 lectures show the exact uses of this powerful mathematical tool, with full discussions of problem methods. Index. Bibliography. 108 figures. x + 189pp. 5⅜ x 8.
S733 Paperbound **$1.35**

ADVANCED CALCULUS, E. B. Wilson. An unabridged reprinting of the work which continues to be recognized as one of the most comprehensive and useful texts in the field. It contains an immense amount of well-presented, fundamental material, including chapters on vector functions, ordinary differential equations, special functions, calculus of variations, etc., which are excellent introductions to these areas. For students with only one year of calculus, more than 1300 exercises cover both pure math and applications to engineering and physical problems. For engineers, physicists, etc., this work, with its 54 page introductory review, is the ideal reference and refresher. Index. ix + 566pp. 5⅜ x 8.
S504 Paperbound **$2.45**

CALCULUS OF VARIATIONS, A. R. Forsyth. Methods, solutions, rather than determination of weakest valid hypotheses. Over 150 examples completely worked-out show use of Euler, Legendre, Jacoby, Weierstrass tests for maxima, minima. Integrals with one original dependent variable; with derivatives of 2nd order; two dependent variables, one independent variable; double integrals involving 1 dependent variable, 2 first derivatives; double integrals involving partial derivatives of 2nd order; triple integrals; much more. 50 diagrams. 678pp. 5⅜ x 8⅜.   S622 Paperbound **$2.95**

LECTURES ON THE CALCULUS OF VARIATIONS, O. Bolza. Analyzes in detail the fundamental concepts of the calculus of variations, as developed from Euler to Hilbert, with sharp formulations of the problems and rigorous demonstrations of their solutions. More than a score of solved examples; systematic references for each theorem. Covers the necessary and sufficient conditions; the contributions made by Euler, Du Bois Reymond, Hilbert, Weierstrass, Legendre, Jacobi, Erdmann, Kneser, and Gauss; and much more. Index. Bibliography. xi + 271pp. 5⅜ x 8.   S218 Paperbound **$**

A TREATISE ON THE CALCULUS OF FINITE DIFFERENCES, G. Boole. A classic in the literature of the calculus. Thorough, clear discussion of basic principles, theorems, methods. Covers MacLaurin's and Herschel's theorems, mechanical quadrature, factorials, periodical constants, Bernoulli's numbers, difference-equations (linear, mixed, and partial), etc. Stresses analogies with differential calculus. 236 problems, answers to the numerical ones. viii + 336pp. 5⅜ x 8.   S695 Paperbound **$1.85**

THE ANALYTICAL THEORY OF HEAT, Joseph Fourier. This book, which revolutionized mathematical physics, is listed in the Great Books program, and many other listings of great books. It has been used with profit by generations of mathematicians and physicists who are interested in either heat or in the application of the Fourier integral. Covers cause and reflection of rays of heat, radiant heating, heating of closed spaces, use of trigonometric series in the theory of heat, Fourier integral, etc. Translated by Alexander Freeman. 20 figures. xxii + 466pp. 5⅜ x 8.   S93 Paperbound **$2.00**

AN INTRODUCTION TO FOURIER METHODS AND THE LAPLACE TRANSFORMATION, Philip Franklin. Concentrates upon essentials, enabling the reader with only a working knowledge of calculus to gain an understanding of Fourier methods in a broad sense, suitable for most applications. This work covers complex qualities with methods of computing elementary functions for complex values of the argument and finding approximations by the use of charts; Fourier series and integrals with half-range and complex Fourier series; harmonic analysis; Fourier and Laplace transformations, etc.; partial differential equations with applications to transmission of electricity; etc. The methods developed are related to physical problems of heat flow, vibrations, electrical transmission, electromagnetic radiation, etc. 828 problems with answers. Formerly entitled "Fourier Methods." Bibliography. Index. x + 289pp. 5⅜ x 8.
                                                                  S452 Paperbound **$1.75**

THE FOURIER INTEGRAL AND CERTAIN OF ITS APPLICATIONS, Norbert Wiener. The only book-length study of the Fourier integral as link between pure and applied math. An expansion of lectures given at Cambridge. Partial contents: Plancherel's theorem, general Tauberian theorem, special Tauberian theorems, generalized harmonic analysis. Bibliography. viii + 201pp. 5⅜ x 8.   S272 Paperbound **$1.50**

INTRODUCTION TO THE THEORY OF FOURIER'S SERIES AND INTEGRALS, H. S. Carslaw. 3rd revised edition. This excellent introduction is an outgrowth of the author's courses at Cambridge. Historical introduction, rational and irrational numbers, infinite sequences and series, functions of a single variable, definite integral, Fourier series, Fourier integrals, and similar topics. Appendixes discuss practical harmonic analysis, periodogram analysis. Lebesgues theory. Indexes. 84 examples, bibliography. xiii + 368pp. 5⅜ x 8.   S48 Paperbound **$2.00**

FOURIER'S SERIES AND SPHERICAL HARMONICS, W. E. Byerly. Continues to be recognized as one of most practical, useful expositions. Functions, series, and their differential equations are concretely explained in great detail; theory is applied constantly to practical problems, which are fully and lucidly worked out. Appendix includes 6 tables of surface zonal harmonics, hyperbolic functions, Bessel's functions. Bibliography. 190 problems, approximately half with answers. ix + 287pp. 5⅜ x 8.   S536 Paperbound **$1.75**

ASYMPTOTIC EXPANSIONS, A. Erdélyi. The only modern work available in English, this is an unabridged reproduction of a monograph prepared for the Office of Naval Research. It discusses various procedures for asymptotic evaluation of integrals containing a large parameter and solutions of ordinary linear differential equations. Bibliography of 71 items. vi + 108pp. 5⅜ x 8.   S318 Paperbound **$1.35**

LINEAR INTEGRAL EQUATIONS, W. V. Lovitt. Systematic survey of general theory, with some application to differential equations, calculus of variations, problems of math, physics. Partial contents: integral equation of 2nd kind by successive substitutions; Fredholm's equation as ratio of 2 integral series in lambda, applications of the Fredholm theory, Hilbert-Schmidt theory of symmetric kernels, application, etc. Neumann, Dirichlet, vibratory problems. Index. ix + 253pp. 5⅜ x 8.   S175 Clothbound **$3.50**
                                                                  S176 Paperbound **$1.60**

ELLIPTIC INTEGRALS, H. Hancock. Invaluable in work involving differential equations containing cubics or quartics under the root sign, where elementary calculus methods are inadequate. Practical solutions to problems that occur in mathematics, engineering, physics: differential equations requiring integration of Lamé's, Briot's, or Bouquet's equations; determination of arc of ellipse, hyperbola, lemiscate; solutions of problems in elastica; motion of a projectile under resistance varying as the cube of the velocity; pendulums; many others. Exposition is in accordance with Legendre-Jacobi theory and includes rigorous discussion of Legendre transformations. 20 figures. 5 place table. Index. 104pp. 5⅛ x 8.
S484 Paperbound **$1.25**

FIVE VOLUME "THEORY OF FUNCTIONS' SET BY KONRAD KNOPP

This five-volume set, prepared by Konrad Knopp, provides a complete and readily followed account of theory of functions. Proofs are given concisely, yet without sacrifice of completeness or rigor. These volumes are used as texts by such universities as M.I.T., University of Chicago, N. Y. City College, and many others. "Excellent introduction . . . remarkably readable, concise, clear, rigorous," JOURNAL OF THE AMERICAN STATISTICAL ASSOCIATION.

ELEMENTS OF THE THEORY OF FUNCTIONS, Konrad Knopp. This book provides the student with background for further volumes in this set, or texts on a similar level. Partial contents: foundations, system of complex numbers and the Gaussian plane of numbers, Riemann sphere of numbers, mapping by linear functions, normal forms, the logarithm, the cyclometric functions and binomial series. "Not only for the young student, but also for the student who knows all about what is in it," MATHEMATICAL JOURNAL. Bibliography. Index. 140pp. 5⅜ x 8.
S154 Paperbound **$1.35**

THEORY OF FUNCTIONS, PART I, Konrad Knopp. With volume II, this book provides coverage of basic concepts and theorems. Partial contents: numbers and points, functions of a complex variable, integral of a continuous function, Cauchy's integral theorem, Cauchy's integral formulae, series with variable terms, expansion of analytic functions in power series, analytic continuation and complete definition of analytic functions, entire transcendental functions, Laurent expansion, types of singularities. Bibliography. Index. vii + 146pp. 5⅜ x 8.
S156 Paperbound **$1.35**

THEORY OF FUNCTIONS, PART II, Konrad Knopp. Application and further development of general theory, special topics. Single valued functions, entire, Weierstrass, Meromorphic functions. Riemann surfaces. Algebraic functions. Analytical configuration, Riemann surface. Bibliography. Index. x + 150pp. 5⅜ x 8.
S157 Paperbound **$1.35**

PROBLEM BOOK IN THE THEORY OF FUNCTIONS, VOLUME 1, Konrad Knopp. Problems in elementary theory, for use with Knopp's THEORY OF FUNCTIONS, or any other text, arranged according to increasing difficulty. Fundamental concepts, sequences of numbers and infinite series, complex variable, integral theorems, development in series, conformal mapping. 182 problems. Answers. viii + 126pp. 5⅜ x 8.
S158 Paperbound **$1.35**

PROBLEM BOOK IN THE THEORY OF FUNCTIONS, VOLUME 2, Konrad Knopp. Advanced theory of functions, to be used either with Knopp's THEORY OF FUNCTIONS, or any other comparable text. Singularities, entire & meromorphic functions, periodic, analytic, continuation, multiple-valued functions, Riemann surfaces, conformal mapping. Includes a section of additional elementary problems. "The difficult task of selecting from the immense material of the modern theory of functions the problems just within the reach of the beginner is here masterfully accomplished," AM. MATH. SOC. Answers. 138pp. 5⅜ x 8. S159 Paperbound **$1.35**

* * *

LECTURES ON THE THEORY OF ELLIPTIC FUNCTIONS, H. Hancock. Reissue of the only book in English with so extensive a coverage, especially of Abel, Jacobi, Legendre, Weierstrasse, Hermite, Liouville, and Riemann. Unusual fullness of treatment, plus applications as well as theory, in discussing elliptic function (the universe of elliptic integrals originating in works of Abel and Jacobi), their existence, and ultimate meaning. Use is made of Riemann to provide the most general theory. 40 page table of formulas. 76 figures. xxiii + 498pp.
S483 Paperbound **$2.55**

THE THEORY AND FUNCTIONS OF A REAL VARIABLE AND THE THEORY OF FOURIER'S SERIES, E. W. Hobson. One of the best introductions to set theory and various aspects of functions and Fourier's series. Requires only a good background in calculus. Provides an exhaustive coverage of: metric and descriptive properties of sets of points; transfinite numbers and order types; functions of a real variable; the Riemann and Lebesgue integrals; sequences and series of numbers; power-series; functions representable by series sequences of continuous functions; trigonometrical series; representation of functions by Fourier's series; complete exposition (200pp.) on set theory; and much more. "The best possible guide," Nature. Vol. I: 88 detailed examples, 10 figures. Index. xv + 736pp. Vol. II: 117 detailed examples, 13 figures. Index. x + 780pp. 6⅛ x 9¼.
Vol. I: S387 Paperbound **$3.00**
Vol. II: S388 Paperbound **$3.00**

ALMOST PERIODIC FUNCTIONS, A. S. Besicovitch. This unique and important summary by a well-known mathematician covers in detail the two stages of development in Bohr's theory of almost periodic functions: (1) as a generalization of pure periodicity, with results and proofs; (2) the work done by Stepanoff, Wiener, Weyl, and Bohr in generalizing the theory. Bibliography. xi + 180pp. 5⅜ x 8.
S18 Paperbound **$1.75**

THEORY OF FUNCTIONALS AND OF INTEGRAL AND INTEGRO-DIFFERENTIAL EQUATIONS, Vito Volterra. Unabridged republication of the only English translation. An exposition of the general theory of the functions depending on a continuous set of values of another function, based on the author's fundamental notion of the transition from a finite number of variables to a continually infinite number. Though dealing primarily with integral equations, much material on calculus of variations is included. The work makes no assumption of previous knowledge on the part of the reader. It begins with fundamental material and proceeds to Generalization of Analytic Functions, Integro-Differential Equations, Functional Derivative Equations, Applications, Other Directions of Theory of Functionals, etc. New introduction by G. C. Evans. Bibliography and criticism of Volterra's work by E. Whittaker. Bibliography. Index of authors cited. Index of subjects. xxxx + 226pp. 5⅜ x 8.　　S502 Paperbound **$1.75**

AN ELEMENTARY TREATISE ON ELLIPTIC FUNCTIONS, A. Cayley. Still the fullest and clearest text on the theories of Jacobi and Legendre for the advanced student (and an excellent supplement for the beginner). A masterpiece of exposition by the great 19th century British mathematician (creator of the theory of matrices and abstract geometry), it covers the addition-theory, Landen's theorem, the 3 kinds of elliptic integrals, transformations, the q-functions, reduction of a differential expression, and much more. Index. xii + 386pp. 5⅜ x 8.
　　S728 Paperbound **$2.00**

THE APPLICATIONS OF ELLIPTIC FUNCTIONS, A. G. Greenhill. Modern books forgo detail for sake of brevity—this book offers complete exposition necessary for proper understanding, use of elliptic integrals. Formulas developed from definite physical, geometric problems; examples representative enough to offer basic information in widely useable form. Elliptic integrals, addition theorem, algebraical form of addition theorem, elliptic integrals of 2nd, 3rd kind, double periodicity, resolution into factors, series, transformation, etc. Introduction. Index. 25 illus. xi + 357pp. 5⅜ x 8.　　S603 Paperbound **$1.75**

THE THEORY OF FUNCTIONS OF REAL VARIABLES, James Pierpont. A 2-volume authoritative exposition, by one of the foremost mathematicians of his time. Each theorem stated with all conditions, then followed by proof. No need to go through complicated reasoning to discover conditions added without specific mention. Includes a particularly complete, rigorous presentation of theory of measure; and Pierpont's own work on a theory of Lebesgue integrals, and treatment of area of a curved surface. Partial contents, Vol. 1: rational numbers, exponentials, logarithms, point aggregates, maxima, minima, proper integrals, improper integrals, multiple proper integrals, continuity, discontinuity, indeterminate forms. Vol. 2: point sets, proper integrals, series, power series, aggregates, ordinal numbers, discontinuous functions, sub-, infra-uniform convergence, much more. Index. 95 illustrations. 1229pp. 5⅜ x 8.　　S558-9, 2 volume set, paperbound **$4.90**

FUNCTIONS OF A COMPLEX VARIABLE, James Pierpont. Long one of best in the field. A thorough treatment of fundamental elements, concepts, theorems. A complete study, rigorous, detailed, with carefully selected problems worked out to illustrate each topic. Partial contents: arithmetical operations, real term series, positive term series, exponential functions, integration, analytic functions, asymptotic expansions, functions of Weierstrass, Legendre, etc. Index. List of symbols. 122 illus. 597pp. 5⅜ x 8.　　S560 Paperbound **$2.45**

ELEMENTS OF THE THEORY OF REAL FUNCTIONS, J. E. Littlewood. Based on lectures given at Trinity College, Cambridge, this book has proved to be extremely successful in introducing graduate students to the modern theory of functions. It offers a full and concise coverage of classes and cardinal numbers, well-ordered series, other types of series, and elements of the theory of sets of points. 3rd revised edition. vii + 71pp. 5⅜ x 8.
　　S171 Clothbound **$2.85**
　　S172 Paperbound **$1.25**

TRANSCENDENTAL AND ALGEBRAIC NUMBERS, A. O. Gelfond. First English translation of work by leading Soviet mathematician. Thue-Siegel theorem, its p-adic analogue, on approximation of algebraic numbers by numbers in fixed algebraic field; Hermite-Lindemann theorem on transcendency of Bessel functions, solutions of other differential equations; Gelfond-Schneider theorem on transcendence of alpha to power beta; Schneider's work on elliptic functions, with method developed by Gelfond. Translated by L. F. Boron. Index. Bibliography. 200pp. 5⅜ x 8.　　S615 Paperbound **$1.75**

THEORY OF MAXIMA AND MINIMA, H. Hancock. Fullest treatment ever written; only work in English with extended discussion of maxima and minima for functions of 1, 2, or n variables, problems with subsidiary constraints, and relevant quadratic forms. Detailed proof of each important theorem. Covers the Scheeffer and von Dantscher theories, homogeneous quadratic forms, reversion of series, fallacious establishment of maxima and minima, etc. Unsurpassed treatise for advanced students of calculus, mathematicians, economists, statisticians. Index. 24 diagrams. 39 problems, many examples. 193pp. 5⅜ x 8.　　S665 Paperbound **$1.50**

DICTIONARY OF CONFORMAL REPRESENTATIONS, H. Kober. Laplace's equation in 2 dimensions solved in this unique book developed by the British Admiralty. Scores of geometrical forms & their transformations for electrical engineers, Joukowski aerofoil for aerodynamists. Schwartz-Christoffel transformations for hydrodynamics, transcendental functions. Contents classified according to analytical functions describing transformation. Twin diagrams show curves of most transformations with corresponding regions. Glossary. Topological index. 447 diagrams. 244pp. 6⅛ x 9¼.　　S160 Paperbound **$2.00**

THE TAYLOR SERIES, AN INTRODUCTION TO THE THEORY OF FUNCTIONS OF A COMPLEX VARIABLE, P. Dienes. This book investigates the entire realm of analytic functions. Only ordinary calculus is needed, except in the last two chapters. Starting with an introduction to real variables and complex algebra, the properties of infinite series, elementary functions, complex differentiation and integration are carefully derived. Also biuniform mapping, a thorough two part discussion of representation and singularities of analytic functions, overconvergence and gap theorems, divergent series, Taylor series on its circle of convergence, divergence and singularities, etc. Unabridged, corrected reissue of first edition. Preface and index. 186 examples, many fully worked out. 67 figures. xii + 555pp. 5⅜ x 8.
S391 Paperbound **$2.75**

INTRODUCTION TO BESSEL FUNCTIONS, Frank Bowman. A rigorous self-contained exposition providing all necessary material during the development, which requires only some knowledge of calculus and acquaintance with differential equations. A balanced presentation including applications and practical use. Discusses Bessel Functions of Zero Order, of Any Real Order; Modified Bessel Functions of Zero Order; Definite Integrals; Asymptotic Expansions; Bessel's Solution to Kepler's Problem; Circular Membranes; much more. "Clear and straightforward . . . useful not only to students of physics and engineering, but to mathematical students in general," Nature. 226 problems. Short tables of Bessel functions. 27 figures. Index. x + 135pp. 5⅜ x 8.
S462 Paperbound **$1.35**

MODERN THEORIES OF INTEGRATION, H. Kestelman. Connected and concrete coverage, with fully-worked-out proofs for every step. Ranges from elementary definitions through theory of aggregates, sets of points, Riemann and Lebesgue integration, and much more. This new revised and enlarged edition contains a new chapter on Riemann-Stieltjes integration, as well as a supplementary section of 186 exercises. Ideal for the mathematician, student, teacher, or self-studier. Index of Definitions and Symbols. General Index. Bibliography. x + 310pp. 5⅝ x 8⅜.
S572 Paperbound **$2.00**

A TREATISE ON THE THEORY OF DETERMINANTS, T. Muir. Unequalled as an exhaustive compilation of nearly all the known facts about determinants up to the early 1930's. Covers notation and general properties, row and column transformation, symmetry, compound determinants, adjugates, rectangular arrays and matrices, linear dependence, gradients, Jacobians, Hessians, Wronskians, and much more. Invaluable for libraries of industrial and research organizations as well as for student, teacher, and mathematician; very useful in the field of computing machines. Revised and enlarged by W. H. Metzler. Index. 485 problems and scores of numerical examples. iv + 766pp. 5⅜ x 8.
S670 Paperbound **$2.95**

THEORY OF DETERMINANTS IN THE HISTORICAL ORDER OF DEVELOPMENT, Sir Thomas Muir. Unabridged reprinting of this complete study of 1,859 papers on determinant theory written between 1693 and 1900. Most important and original sections reproduced, valuable commentary on each. No other work is necessary for determinant research: all types are covered—each subdivision of the theory treated separately; all papers dealing with each type are covered; you are told exactly what each paper is about and how important its contribution is. Each result, theory, extension, or modification is assigned its own identifying numeral so that the full history may be more easily followed. Includes papers on determinants in general, determinants and linear equations, symmetric determinants, alternants, recurrents, determinants having invariant factors, and all other major types. "A model of what such histories ought to be," NATURE. "Mathematicians must ever be grateful to Sir Thomas for his monumental work," AMERICAN MATH MONTHLY. Four volumes bound as two. Indices. Bibliographies. Total of lxxxiv + 1977pp. 5⅜ x 8.
S672-3 The set, Clothbound **$10.00**

A COURSE IN MATHEMATICAL ANALYSIS, Edouard Goursat. Trans. by E. R. Hedrick, O. Dunkel. Classic study of fundamental material thoroughly treated. Exceptionally lucid exposition of wide range of subject matter for student with 1 year of calculus. Vol. 1: Derivatives and Differentials, Definite Integrals, Expansion in Series, Applications to Geometry. Problems. Index. 52 illus. 556pp. Vol. 2, Part I: Functions of a Complex Variable, Conformal Representations, Doubly Periodic Functions, Natural Boundaries, etc. Problems. Index. 38 illus. 269pp. Vol. 2, Part 2: Differential Equations, Cauchy-Lipschitz Method, Non-linear Differential Equations, Simultaneous Equations, etc. Problems. Index. 308pp. 5⅜ x 8.
Vol. 1 S554 Paperbound **$2.25**
Vol. 2 part 1 S555 Paperbound **$1.65**
Vol. 2 part 2 S556 Paperbound **$1.65**
3 vol. set **$5.00**

INFINITE SEQUENCES AND SERIES, Konrad Knopp. First publication in any language! Excellent introduction to 2 topics of modern mathematics, designed to give the student background to penetrate farther by himself. Sequences & sets, real & complex numbers, etc. Functions of a real & complex variable. Sequences & series. Infinite series. Convergent power series. Expansion of elementary functions. Numerical evaluation of series. Bibliography. v + 186pp. 5⅜ x 8.
S152 Clothbound **$3.50**
S153 Paperbound **$1.75**

TRIGONOMETRICAL SERIES, Antoni Zygmund. Unique in any language on modern advanced level. Contains carefully organized analyses of trigonometric, orthogonal, Fourier systems of functions, with clear adequate descriptions of summability of Fourier series, proximation theory, conjugate series, convergence, divergence of Fourier series. Especially valuable for Russian, Eastern European coverage. Bibliography. 329pp. 5⅜ x 8.
S290 Paperbound **$1.50**

COLLECTED WORKS OF BERNHARD RIEMANN. This important source book is the first to contain the complete text of both 1892 Werke and the 1902 supplement, unabridged. It contains 31 monographs, 3 complete lecture courses, 15 miscellaneous papers, which have been of enormous importance in relativity, topology, theory of complex variables, and other areas of mathematics. Edited by R. Dedekind, H. Weber, M. Noether, W. Wirtinger. German text. English introduction by Hans Lewy. 690pp. 5⅜ x 8. S226 Paperbound **$2.85**

See also: A HISTORY OF THE CALCULUS, C. B. Boyer; CALCULUS REFRESHER FOR TECHNICAL MEN, A. A. Klaf; MONOGRAPHS ON TOPICS OF MODERN MATHEMATICS, ed. by J. W. A. Young; THE CONTINUUM AND OTHER TYPES OF SERIAL ORDER, E. V. Huntington.

Symbolic logic

AN INTRODUCTION TO SYMBOLIC LOGIC, Susanne K. Langer. Probably the clearest book ever written on symbolic logic for the philosopher, general scientist and layman. It will be particularly appreciated by those who have been rebuffed by other introductory works because of insufficient mathematical training. No special knowledge of mathematics is required. Starting with the simplest symbols and conventions, you are led to a remarkable grasp of the Boole-Schroeder and Russell-Whitehead systems clearly and quickly. PARTIAL CONTENTS: Study of forms, Essentials of logical structure, Generalization, Classes, The deductive system of classes, The algebra of logic, Abstraction of interpretation, Calculus of propositions, Assumptions of PRINCIPIA MATHEMATICA, Logistics, Logic of the syllogism, Proofs of theorems. "One of the clearest and simplest introductions to a subject which is very much alive. The style is easy, symbolism is introduced gradually, and the intelligent non-mathematician should have no difficulty in following the argument," MATHEMATICS GAZETTE. Revised, expanded second edition. Truth-value tables. 368pp. 5⅜ x 8.
S164 Paperbound **$1.75**

THE ELEMENTS OF MATHEMATICAL LOGIC, Paul Rosenbloom. First publication in any language. This book is intended for readers who are mature mathematically, but have no previous training in symbolic logic. It does not limit itself to a single system, but covers the field as a whole. It is a development of lectures given at Lund University, Sweden, in 1948. Partial contents: Logic of classes, fundamental theorems, Boolean algebra, logic of propositions, logic of propositional functions, expressive languages, combinatory logics, development of mathematics within an object language, paradoxes, theorems of Post and Goedel, Church's theorem, and similar topics. iv + 214pp. 5⅜ x 8. S227 Paperbound **$1.45**

A SURVEY OF SYMBOLIC LOGIC: THE CLASSIC ALGEBRA OF LOGIC, C. I. Lewis. Classic survey of the field, comprehensive and thorough. Indicates content of major systems, alternative methods of procedure, and relation of these to the Boole-Schroeder algebra and to one another. Contains historical summary, as well as full proofs and applications of the classic, or Boole-Schroeder, algebra of logic. Discusses diagrams for the logical relations of classes, the two-valued algebra, propositional functions of two or more variables, etc. Chapters 5 and 6 of the original edition, which contained material not directly pertinent, have been omitted in this edition at the author's request. Appendix. Bibliography. Index. viii + 352pp. 5⅝ x 8⅜.
S643 Paperbound **$2.00**

INTRODUCTION TO SYMBOLIC LOGIC AND ITS APPLICATIONS, R. Carnap. One of the clearest, most comprehensive, and rigorous introductions to modern symbolic logic by perhaps its greatest living master. Symbolic languages are analyzed and one constructed. Applications to math (symbolic representation of axiom systems for set theory, natural numbers, real numbers, topology, Dedekind and Cantor explanations of continuity), physics (the general analysis of concepts of determination, causality, space-time-topology, based on Einstein), biology (symbolic representation of an axiom system for basic concepts). "A masterpiece," Zentralblatt für Mathematik und ihre Grenzgebiete. Over 300 exercises. 5 figures. Bibliography. Index. xvi + 241pp. 5⅜ x 8. S453 Paperbound **$1.85**
Clothbound **$4.00**

SYMBOLIC LOGIC, C. I. Lewis, C. H. Langford. Probably the most cited book in symbolic logic, this is one of the fullest treatments of paradoxes. A wide coverage of the entire field of symbolic logic, plus considerable material that has not appeared elsewhere. Basic to the entire volume is the distinction between the logic of extensions and of intensions. Considerable emphasis is placed on converse substitution, while the matrix system presents the supposition of a variety of non-Aristotelian logics. It has especially valuable sections on strict limitations, existence of terms, 2-valued algebra and its extension to propositional functions, truth value systems, the matrix method, implication and deductibility, general theory of propositions, propositions of ordinary discourse, and similar topics. "Authoritative, most valuable," TIMES, London. Bibliography. 506pp. 5⅜ x 8. S170 Paperbound **$2.00**

THE LAWS OF THOUGHT, George Boole. This book founded symbolic logic some hundred years ago. It is the 1st significant attempt to apply logic to all aspects of human endeavour. Partial contents: derivation of laws, signs & laws, interpretations, eliminations, conditions of a perfect method, analysis, Aristotelian logic, probability, and similar topics. xviii + 424pp. 5⅜ x 8. S28 Paperbound **$2.00**

THE PRINCIPLES OF SCIENCE, A TREATISE ON LOGIC AND THE SCIENTIFIC METHOD, W. S. Jevons. Treating such topics as Inductive and Deductive Logic, the Theory of Number, Probability, and the Limits of Scientific Method, this milestone in the development of symbolic logic remains a stimulating contribution to the investigation of inferential validity in the natural and social sciences. It significantly advances Boole's logic, and contains a detailed introduction to the nature and methods of probability in physics, astronomy, everyday affairs, etc. In his introduction, Ernest Nagel of Columbia University says, "[Jevons] continues to be of interest as an attempt to articulate the logic of scientific inquiry." Index. liii + 786pp. 5⅜ x 8. S446 Paperbound **$2.98**

Group theory, algebra, sets

LECTURES ON THE ICOSAHEDRON AND THE SOLUTION OF EQUATIONS OF THE FIFTH DEGREE, Felix Klein. The solution of quintics in terms of rotation of a regular icosahedron around its axes of symmetry. A classic & indispensable source for those interested in higher algebra, geometry, crystallography. Considerable explanatory material included. 230 footnotes, mostly bibliographic. 2nd edition, xvi + 289pp. 5⅜ x 8. S314 Paperbound **$1.85**

LINEAR GROUPS, WITH AN EXPOSITION OF THE GALOIS FIELD THEORY, L. E. Dickson. The classic exposition of the theory of groups, well within the range of the graduate student. Part I contains the most extensive and thorough presentation of the theory of Galois Fields available, with a wealth of examples and theorems. Part II is a full discussion of linear groups of finite order. Much material in this work is based on Dickson's own contributions. Also includes expositions of Jordan, Lie, Abel, Betti-Mathieu, Hermite, etc. "A milestone in the development of modern algebra," W. Magnus, in his historical introduction to this edition. Index. xv + 312pp. 5⅜ x 8. S482 Paperbound **$1.95**

INTRODUCTION TO THE THEORY OF GROUPS OF FINITE ORDER, R. Carmichael. Examines fundamental theorems and their application. Beginning with sets, systems, permutations, etc., it progresses in easy stages through important types of groups: Abelian, prime power, permutation, etc. Except 1 chapter where matrices are desirable, no higher math needed. 783 exercises, problems. Index. xvi + 447pp. 5⅜ x 8. S299 Clothbound **$3.95**
S300 Paperbound **$2.00**

THEORY OF GROUPS OF FINITE ORDER, W. Burnside. First published some 40 years ago, this is still one of the clearest introductory texts. Partial contents: permutations, groups independent of representation, composition series of a group, isomorphism of a group with itself, Abelian groups, prime power groups, permutation groups, invariants of groups of linear substitution graphical representation, etc. 45pp. of notes. Indexes. xxiv + 512pp. 5⅜ x 8. S38 Paperbound **$2.45**

THEORY AND APPLICATIONS OF FINITE GROUPS, G. A. Miller, H. F. Blichfeldt, L. E. Dickson. Unusually accurate and authoritative work, each section prepared by a leading specialist: Miller on substitution and abstract groups, Blichfeldt on finite groups of linear homogeneous transformations, Dickson on applications of finite groups. Unlike more modern works, this gives the concrete basis from which abstract group theory arose. Includes Abelian groups, prime-power groups, isomorphisms, matrix forms of linear transformations, Sylow groups, Galois' theory of algebraic equations, duplication of a cube, trisection of an angle, etc. 2 Indexes. 267 problems. xvii + 390pp. 5⅜ x 8. S216 Paperbound **$2.00**

CONTINUOUS GROUPS OF TRANSFORMATIONS, L. P. Eisenhart. Intensive study of the theory and geometrical applications of continuous groups of transformations; a standard work on the subject, called forth by the revolution in physics in the 1920's. Covers tensor analysis, Riemannian geometry, canonical parameters, transitivity, imprimitivity, differential invariants, the algebra of constants of structure, differential geometry, contact transformations, etc. Likely to remain one of the standard works on the subject for many years . . . principal theorems are proved clearly and concisely, and the arrangement of the whole is coherent," MATHEMATICAL GAZETTE. Index. 72-item bibliography. 185 exercises. ix + 301pp. 5⅜ x 8. S781 Paperbound **$1.85**

THE THEORY OF GROUPS AND QUANTUM MECHANICS, H. Weyl. Discussions of Schroedinger's wave equation, de Broglie's waves of a particle, Jordan-Hoelder theorem, Lie's continuous groups of transformations, Pauli exclusion principle, quantization of Maxwell-Dirac field equations, etc. Unitary geometry, quantum theory, groups, application of groups to quantum mechanics, symmetry permutation group, algebra of symmetric transformation, etc. 2nd revised edition. Bibliography. Index. xxii + 422pp. 5⅜ x 8. S268 Clothbound **$4.50**
S269 Paperbound **$1.95**

ALGEBRAIC THEORIES, L. E. Dickson. Best thorough introduction to classical topics in higher algebra develops theories centering around matrices, invariants, groups. Higher algebra, Galois theory, finite linear groups, Klein's icosahedron, algebraic invariants, linear transformations, elementary divisors, invariant factors; quadratic, bi-linear, Hermitian forms, singly and in pairs. Proofs rigorous, detailed; topics developed lucidly, in close connection with their most frequent mathematical applications. Formerly "Modern Algebraic Theories." 55 problems. Bibliography. 2 indexes. 285pp. 5⅜ x 8. S547 Paperbound **$1.50**

ALGEBRAS AND THEIR ARITHMETICS, L. E. Dickson. Provides the foundation and background necessary to any advanced undergraduate or graduate student studying abstract algebra Begins with elementary introduction to linear transformations, matrices, field of complex numbers; proceeds to order, basal units, modulus, quaternions, etc.; develops calculus of linear sets, describes various examples of algebras including invariant, difference, nilpotent semi-simple. "Makes the reader marvel at his genius for clear and profound analysis," Amer Mathematical Monthly. Index. xii + 241pp. 5⅜ x 8. S616 Paperbound **$1.3**

THE THEORY OF EQUATIONS WITH AN INTRODUCTION TO THE THEORY OF BINARY ALGEBRAIC FORMS, W. S. Burnside and A. W. Panton. Extremely thorough and concrete discussion of the theory of equations, with extensive detailed treatment of many topics curtailed in later texts Covers theory of algebraic equations, properties of polynomials, symmetric functions, derivative functions, Horner's process, complex numbers and the complex variable, determinants and methods of elimination, invariant theory (nearly 100 pages), transformations, introduction to Galois theory, Abelian equations, and much more. Invaluable supplementary work for modern students and teachers. 759 examples and exercises. Index in each volume. Two volume set Total of xxiv + 604pp. 5⅜ x 8.
S714 Vol I Paperbound **$1.85**
S715 Vol II Paperbound **$1.85**
The set **$3.70**

COMPUTATIONAL METHODS OF LINEAR ALGEBRA, V. N. Faddeeva, translated by C. D. Benster First English translation of a unique and valuable work, the only work in English presenting a systematic exposition of the most important methods of linear algebra—classica and contemporary. Shows in detail how to derive numerical solutions of problems in mathematical physics which are frequently connected with those of linear algebra. Theory as well as individual practice. Part I surveys the mathematical background that is indispensable to what follows. Parts II and III, the conclusion, set forth the most important methods of solution, for both exact and iterative groups. One of the most outstanding and valuable features of this work is the 23 tables, double and triple checked for accuracy. These tables will not be found elsewhere. Author's preface. Translator's note. New bibliography and index. x + 252pp. 5⅜ x 8. S424 Paperbound **$1.95**

ALGEBRAIC EQUATIONS, E. Dehn. Careful and complete presentation of Galois' theory of algebraic equations; theories of Lagrange and Galois developed in logical rather than historical form, with a more thorough exposition than in most modern books. Many concrete applications and fully-worked-out examples. Discusses basic theory (very clear exposition of the symmetric group); isomorphic, transitive, and Abelian groups; applications of Lagrange's and Galois' theories; and much more. Newly revised by the author. Index. List of Theorems xi + 208pp. 5⅜ x 8. S697 Paperbound **$1.45**

THEORY OF SETS, E. Kamke. Clearest, amplest introduction in English, well suited for independent study. Subdivision of main theory, such as theory of sets of points, are discussed but emphasis is on general theory. Partial contents: rudiments of set theory, arbitrary sets and their cardinal numbers, ordered sets and their order types, well-ordered sets and their cardinal numbers. Bibliography. Key to symbols. Index. vii + 144pp. 5⅜ x 8.
S141 Paperbound **$1.35**

Number theory

INTRODUCTION TO THE THEORY OF NUMBERS, L. E. Dickson. Thorough, comprehensive approach with adequate coverage of classical literature, an introductory volume beginners can follow. Chapters on divisibility, congruences, quadratic residues & reciprocity, Diophantine equations, etc. Full treatment of binary quadratic forms without usual restriction to integral coefficients. Covers infinitude of primes, least residues, Fermat's theorem, Euler's phi function, Legendre's symbol, Gauss's lemma, automorphs, reduced forms, recent theorems of Thue & Siegel, many more. Much material not readily available elsewhere. 239 problems. Index. J figure. viii + 183pp. 5⅜ x 8. S342 Paperbound **$1.65**

ELEMENTS OF NUMBER THEORY, I. M. Vinogradov. Detailed 1st course for persons without advanced mathematics; 95% of this book can be understood by readers who have gone no farther than high school algebra. Partial contents: divisibility theory, important number theoretical functions, congruences, primitive roots and indices, etc. Solutions to both problems and exercises. Tables of primes, indices, etc. Covers almost every essential formula in elementary number theory! Translated from Russian. 233 problems, 104 exercises. viii + 227pp. 5⅜ x 8. S259 Paperbound **$1.60**

THEORY OF NUMBERS and DIOPHANTINE ANALYSIS, R. D. Carmichael. These two complete works in one volume form one of the most lucid introductions to number theory, requiring only a firm foundation in high school mathematics. "Theory of Numbers," partial contents: Eratosthenes' sieve, Euclid's fundamental theorem, G.C.F. and L.C.M. of two or more integers, linear congruences, etc "Diophantine Analysis": rational triangles, Pythagorean triangles, equations of third, fourth, higher degrees, method of functional equations, much more. "Theory of Numbers": 76 problems. Index. 94pp. "Diophantine Analysis": 222 problems. Index. 118pp. 5⅜ x 8. S529 Paperbound **$1.35**

CONTRIBUTIONS TO THE FOUNDING OF THE THEORY OF TRANSFINITE NUMBERS, Georg Cantor. These papers founded a new branch of mathematics. The famous articles of 1895-7 are translated, with an 82-page introduction by P. E. B. Jourdain dealing with Cantor, the background of his discoveries, their results, future possibilities. Bibliography. Index. Notes. ix + 211 pp. 5⅜ x 8. S45 Paperbound **$1.25**

See also: **TRANSCENDENTAL AND ALGEBRAIC NUMBERS, A. O. Gelfond.**

Probability theory and information theory

A PHILOSOPHICAL ESSAY ON PROBABILITIES, Marquis de Laplace. This famous essay explains without recourse to mathematics the principle of probability, and the application of probability to games of chance, natural philosophy, astronomy, many other fields. Translated from the 6th French edition by F. W. Truscott, F. L. Emory, with new introduction for this edition by E. T. Bell. 204pp. 5⅜ x 8. S166 Paperbound **$1.35**

MATHEMATICAL FOUNDATIONS OF INFORMATION THEORY, A. I. Khinchin. For the first time mathematicians, statisticians, physicists, cyberneticists, and communications engineers are offered a complete and exact introduction to this relatively new field. Entropy as a measure of a finite scheme, applications to coding theory, study of sources, channels and codes, detailed proofs of both Shannon theorems for any ergodic source and any stationary channel with finite memory, and much more are covered. Bibliography. vii + 120pp. 5⅜ x 8. S434 Paperbound **$1.35**

SELECTED PAPERS ON NOISE AND STOCHASTIC PROCESS, edited by **Prof. Nelson Wax,** U. of Illinois. 6 basic papers for newcomers in the field, for those whose work involves noise characteristics. Chandrasekhar, Uhlenbeck & Ornstein, Uhlenbeck & Ming, Rice, Doob. Included is Kac's Chauvenet-Prize winning Random Walk. Extensive bibliography lists 200 articles, up through 1953. 21 figures. 337pp. 6⅛ x 9¼. S262 Paperbound **$2.35**

THEORY OF PROBABILITY, William Burnside. Synthesis, expansion of individual papers presents numerous problems in classical probability, offering many original views succinctly, effectively. Game theory, cards, selections from groups; geometrical probability in such areas as suppositions as to probability of position of point on a line, points on surface of sphere, etc. Includes methods of approximation, theory of errors, direct calculation of probabilities, etc. Index. 136pp. 5⅜ x 8. S567 Paperbound **$1.00**

Vector and tensor analysis

VECTOR AND TENSOR ANALYSIS, A. P. Wills. Covers the entire field of vector and tensor analysis from elementary notions to dyads and non-Euclidean manifolds (especially detailed), absolute differentiation, the Lamé operator, the Riemann-Christoffel and Ricci-Einstein tensors, and the calculation of the Gaussian curvature of a surface. Many illustrations from electrical engineering, relativity theory, astro-physics, quantum mechanics. Presupposes only a good working knowledge of calculus. Exercises at end of each chapter. Intended for physicists and engineers as well as pure mathematicians. 44 diagrams. 114 problems. Bibliography. Index. xxxii + 285pp. 5⅜ x 8. S454 Paperbound **$1.75**

APPLICATIONS OF TENSOR ANALYSIS, A. J. McConnell. (Formerly APPLICATIONS OF THE ABSOLUTE DIFFERENTIAL CALCULUS.) An excellent text for understanding the application of tensor methods to familiar subjects such as dynamics, electricity, elasticity, and hydrodynamics. Explains the fundamental ideas and notation of tensor theory, the geometrical treatment of tensor algebra, the theory of differentiation of tensors, and includes a wealth of practical material. Bibliography. Index. 43 illustrations. 685 problems. xii + 381pp. 5⅜ x 8. S373 Paperbound **$1.85**

VECTOR AND TENSOR ANALYSIS, G. E. Hay. One of the clearest introductions to this increasingly important subject. Start with simple definitions, finish the book with a sure mastery of oriented Cartesian vectors, Christoffel symbols, solenoidal tensors, and their applications. Complete breakdown of plane, solid, analytical, differential geometry. Separate chapters on application. All fundamental formulae listed & demonstrated. 195 problems, 66 figures. viii + 193pp. 5⅜ x 8. S109 Paperbound **$1.75**

Dover publishes books on art, music, philosophy, literature, languages, history, social sciences, psychology, handcrafts, orientalia, puzzles and entertainments, chess, pets and gardens, books explaining science, intermediate and higher mathematics, mathematical physics, engineering, biological sciences, earth sciences, classics of science, etc. Write to:

Dept. catrr.
Dover Publications, Inc.
180 Varick Street, N. Y. 14, N. Y.